Social capital

—

Words by Rory Olcayto

In many ways, London feels more 'social' than ever. That feeling can spring from the deep connection we make with our habitat when we take in a view of the city we spend our lives in from a new rooftop venue. (Many of which we highlighted during National Park City Festival in July and yes, the top deck of Peckham car park, open throughout the summer for Bold Tendencies, the art show, remains our favourite.) Or it can emerge from more intimate moments – a ceramics workshop you've signed up for, at Open House regular Turning Earth perhaps.

Or maybe it's a tour you've taken of a very special building, during one of our own 'Evening With' events, at Walmer Yard maybe, renowned for its 'slow food' approach to design (it took the architect Peter Salter years to conceive and build).

You could even argue that the skyline is friendlier looking than ever before, the jaunty – some might say silly – nature of it (have you seen the City's cluster of towers recently?!) transcending the negativity – the gloom of shadows, the typically boxy dullness, that towering skylines so often bring.

And most of it is new-ish: Marks Barfield's London Eye, for example, which to fresh eyes must seem to have always sidled up to the South Bank. But also Norman Foster's Gherkin, Renzo Piano's Shard, Rogers Stirk and Harbour's Cheesegrater, Anish Kapoor's twisty Olympic folly tower and Rafael Viñoly's Walkie Talkie. All built since the turn of the millennium.

But there is another layer of newness re-making the City too: housing, in all shapes and sizes, after years of playing second fiddle to commercial and cultural architecture, is having a moment. From Barratts' brick towers at Aldgate Cross (designed by Allies & Morrison) to the not-yet-finished One Park Drive in Canary Wharf by Tate Modern *starchitects* Herzog de Meuron.

Nevertheless, while luxury housing of this order is clearly for the few, Open House London has always been for the many. Which is why we've teamed up this year with Clarion Housing, the UK's largest housing association (its circular economy article on P14 is essential reading) and architects Pollard Thomas Edwards, whose broad range of projects, from a renewed North London housing estate to a women-only co-housing scheme, captures the breadth of residential design thinking in the capital today.

• Left: Trellick Tower ©James Davies

As well as celebrating the culture of a long-standing, dynamic community, Beck Road's 'gallery' should make for a fascinating street party

The residents of Hackney's Beck Road, have taken this notion of 'social' further still with a two-day art exhibition this Open House Weekend. Spanning the length of the street, the show – conceived by residents Alastair Carruthers and Kathryn Lovering – will be presented in rooms and studios of private homes, local businesses, and not-for-profit studios and charity spaces under railway arches.

All art on show will be by current and former residents, tenants and employees of Beck Road. As well as celebrating the culture of a long-standing, dynamic community, it should make for a fascinating street party.

Meanwhile, on the other side of town we've partnered with Savile Row this year to explore the social history of one of the most famous streets in the world.

Together with our other supporters – Fosters, the Old Oak Common and Park Royal Development Company among them – they ensure the quality of buildings and places to visit this year are top notch and ready to welcome you. Crowdfund London is also on board with Open House in 2019, meaning some of the best crowdfunded projects – citizen-led schemes match-funded by the Mayor – are among the highlights of this year's programme. Social? Of course it is. As we've been saying for a while now: people make Open House.

• Left-hand page: By Beck Road 19 © Becky Bailey.
Right-hand page – Top right: Sugar House Island. Bottom left: Aga Khan Centre © Steve Lavers. Bottom right: Alexandra and Ainsworth Estate © Anthony Coleman

Crowdfund London

—

Crowdfund London is spotlighting five of the best community-led projects across the capital that the *Mayor's programme* is supporting PLUS – *How to get involved* and win funding towards your own project

The Mayor of London's programme, Crowdfund London gives you the opportunity to pitch new ideas – big or small – for community-led projects to make your local area even better. The best projects running campaigns on Spacehive, the Greater London Authority's crowdfunding platform partner, could get a pledge of up to £50,000 from City Hall.

But what does 'best' mean? "The Mayor wants to back creative and distinctive ideas that can show local support," explains the Greater London Authority's James Parkinson, who has run the programme since its inception in 2015 and which this year has up to £1m to pledge.

"We're really open-minded to different types of ideas but typically they will be civic improvement projects (think buildings, spaces or local resources) led by local people for the benefit of everyone in the wider community.

"They must be not-for-profit and we're using crowdfunding to help local people to access cash, skills and resources from multiple sources and their campaigns can be a powerful local engagement tool."

115
Successful Crowdfund campaigns

£2m+
Pledged by the Mayor of London towards new projects

£3m
Matched by 20,000 crowd backers

How to get involved with *Crowdfund London*

• Mayor of London Sadiq Khan visiting Tottenham Café Connect – a project that transformed a dilapidated park bowls club into a new community meeting place.

You and your community need to come together to create something new and exciting to benefit the whole neighbourhood.

Projects must be
- In Greater London
- Well-resourced with a clear plan and budget
- Managed by an organisation representing their community
- Not-for-profit proposals that serve the local community

The Mayor wants to pledge to projects that
- Celebrate and strengthen the special character of your area
- Respond to a local challenge or opportunity in a creative way
- Give an unused space a new lease of life
- Help the local economy
- Give local people lasting skills and opportunities
- Make everyone in the community feel welcome and involved
- Attract strong support from the community – shown through a spirited crowdfunding campaign
- Are environmentally sustainable
- Provide access to affordable workspace for creative or start-up businesses
- Engage local people in a co-design process to improve a local public space or park

Projects could
- Help to make your high street a better place to visit or do business
- Improve or establish a local market
- Give a new lease of life to an unloved space or empty building
- Improve access to healthy and affordable food
- Create a beautiful new green space or cultural feature that attracts people to the area

Crowdfund London is looking for ideas that show innovation and enterprise and aspire to achieve a wider social good. Attend support events in the autumn to help you plan ahead of the next deadline, to begin campaigns on Spacehive in early 2020.

Need more Information?
london.gov.uk/crowdfunding

Explore some of the best Crowdfund London projects from 2019, free to visit during *Open House*

PEER Gallery, Hackney, pg62
With its community garden, PEER has transformed the public realm where Hoxton Street meets Fanshawe Street with trees, paving, a raised bed of planting, seating and bike parking and public art commissions by Chris Ofili and London Fieldworks. Planting design was undertaken by Yvonne Say and Jane Heather and local practice Trevor Horne Architects developed the original designs for the layout of the space.

Phoenix Garden and Community Building, Camden, pg117 →
Designed by Sian Architecture + Design, this purpose-built community centre provides space for hosting events, community parties and school groups. "The design," says the architect, "was developed from an early concept of garden walls – a metaphor for ideas of enclosure, secrecy, and boundaries." With a strong emphasis on local context and sustainable design, the building features robust brickwork detailing, super-insulating materials, air-source heat pumps, water harvesting and green roofs.

Ladywell Self-Build Community Space, Lewisham, pg67
This new civic space In Lewisham is being constructed with self-build volunteers led by the Rural Urban Synthesis Society (RUSS) to create a knowledge hub for community-led housing. Designed as a demountable structure using reclaimed materials, the project will open in time for Open House 2019. The goal is provide a community space to bring locals and new self-build residents together – and inspire other self-builders.

Camden Highline, Camden, pg119
The Camden Highline, built in 1852 for the North London Railway, has been disused for more than 30 years. A community group of the same name is proposing to bring back the 1.2km railway line into public use as an elevated park and garden walk linking Camden Town with King's Cross - a 10-minute walk. The project is currently working to achieve the permissions (e.g. landowner approval, planning permission) and fundraising the construction cost.

Clitterhouse Farm, Barnet, pg44 →
The project aims to restore the historic Clitterhouse Farm Buildings in Brent Cross and bring them back into community use. Crowdfund London pledged the maximum £50,000 to help build a small on-site café and open three of the derelict workshops. The buildings have a long history, with the site playing host to a woodland sub-manor held by John de Langton in 132 with the area officially recognised by the London Borough of Barnet as one of "special archaeological significance".

A selection of other *notable* Crowdfund projects from 2019

Please note
These projects are not in the Open House 2019 programme.

Livesey Exchange →

Design engagement event for the Livesey Exchange – a series of pop-up workspaces created in a disused underground car park of a public housing estate on the Old Kent Road. The Livesey Exchange aims at bringing life, new skills and jobs to a neglected corner of South East London. Proposals for the Livesey Exchange have been developed by local residents Nicholas Okwulu of social enterprise Pempeople and architect Ulrike Steven of what if: projects.

Colour in Romford →

A history making project in the London Borough of Havering, successfully commissioning and installing 4 large-scale murals in and around the town centre. Completed in 2017 with artists such as Ben Eine, Lucy Tiffany, Art+Believe and DZIA all on board, creating inspiring pieces of art for the whole town to enjoy.

Clapton Common →

Campaign image for 'A Village Hall for Clapton Common', with residents proposing future uses for a disused toilet block to be revived as a new community resource. The plan is to turn the abandoned eyesore into a beautiful new community kitchen and meeting place - Liberty Hall. Provide a community cookery school - sharing simple and fun ideas that will be accessible to everybody, including local communities who keep kosher. The Hall will be made available for community use, and the surrounding area will be landscaped to maximise biodiversity.

In Partnership with:

MAYOR OF LONDON

Exploring Old Oak and Park Royal

—

Once again **Open House London** is partnering with the Old Oak and Park Royal Development Corporation (OPDC) to celebrate the Mayor's plans to enhance this diverse neighbourhood with thousands of new homes and jobs

In terms of numbers, the mayoral development corporation bringing forward this new West London district will oversee the delivery of 25,500 new homes, generating 65,000 new jobs for the capital. At the forefront of OPDC's plan for regeneration is the celebration that makes Old Oak and Park Royal a 'Great Place, in the Making' by uncovering, connecting and showcasing its unique culture, creativity and heritage.

Connectivity is at the heart of Old Oak and Park Royal. Its origins were formed by the creation of the Grand Union Canal in 1801 and the railway network from 1838. These pieces of infrastructure are significant to the UK's wider transport and industrial history, but also had huge ramifications for the local area's sense of place and identity.

The transport infrastructure enabled a variety of industries and saw marked industrial growth in the early twentieth century. The area is now home to 2,000 businesses and over 40,000 employees, including big-name brands like McVitie's, Diageo and Boden.

Transport will again be the catalyst for growth at Old Oak and Park Royal. It is the only place in the country where High Speed 2 and Crossrail will meet, bringing a wealth of new development planned over the next 25 years, which will once more see this area change and evolve.

As landscapes change, however, communities can often feel that this change is happening to them, not for them. Recognising this, OPDC was awarded funding from the Great Place Scheme supported by the National Lottery through Arts Council England and the Heritage Lottery Fund. This national fund puts arts, culture and heritage at the heart of successful communities, both existing and new.

OPDC's Great Place Programme, titled 'In the Making', engages residents and businesses by putting on cultural and place-making activites; whether supporting small businesses with grants, delivering public space improvements and artwork, or supporting the production of limited-edition artist-made and designer products – all made in Park Royal.

This year, we are embracing Open House's 'social' theme by showcasing the workshops, engagement activities and exhibitions that 'In the Making' and the Great Place Programme are delivering, reflecting how people can influence their built environment. Playing on every meaning of 'social', John Lewis's Distribution Centre and Content Development, where all the company's social media and website content is produced, will be opening its doors.

We are also welcoming Preedy Glass artisan glass-makers and ETC Lighting, a global leader in lighting and rigging technology, as well as the Chapel at Wormwood Scrubs and our local Fire Station.

We would like to thank everyone who has agreed to open up for Open House and would encourage anyone who hasn't visited this fascinating part of North West London to visit, join a heritage walk or take part in one of our family workshops. Experience this part of London on the threshold of change, but change that will celebrate its heritage as well as telling its new story.

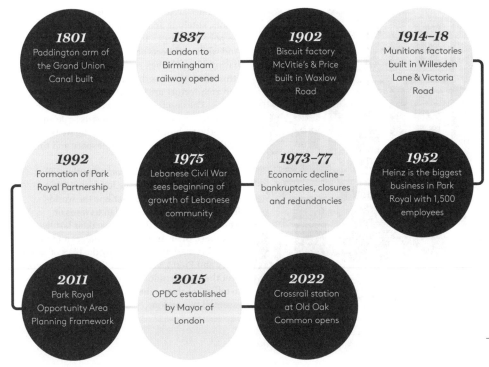

1801 Paddington arm of the Grand Union Canal built

1837 London to Birmingham railway opened

1902 Biscuit factory McVitie's & Price built in Waxlow Road

1914–18 Munitions factories built in Willesden Lane & Victoria Road

1992 Formation of Park Royal Partnership

1975 Lebanese Civil War sees beginning of growth of Lebanese community

1973–77 Economic decline – bankruptcies, closures and redundancies

1952 Heinz is the biggest business in Park Royal with 1,500 employees

2011 Park Royal Opportunity Area Planning Framework

2015 OPDC established by Mayor of London

2022 Crossrail station at Old Oak Common opens

Tailor-made townscape

—

As part of our *Social* themed programme this year we've teamed up with five renowned tailoring houses – Chittleborough and Morgan, Norton and Sons, Huntsman, Cad and The Dandy and Richard Anderson – to refresh your perspective on Savile Row, London's world leader in luxury tailoring

• Henry Poole © Ed Reeve

Sometimes architects think of themselves as tailors, stitching and weaving their designs – bespoke buildings – into the fabric of the city. And while architects are prone to metaphor – having a bagful when selling your idea is essential – this affectation has the ring of truth. Fashion and architecture are inherently linked: by our bodies. The best fashion, the best architecture, is always a response to us – our size, scale and proportions, how we move, how long we take to do things – and how we inhabit space and time.

Fashion and architecture come together effortlessly on Savile Row: in the luxury tailoring houses and art galleries that line the world-famous street, in the Georgian terraces on whose rooftops the Beatles gave their last live gig (above their Apple Records office) and in the smart modern additions by the likes of Eric Parry and Piercy & Company that have emerged over the past decade. This is a street with stories to tell, all of them inherently social, all of them essential to London.

Indeed Savile Row is so deeply embedded in our popular culture that it, like Baker Street and Sherlock Holmes, is home to a residence of a world-famous fictional person: Jules Verne has Phileas Fogg living at number 14 while Wodehouse butler Jeeves takes his name from Tailor Gieves and Hawkes at number 1.

Tailors however did not arrive on the street until the early 1800s, when high society alighted upon the district of Mayfair. Until then, from when it was first laid out in the 1690s and built upon the kitchen gardens of Burlington House (now the Royal Academy) it was home to military officers and politicians. And if the street built its reputation on the custom of Beau Brummel and the Prince Regent, and that era famed for excess, it has also proved to be adept at recognising and inspiring change as time has marched onwards.

Whether dressing Fred Astaire for his 1930s movie *Top Hat*, which saw Cary Grant, Bing Crosbie and Frank Sinatra, come here for their own makeover, or kitting out John Lennon,

Ringo Star and Paul McCartney in Tommy Nutter suits for the Abbey Road photoshoot at the tail end of the 1960s, Savile Row has consistently attuned with popular culture. The Edwardian 'Teddy Boy' look emerged here too, in the late 1940s.

Today, the revolution is in diversity and equality, with more female tailors and tailoring for women comfortably at home in a neighbourhood once exclusively male. And while the first female head cutter was appointed as recently as 2011, the street now plays host to Gormley & Gamble, the first tailor on Savile Row to cater exclusively to women.

As for the words tailors use day to day that architects happily steal, Savile Row can also lay claim to originating one of them, *bespoke*, whose original definition 'discussed in advance' was first used to describe tailor-made garments by craftsmen on this very street.

• Top-image: Huntsman © Ed Reeve. Bottom-image: Campbell Carey, Creative Director at Huntsman

• Savile Row © Ed Reeve

In Partnership with:

CLARION
HOUSING GROUP

Clarion's calling

—

What is the *circular economy* and how
is it shaping the future of London's built
environment, asks Clarion Housing, the
UK's largest housing association

In the world of the built environment, new homes and place-making there is a quiet revolution underway. The term *circular economy* has made the jump from academia, a handful of influential books and think-tanks, and into the mainstream.

To reinforce that mainstreaming, you only have to look at the new draft London Plan. The final version looks certain to include a requirement for circular economy statements for all referable schemes (those that need GLA review before planning can be secured).

**Those statements will need to confirm
how constructors will:**
- Conserve resources, increase efficiency and source ethically
- Design to eliminate waste (and for ease of maintenance)
- Manage waste sustainably at the highest value

Alongside a suite of new design policy requirements (including designing for disassembly) it's clear that if you want to build anything in London at even moderate scale, you will have to adapt. For an industry that is responsible for 59% of the UK's total 202 million tonnes of waste (DEFRA, 2018) a significant change is required.

But what do we mean by circular economy? There are many definitions but one of the better ones comes from The Waste and Resources Action Programme: "A circular economy is an alternative to a traditional linear economy (make, use, dispose) in which we keep resources in use for as long as possible, extract the maximum value from them whilst in use, then recover and regenerate products and materials at the end of each service life."

This circularity is a principle Clarion embraces through our £2.6billion regeneration programme. We recognise the importance of the approach for the communities we serve. But we also acknowledge our responsibility as the UK's largest social landlord to help steer our industry in a direction which better recognises the need to retain finite resources and think about the impact of our activities in much longer timeframes. Our regeneration programmes, with a particular focus on the 1,800-home High Path project in South Wimbledon, give us an ideal opportunity to begin to apply those principles.

As you might expect of a social landlord, our own take on the circular economy includes not only the emphasis on waste reduction and design seen in the new London Plan, but also social value – supporting community reuse projects, meanwhile strategies for underused spaces, promoting sharing economy initiatives and actively promoting higher rates of household and community recycling.

Embedding these sometimes competing aspirations (designing highly efficient new buildings whilst at the same time allowing for their deconstruction into their component parts in 80 or 90 years time is a quandary for architects) will in some cases be a case of trial and error. But learning and doing better next time is in itself a circular activity.

We will not be alone in this learning. All major procurement for Clarion regeneration activities now includes specific questions and expectations around circular economy. We are looking for suppliers and partners who embrace these same principles and learn and share learning alongside us and the communities we serve.

Perhaps most positive of all has been the reaction of residents who are often far more aware of and concerned about these issues than many in our industry, asking the awkward questions and pushing for better answers. So as we celebrate all that is wonderful in London's built environment during Open House Weekend, it is Clarion's belief that the circular economy has a very significant contribution to make to the future of London. It really is an idea whose time has come.

Find out more
Search 'Clarion Circular Economy Strategy Merton' to learn more about Clarion's South Wimbledon regeneration plans.

• Artist impression of High Path, Wimbledon

Designed with all five senses in mind

—

Wembley Park is changing perceptions of *'home'* with new rental models and pioneering sense-based design

We're in Peckham, the diagonally opposite end of London to where Julian Tollast, Wembley Park's head of masterplanning and design, usually plies his trade. And the tour he's leading isn't a typical exploration of local heritage, rather, it is centred on how we can design better places if we engage all five of our senses.

What does it mean to go beyond seeing – to feel and touch, for example, or even smell the buildings and places we design and make? These were among the questions Julian, participating in Open City's Citymaking Sessions (p.36-7) asked as he wound his way through the main roads and side streets of Del Boy's stomping ground.

It is this intense line of enquiry, this dedication to the value of great design and how it can be opened up as an idea for everyone to enjoy, that is driving Julian's approach in shaping Wembley Park. Designing for the five senses is just one way Julian's team is shaping the future of London's neighbourhoods. A great example of this approach can be found on Olympic Way, the main pedestrian promenade between Wembley Stadium and Wembley Park's railway station. A clutch of new trees, a variety of species selected from the temperate zones around the world and planted earlier this year, now line the avenue, their textures, colours and smells transforming the feel of the emerging townscape.

Julian's goal is to develop a culture of sociality at Wembley Park, that sense of being involved in a place alongside others: all 20,000 of them. Because what marks out Wembley Park most significantly, is its status as the largest single-site purpose-built PRS development anywhere in the UK.

And renting necessitates a different approach to urban living. "We want people to really use the buildings here – the homes they rent with their built-in facilities, from rooftop gardens (with cinema screens) to gyms, shared lounges, landscaped gardens and private dining rooms," says Julian.

Did you know

Initial records of a place called Wembley dates from 825AD. Saxon people from northern Germany had occupied this part of England (known as Middlesex – land of the Middle Saxons). One family had settled here, and their home was known as "Wemba lea" – Wemba's clearing in the forest. Over hundreds of years, more woodland was cleared, and by 1500 most of the Wembley area was made up of hedged fields.

There are four completed rental developments so far: Alto, with its sky terrace, pet-friendly Landsby; Alameda, with its rooftop cinema; and Montana and Dakota, the first two blocks to complete, overlooking manicured gardens and expansive ponds.

Nestled among them, residents are served by a blend of small independent shops, London's largest Boxpark, a new theatre, London Designer Outlet and access to the tube. Technology and comms play a key role too in helping to shape a local culture, explains Julian, for everyone who lives there. Tipi, the lifestyle-focused rental brand managing the residents' rental experience, for example, uses social media to build communities around shared interests and group events (a weekly quiz night, for example, but also supperclubs with Masterchef finalists!).

Much of the ethos Julian and his team have fostered in Wembley Park comes together in The Yellow – a visually striking and spatially generous community building for everyone who lives, works and studies in Wembley Park. As Julian explains Yellow's offer all comes back to the five senses and how we engage with them.

"The Yellow is crucial in this respect," he says. "You can get fit there or learn new skills. It encourages residents to socialise in creative ways: like the Saturday morning cookery class run by a City of London worker – where smell, taste, touch, sight and sound come together, against a backdrop of contemporary design."

New London: The scale of development at Wembley Park
Wembley Park: *85 acres*
Nine Elms: *70 acres*
Earl's Court: *69 acres*
Kings Cross: *66 acres*
Canada Water: *46 acres*
Elephant & Castle: *24 acres*

In Partnership with:

**Pollard
Thomas
Edwards**

Reconciling cité and ville

—

Pollard Thomas Edwards Architects is
playing a *leading role* in shaping the future
of London's residential townscape

New Ground, pg45

Designed for – and with – a group of older
women keen on the benefits of co-housing,
New Ground provides 25 homes with shared
facilities and communal gardens. "We're
unique, but we don't want to be!" as founder
member Shirley Meredeen puts it.

Housing. When you read that word what
picture forms in your mind's eye? A tower?
A mansion block? A suburban semi? Or a kind
of metropolitan cocktail with a restaurant on
the ground floor over a subterranean cinema,
with flats and balconies above?

For the hundred-plus architects at Pollard
Thomas Edwards in Islington, it's probably all
of these things and more, so absorbed is the
team in the challenge of providing London with
well-designed housing for all ages and incomes.

But creating good housing – and neighbourhoods people want to live in – is as much art
as science. And it's really quite hard to do. In
his book *Building and Dwelling*, which explores
'ethics and the city', Richard Sennett describes
the city as an artefact composed of two distinct
elements; the cité, which represents the
traditions, behaviours and beliefs of a place,
and the ville – the buildings, streets, squares
and parks, that are its physical substance.
In other words, a city's mind and body.

Colby Lodge, pg79
This five-storey almshouse-inspired scheme of 20 one-bedroom dual aspect flats is for older locals in Walthamstow. It is characterised by its richly appointed communal facilities, including a large garden room, a hairdressing and therapy salon, a laundry and guest suite.

Sennett argues that cité can refer to a kind of consciousness – how people want to live collectively. But if this is inhibited by the ville, the physical stage... well, we have a problem, a trust deficit even. This is the challenge then that designing good housing – and neighbourhoods – presents. And it is one PTE is considering with thoughtfulness and aplomb.

You can sense how PTE approaches its craft – places where people enjoy being part of something bigger than their own home, where 'cité' and 'ville' are in concert – in the variety of projects the canal-side architect is showcasing during the Open House Weekend this year. From its New Ground third-age housing in Barnet, designed in partnership with the client, an all-women co-housing group, to its Deptford Lounge project, which draws together a public library, computer labs, study areas, a café, artists' studios and keyworker housing, a rooftop ball court and a new town square – the evidence on show is of an architect at full tilt, shaping a new London predicated on sociality.

St Paul's Way, pg73
A ground-breaking project encompassing a new school, a new mosque and over a hundred new homes. Its green credentials are notable with great energy efficiency, 183 cycle storage spaces and easy access to public transport. Mile End underground station is a 10 minute walk away.

Sociality, as Sennett has it, is a kind of modest fraternity that arises when people are doing something together rather than simply being together, offering "an emotional counterpoint to impersonality" he writes. It begs the question whether architecture can enable this condition – not simply bring people together but gather people in one place to do something together. Indeed, should this be the minimum that architecture gifts the citymaking process?

PTE's Open House Weekend projects seem to be saying yes. In Tower Hamlets, Bow Garden Square mosque, school, community centre and flats for Poplar HARCA and Telford Homes is as it sounds – a whole neighbourhood design that also includes a community park and playground, providing safe areas for children to play.

Not forgetting Colby Lodge too, in Waltham Forest. It's more modest in its third-age housing scope but with the added bonus of being both secluded by trees and richly textured with social spaces, while also being a short walk from the heart of Walthamstow, its restaurants and cinema screens in PTE's Scene complex. The emphasis is always on people and how best to put them in contact with others.

PTE will also be opening up the (film-set pretty) Diespeker Wharf, where its industrial-arcadian studios are located. For a sense of its long-term thinking, turn up for their 'back-yard' tours – informed wanders around the Packington neighbourhood and City Road basin in Islington, which they have been transforming for years now, street by street, block by block.

Tidemill, incl. Deptford Lounge
& Market Yard, pg78
Part of Lewisham's regeneration masterplan for central Deptford, this project is unique, truly. The 'co-locational' design includes a district library, a new building for Tidemill Academy and Resolution Studios, a complex of new duplex homes over studios and exhibition space for local artists.

Social City
The Developer's View

In Partnership with:

ROCKET
PROPERTIES

Chairman and co-founder of Rocket Properties Tom Appleton describes how building more public realm can be good for business

Public realm has been in the conscience of developers, if not the actual public that it is intended to please, for a number of years now. The rather cynical view of, 'well if you want to get a decent planning consent you might need to squeeze a bit of public realm in there' has been prevalent for years. Indeed, the wider public are more likely to be unaware that the brand new micro park across from their workplace, or the benches and box hedging outside all 300,000 square feet of glass and steel making up the office next door, was actually put there for them.

Thankfully this attitude – among developer and the public – has matured in recent years. As has the concept of public realm. The term now covers parts of a building, the crossover spaces – often the ground floor, sometimes the rooftop, but in stairwells and other communal areas too – where office workers and residential dwellers can mix, in some cases with the passing public.

In urban-scaled developments such spaces can come in the form of gardens (with eye-pleasing topiary) but more commonly and more usefully (in terms of pure business and forging a social culture) these spaces are increasingly taken up as softer commercial offerings with food courts and pop-up retail.

You can see this at Thomas More Square (near St. Katherine's Dock) where the fairly bland gaps (not even old school public realm!) come alive at lunchtime to offer food from all four corners of the world. This brings people together not just from the same office, but also other blocks creating one supersized lunchtime co-working space.

But how the property sector can make a genuine contribution to the social life of a city is of course tied up with economics. Going forward, public realm – or social spaces as perhaps we should re-name this aspect of our cities – has to offer an amenity for people in the buildings alongside, as well as people passing by. And while this will increase the attractiveness of the development to incoming tenants, in most cases it will allow the landlord to charge a premium too.

Housing charity Shelter on the pressing need to build more, bigger and better social homes – for everyone

Looking at some of the gems included in this year's Open House there is much to admire – London can be a hugely impressive site when it comes to our buildings. Yet there is one area where our track record, particularly in recent years, leaves much to be desired – the building of social homes.

One hundred years ago this year, the Addison Act kick-started a widespread programme of social house building with the aim that everyone, no matter their income, could have a place to call home. A century on and last year only 741 social homes were built in London, while 232,409 households in the capital are stuck on housing waiting lists.

This failure to provide enough social homes is the root cause of our housing emergency. In January 2018, Shelter brought together 16 commissioners from across the political spectrum, as well as the Grenfell community, to form its social housing commission. Earlier this year the commission launched its findings, calling for a 20-year programme to deliver 3.1 million more social homes. Social housing is currently an ambulance service for the most vulnerable.

As important as that is, we need a new approach to social housing that will provide a decent, affordable home for all those currently priced out and struggling. This will make social housing not just a safety net for those in greatest need, but also a step up for young families trying to get on and save for their future. A step up that will enable them to put down roots, to thrive, to plan for their futures and their children's futures.

To realise this vision we need to build more social homes. And we need to make sure the sector is not just bigger, but better – good-quality homes built in the right places for tenants who feel able to make their voices heard.

This is not an easy task, but it is doable if the will is there. To find our more, or to show your support for building more social housing: visit shelter.org.uk/buildmore

England's housing crisis in numbers
- 741 social homes were built in 2018
- 232,409 households stuck on housing waiting lists
- 3.1m new homes across England needed by 2039

Few London buildings command their neighbourhood as completely as Balfron Tower does

Even from East India Dock Road, speeding past in a car, you can feel it: The Modernism. The continental tang. This is architecture with a capital S - for 'Swagger'. It's architect, Erno Goldfinger, Hungarian by birth, Modernist by creed, moved to London in the 1930s, after a stint in Le Corbusier's Paris studios. Is it any wonder his vision would be this bold?

You can get up close to the Grade II*-listed edifice during Open House Weekend this year. It's back in the programme after a soon to be completed revamp by Londonewcastle, a joint venture with partners Poplar HARCA and Telford Homes first announced in 2015.

As part of the refurbishment works, the architects on the project, Studio Egret West, has upgraded its thermal and acoustic performance, targeting BREEAM "Excellent". Working in collaboration with Ab Rogers Design, they have also overseen the careful selection of the interior finishes of the tower's apartments and maisonettes. The tower's iconic form and concrete façade remain and have been carefully restored, repaired and cleaned, now with an additional rooftop garden, for use by the residents, and the playground will be restored and updated at ground level for public use.

In addition, inspired by Goldfinger's communal Jazz/Pop room, the service tower will include shared spaces for the residents, such as a music room, workshop, screening room, as well as cookery and dining rooms.

Six heritage apartments, one of each of the original flat typologies designed by Goldfinger, are being reinstated, including the original apartment that Erno and Ursula Goldfinger famously lived in during 1968 to experience high-rise living. Designed by Studio Egret West, they will be working as close as possible to Goldfinger's design, remaining faithful to the original room layouts while meeting today's needs – such as the inclusion of modern appliances – alongside reclaimed heritage details and a historic colour palette.

Whether Goldfinger's experiment worked is a debate often heard, and it will be interesting to see how Londonewcastle's regeneration of Balfron and the wider Brownfield Estate begins to connect with a new generation of Londoners intrigued by the capital's social and aesthetic histories. It's a great place to start.

Social City
The Architect's View

Britain's biggest – and most admired – architect,
Foster + Partners, welcomes the world to its
Battersea riverside home once again this year

For the past 22 years, we have opened our London studios to visitors for the annual Open House Weekend, giving them a glimpse into the creative process behind some of the projects at the practice. Last year, we welcomed over 4,000 visitors, offering them an opportunity to see the way we work, with interactive displays that provides insight into the work of our specialist teams, alongside an exhibition focusing on upcoming projects.

This year's special event coincides with the publication of the Foster + Partners Portfolio, a complete and extraordinary account of the first 50 years of the practice. For the first time ever, Portfolio features photography of every project completed in the practice's first five decades, as well as drawings of its most important unrealised designs. With over 480 carefully selected images – many previously unpublished – the book highlights the enormous contribution the practice has made to a range of design disciplines.

Visitors to Foster + Partners' Riverside studio who register at the door will get a chance to win a free copy of Portfolio, which will also be available to buy from the practice bookshop throughout the Open House Weekend.

See the fold-out at back of the guide for a one-day itinerary of Foster + Partners buildings to visit.

All Foster+Partners buildings in Open House this year
- Foster + Partners (studio) in Wandsworth
- City Hall in Southwark
- One Bishops Square in Tower Hamlets
- Capital City Academy in Brent
- Bloomberg European Headquarters in City of London
- Crossrail Place Roof Garden in Tower Hamlets
- HM Treasury in Westminster

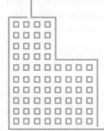

Social City
The Cultural View

Open House has teamed up with Art Fund to explore sociality – doing things together – by visiting museums and galleries, all while getting to know each other better in an inspiring setting

Think of gazing up at Hope, the blue whale in the Natural History Museum, puzzling over Salvador Dalí's Lobster Telephone together at Tate Modern, or taking in the opulence of the Arab Hall at Leighton House. Some things are better when you're bouncing off someone else. Art Fund's new podcast, Meet Me at the Museum, is all about these shared experiences. Listen to well-known guests as they take someone they love to a favourite museum or gallery and enjoy their musings on life stirred up by some of the UK's best-loved cultural venues.

If you want to get more out of art, and maybe take a loved one too, the National Art Pass gives you free access to over 240 museums, galleries and historic houses across the UK, as well as 50% off entry to major exhibitions – all for just £70 a year. You'll also be helping Art Fund to raise vital funds for museums and galleries so that they can buy and share more art with everyone.

Discover new museums, galleries and historic places all year round with a National Art Pass.

Annual membership includes
- Art Map – a comprehensive annual guidebook on using your pass at over 700 venues
- A subscription to Art Quarterly magazine with insightful and exclusive features
- Art in your inbox email subscription – your fortnightly guide to great art across the UK
- Free entry to 240 venues, including Kensington Palace, Handel & Hendrix in London and Cardiff Castle
- 50% off major exhibitions, including British Museum, Design Museum, Tate and the V&A

Learn more at artfund.org/opencities

In Partnership with:

MARGARET
HOWELL

Privately owned public spaces

—

Are POPS the future of London's *public realm*
asks Rory Olcayto ahead of the Margaret Howell
debate this October

From Wimbledon Common to Hyde Park,
Hampstead Heath to Epping Forest, as *Observer*
architecture critic Rowan Moore reminded us
in the 2016 Open House Guide, "they are there
to be enjoyed (because) of battles fought against
their enclosure and development". Public space
in London has often been hard won, and almost
always hard fought for.

Yet in 2019, the best new public space – or rather
the seemingly most flocked to, most vibrant,
most talked about public space in London –
isn't public at all. Rather, it's a POPS – a privately
owned public space, run by the neighbourhood
developer Argent. It's called Granary Square, and
it's slap bang in the middle of London, the very
heart of the new Kings Cross.

Are privately owned public spaces the future of London's 'public' realm?

Open House Presents:
Join us for a debate on privately owned public spaces with Sarah Gaventa, Founder of Made Public. Director of the Illuminated River Foundation. Hosted by Margaret Howell.

Date
2 October 2019

Find out more
Visit open-city.org.uk/talks for more info and how to book.

Granary Square has been up and running since 2012. Designed by Townshend Landscape Architects, it occupies the land in front of Lewis Cubitt's granary building (designed in 1852 to store Lincolnshire wheat for London's bakers) that now houses the world-class art school Central St Martin's.

It's big, around 8,000m², similar in size to Trafalgar Square. Both squares are famous for their fountains – although at Kings Cross they encourage citizens to linger on a hot summer day while Trafalgar's Lutyen-designed efforts form part of a wider urban plan for the square that subtly limits potential for "riotous assembly" – a perennial concern for the rulers of London – of all capital cities – down the ages.

You can find POPS everywhere in London. Another long-established POPS is MORE London, the flagstoned-expanse of bankside land in Southwark on which City Hall is built.

If you've ever wondered why you don't see protests outside Norman Foster's 'crash-helmet' HQ for the GLA – placards targeting the Mayor in the same way we see countless political gatherings in Westminster at Parliament Square – it's because MORE London's owner, doesn't permit them to happen.

The quandry is clear: in some cases POPS make better use of the public realm, giving the public more of London to enjoy together – anyone who compares and contrasts the spatial freedoms offered by Granary Square with those of London's most famous piazza at Trafalgar gets this. On the other hand, POPS can limit the kind of behaviour we have come to take for granted in British culture and public life – the right to protest, for example, a point made clearly at MORE London.

And it's this rub – this very obvious conflict of interests – that set the stage for our next event hosted by Margaret Howell, POPS culture: are privately owned public spaces the future of London's 'public' realm?

In Partnership with:

jackson|coles

The invisible hand

—

Who actually makes cities? How do they come about?
And who makes sure the *buildings we create* for our
cities actually work the way they are meant to?

Designing and making buildings, neighbourhoods and cities is the ultimate social act. It makes us who we are. To build cities is to be civilised. Cities are civilisation. And most of us today, all over the planet, live in cities.

Yet architects, engineers, developers, builders and clients tend to attract the plaudits because their work is so obviously tangible – you can see it! – but today, it is the cost consultant, the project manager, sometimes an organisation that provides both services, that ultimately advises on the key decisions around a project's prospects. It's all about time and money. In addition statutory roles under Construction Design Management (CDM) Regulations, which oversee health, safety and welfare and manages a project team's wider, longer term responsibilities - have also emerged as one of the key skillsets at play in the art of citymaking.

Open House partner Jackson Coles is one such company doing all of these things. The firm has a rich portfolio of projects that includes two Stirling Prize winners, a pioneering co-working hotspot in East London; an old tea warehouse in the heart of Shoreditch, an experimental workplace with a running track on its roof and, although it is yet to open, a 'cooking community' building in the New Covent Garden Market in Nine Elms.

This year, two Jackson Coles buildings, the White Collar Factory (of running track fame) designed by architects AHMM, and Congress House, designed in the 1940s and built in the 1950s for the TUC, and refurbished more recently by Hugh Broughton Architects, are featured in the Open House programme. The first of them, the White Collar Factory, is a construction industry favourite, inspiring the professionals who worked on it – including the Jackson Coles team. As the firm's Ruth Lees says, "It's more than a building; it's a neighbourhood". It's often seen as a single tower but is in fact a group of buildings (Old Street Yard) that includes restaurants and homes. And the new public space creates new pedestrian routes – it's proper city-making."

Architecture after all, is a pragmatic art, it provides a function, it needs to work

Nestling on a side street in Bloomsbury, Congress House, says the 20th Century Society, is one of the most important British buildings of the 1950s. This was recognised in 1988 when it was listed (Grade II*) but by that point it was already falling into disrepair. Maintenance and restoration work began in the late nineties overseen by Hugh Broughton Architects and by 2016, with Jackson Coles' involvement, a transparent ETFE roof – a translucent polymer 'sheet' that transmits more light than glass and insulates better too – was installed over the internal courtyard. This facilitated the reinstatement of the original glass roof over the conference hall below and the conservation of original fabric, including an important sculpture by Sir Jacob Epstein.

Ensuring these projects are built safely, that they comply with an array of building regulations, that they are costed properly and to the specifications agreed by the design team and client – this is the reality of citymaking. Architecture, after all, is a pragmatic art, it provides a function, it needs to work – and to cost what you thought it would before you dug the foundations. Projects really do stray from their original design intent under time or cost pressures. Jackson Coles approach is to maintain the joy in the projects they advise on, working so the whole delivery team can stay true to a shared vision. It's hard work, and even harder to see. But without these skills we'd struggle to be sure that the buildings we create for our cities are actually fit for purpose.

Elements Photography Competition

Following on from the success of 2018, the Elements photography competition returns for Open House London 2019 weekend this September.

We want you to scour London's magnificent townscape in search of the best building 'elements' in the city. The best façade, the best corridor, the best door, the best staircase and so on. Why? Because London's best buildings – like all great architecture – are assemblages formed of elements, that come together to make a functional, inspiring whole.

This year we have partnered with the writers behind Curiocity – a 26-chapter book weaving together facts, myths, stories, riddles, essays, diagrams, illustrations and itineraries that explore every aspect of life in the capital. At the heart of each chapter is a hand-drawn map, charting everything from the city's islands and underground spaces to its erogenous zones and dystopian futures. Taking you from Atlas to Zones, via Congestion, Folkmoot, Pearls and Xenophilia, Curiocity will transform the way you see London.

The best photograph posted on Instagram for each of the 10 elements will receive a copy of Curiocity. Competition closes 4 October and winners, chosen by a panel of judges, will be announced 11 October.

How to enter
- Look at architecture in a fresh way and get involved in our 'Elements' photography competition
- Follow @openhouselondon on Instagram
- Post your Elements photos onto Instagram
- Make sure to hashtag *#OHL19*, the building and include the tag for the element you've found (see list)

Elements
Floor *#openhousefloor*
Ceiling *#openhouseceiling*
Room *#openhouseroom*
Door *#openhousedoor*
Window *#openhousewindow*
Façade *#openhousefacade*
Corridor *#openhousecorridor*
Fireplace *#openhousefireplace*
Stair *#openhousestair*
Bathroom *#openhousebathroom*

Follow us

 @openhouselondon2019
 @openhouselondon
 @openhouselondon

2018 Winning Entry
Swiss Cottage Library, captured by Peter Berzanskis
@thespacecowboyphotography

#SocialMediainArchitecture

Earlier this year we asked our online followers how important social media is to the live experience of architecture and if architects should start to pay attention to the comments and their role on social media. We asked the public a series of questions and polls to find out their thoughts

Open House social media stats: June 2019

 15.8k   *32.9k*   *27.7k*

---

01 **Do you use social media for professional or personal accounts?**

 Personal

 Professional

86%   **14%**

---

02 **If you see a picture of a building or place you like which is near you, would that encourage you to go out and visit that building?**

Yes! Gives good inspiration and ideas for seeing new buildings and places or holiday destinations.

"

Absolutely – people need to know about places to visit them and social media is one of the best ways to get building/places in front of people.

---

03 **Do you feel architecture has been made more accessible to others outside the industry through social media?**

 Yes

No

78%   **22%**

04 We asked our followers "Do you know what an _Instagrammable building_ is?"

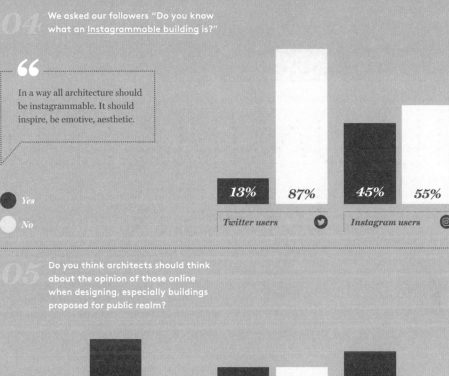

> ❝ In a way all architecture should be instagrammable. It should inspire, be emotive, aesthetic.

● Yes
○ No

13%	87%
Twitter users 🐦	
45%	55%
Instagram users 📷	

---

05 Do you think architects should think about the opinion of those online when designing, especially buildings proposed for public realm?

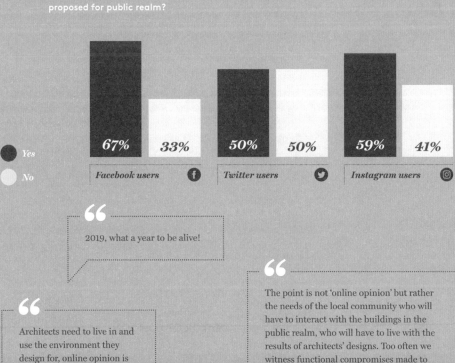

● Yes
○ No

67%	33%	50%	50%	59%	41%
Facebook users f		Twitter users 🐦		Instagram users 📷	

> ❝ 2019, what a year to be alive!

> ❝ Architects need to live in and use the environment they design for, online opinion is irrelevant.

> ❝ The point is not 'online opinion' but rather the needs of the local community who will have to interact with the buildings in the public realm, who will have to live with the results of architects' designs. Too often we witness functional compromises made to enable the most striking or pure design.

ILLUMINATED RIVER

We hope you enjoy!
 @IlluminatedRiver
 @IlluminatedRiver
 @IlluminatedRiv
#IlluminatedRiver
www.illuminatedriver.london

Illuminated River is a new public art commission to light up to 15 bridges on the Thames. The first phase of the project is now lit — London, Cannon Street, Southwark and Millennium Bridges. Conceived by American light artist Leo Villareal and British architects Lifschutz Davidson Sandilands, the project is delivered by the Illuminated River Foundation.

On September 21st 2019, as part of Open House London weekend, there will be an evening boat tour of the Illuminated River first four bridges (full details in Open House weekend programme listings). This event forms part of the wider Illuminated River programme of public events, please visit our website for further details.

To celebrate the project, composers from Guildhall School of Music & Drama have been commissioned by the Illuminated River Foundation to create new music inspired by the bridges and artwork, available for free download from our website.

FUNDERS

 ARCADIA

 BLAVATNIK
FAMILY FOUNDATION

SUPPORTED BY
MAYOR OF LONDON

ROTHSCHILD
FOUNDATION

Open House Friends

Join Open House as a Friend today to ensure that we can continue to open up London's best buildings.

Friends' subscriptions, donations and benefactors all fund our vital work in opening up London's architecture to all, for free. Become a Friend to receive a range of benefits.

Friend of Open House

- 20% discount on all purchases online, including our Open House Architecture year-round tours
- Advance FREE booking for annual Thornton Lecture, with a speaker of international repute
- Free annual Citymaking publication
- Free Open House Guide – be among the first to receive the annual Open House Guide, printed in August – starting 2020
- Exclusive quarterly newsletter content

Subscription Cost
£45 by direct debit, otherwise £50

opencityshop.myshopify.com
/products/friend-of-open-house

Student Friend

For student or low-income Open House enthusiasts, we offer a heavily discounted rate. Contact Open City to find out more:
hello@open-city.org.uk

Subscription Cost
£15 discounted rate

Premium Friend of Open House

- Free ticket to the annual Thornton Lecture
- Free annual Citymaking publication
- 20% discount on all purchases online, including our Open House Architecture year-round tours
- Free Open House Guide – be among the first to receive the annual Open House Guide, printed in August – Starting 2020.
- Exclusive quarterly newsletter content

* 2 free tickets to an exclusive Premium Friend 'Evening with…' event at an outstanding private home, with the architects
* 2 free tickets to the Open House launch party in mid-September, at an outstanding building
* Acknowledgement on website and in the Open House Guide – starting 2020.

Subscription Cost
£180 by direct debit, otherwise £200

opencityshop.myshopify.com
/products/premium-friend-of-open-house

Citymaking Sessions

Citymaking Sessions is a new events programme produced by Open City for professionals and anyone interested in how cities are made.

It has five aims:

- Promote an equitable approach to citymaking at every scale
- Promote true collaboration between professional disciplines, public organisations and citizen-led initiatives
- Engage with raw, new, powerful ideas that reconceive what cities can be
- Build a dedicated audience and network of citymakers from all walks of life
- Hold Citymaking Sessions in relevant locations, from which delegates can learn

The first Citymaking Sessions was on 27 June at Bold Tendencies in Peckham's Multi-storey Car Park, and featured a range of talks, debates, workshops and interactive design challenges curated by educator and urban development expert Sven Muendner of Beispiel (and formerly Bold Tendencies). Inspired by Open House, the choice of venue matters.

"We want our Citymaking delegates to learn from the environment they're in too and Bold Tendencies' transformation of the car park off Rye Lane into a world-beating arts venue is the stuff of legend," says Open City director Rory Olcayto. "It's genuine ground-up development of a kind we still see too little of in London."

Delegates enjoyed learning from a wide range of speakers including Argent's Nick Searl, architects Julia Barfield – who gave the keynote Thornton Lecture – and Roz Barr and Katerina Dionysopoulou, who in conversation discussed the merits of making 'stuff' in an increasing digital, ephemeral age.

"A superb first symposium and I look forward to more to come over the years!" – Sharmaine Lovegrove, Founder & Publisher of Dialogue Books.

citymaking.org

• Photography © Steve Lavers

Open House Tours

Our year-round programme of architecture tours by foot, bike and boat are led by specialist guides helping you look at the themes and issues shaping the capital today – from the design of homes, to infrastructure and urban landscapes.

Photography tours
Join architectural photographers to learn how to snap great buildings:
- Wren to Rogers: an exploration of the City of London and its hugely impressive mix of history and modernity
- Architecture by Night: photographing the City's iconic structures where lighting dramatically re-enforces their night time presence (spring and autumn)
- Capturing Battersea: photograph this rapidly changing urban landscape

Walking tours
- Transforming Nine Elms & Battersea
- Olympics and Beyond
- Mostly PoMo
- King's Cross Renaissance
- Navigating East London: the Lea Valley, linking Stratford & Canary Wharf
- The Real Lea Valley: industry and art beyond the Olympic Park

Boat Tours: Architecture on the Thames
Journey down the Thames looking at iconic landmarks that make London so architecturally diverse. Led by our specialist guide, architect Benedict O'Looney, whose in-depth knowledge guarantees deep insight and thoughtful commentary. Select from two different tours exploring different sections of the Thames, with a different guest speaker on board each tour highlighting a different theme.

- Architecture on the Thames East
- Architecture on the Thames Central

An Evening With...
Exclusive opportunities to tour award-winning and unique London homes with the architect and/or owner, over drinks and nibbles. Now including out of London houses too!

tours@open-city.org.uk
open-city.org.uk/tours

Open City Learning

Our learning programmes for schools and communities use the city and its buildings, infrastructure and the public realm – to inform and inspire.

Architecture in Schools
A creative learning programme for Key Stage Two primary school pupils.

The aim of the programme is to inspire the next generation of city-shapers and for participants to understand how architecture informs the world around us. The programme also aims to train teachers on how architecture can be used to teach a variety of subjects including Art, Design, Numeracy, Literacy, Geography and Science while improving children's drawing, model-making, communication and problem-solving skills.

Accelerate
A pioneering education and mentoring programme aimed at increasing diversity in the architecture profession.

It gives students the confidence and skills needed to make strong university applications to study architecture and subjects linked to the built environment.

Each year Accelerate provides 30-40 academically able and ambitious Year 12 and 13 students from across London with:

- One-to-one mentoring with an architect at their London practice
- Skills development workshops in a university environment
- Peer-to-peer learning with university students
- An architecture project brief devised by UCL and Open City
- Guidance workshops on portfolio production and university applications

Creative Curriculum
Each year the Creative Curriculum programme enables 280 pupils from Camden, Hackney, Tower Hamlets and Westminster to explore spaces they previously haven't visited. It supports children's learning through facilitating the investigation of public works of art and surrounding architecture and the creation of high-quality sculptures and animations.

Open House Families

Open House Families is London's free festival of architecture exclusively for children and their families.

Each year in June, families can take part in a huge variety of hands-on workshops including craft and design activities, Lego building, storytelling sessions and messy play against the backdrop of some of London's most exciting urban landscapes.

In 2019 Open House Families were excited to introduce family-friendly building tours hosted by local children and workshops designed specifically for families with special education needs and/or disabilities.

Open House Families this September
From April to June an incredible team of children from St Paul's and St John's Primary Schools researched, curated and led tours of St Paul's Cathedral, the Barbican (pictured right), NLA and the Museum of London as part of the June festival. This September, look out for the Open House Families activity trail created by these children, so you and your family can join them on their adventure.

Check open-city.org.uk for updates on what other activities will be held just for families over the big weekend!

The learning team would like to thank its incredible sponsors for supporting all of Open City's learning programmes, including the Canary Wharf Group, Build Studios, the National Education Union, The Bartlett, British Land, the City of London, the John Lyon's Charity, 30 St Mary Axe, Kings Cross and Here East.

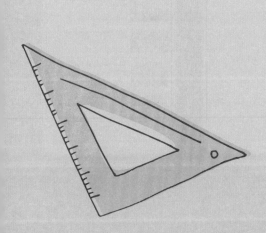

The Open House App

A free guide to London's best buildings & places.
Download the Open House app to view the festival programme on the go with up-to-date listings, opening times and pictures of every building participating. By using the app during the weekend you will be able to discover new buildings near your current location.

- Save favourites to plan your weekend
- Filter results by day, accessibility, architectural type and period
- Explore Open House-curated highlights and collections
- Directions to buildings near you

 Our App also lets you donate and support Open City straight from your phone!

Essential information

How to use this guide

Open House is part-funded by individual local authorities, all 33 of which are participating in our 27th year. We hope to continue to be able to showcase the whole of the capital. Keep lobbying your local councillors to ensure their inclusion for next year!

Events to celebrate Car Free Day will be taking place across London on Sunday 22 September. For the most up-to-date information and to plan your journey, please visit london.gov.uk/reimagine

How can I get another copy of the programme?

You can buy copies from online at opencityshop.myshopify.com or in store at the RIBA book shop, Museum of London book shop and selected Foyles stores. Copies can also be picked up free from participating London libraries from 20 August onwards. The 2020 Guide will be available to pre-order online from 25 September 2019.

Audio-described tours

VocalEyes, a national charity bringing art, architecture and heritage to life for blind and partially sighted people, will be leading audio-described tours at selected buildings again this year. Visit vocaleyes.co.uk to find out more.

Do I need to book?

Most buildings are on a first-come basis, however a few of the properties will require you to book in advance. Where this is through the building, contact details are given. Open House regrets that we cannot guarantee availability of places.

Feedback & suggestions

Feedback is very welcome and if you have any complaints please write to our Director, Open City, 18 Ensign Street, London, E1 8JD, or you can complete our online survey at the address below: surveymonkey.co.uk/r/OHL19

Key to listings

B   Bookshop
D   Disabled access
P   Parking
R   Refreshments
T   Toilets
O   Open normally for free
F   Family activities
A   Architect on site
X   Photography NOT allowed

🚶 Address of building/meeting point
🕐 Opening times
❗ Booking required
🚇 Nearest tube/rail
🚌 Useful bus routes

Ballots

The following buildings are only accessible by entering our public ballot:

10 Downing Street: pg 147
Bloomberg European Headquarters: pg 122
BT Tower: pg 114
New Scotland Yard: pg 151
The Shard: pg 146
U.S. Embassy: pg 94

Please note

The ballots open from 20 August to 9 September. Go to each building's entry online to enter. Please note, only successful applicants will be notified.

Open House London Programme

The programme listings on the following pages are ordered geographically in *North, South, East, West* and *Central London*, with each area split by London borough

Tower Hamlets
Boundary Estate was the world's first Council estate, created by the LCC on the demolished site of a notorious slum, Old Nichol.

Barking & Dagenham (Becontree Estate)
In the 1930s Becontree estate was the largest public housing development in the world, today it houses 50% of the Borough's population.

Lambeth
Edward Hollamby OBE (8 January 1921 – 29 December 1999), known for restoring William Morris's and Philip Webb's Red House, was Lambeth's chief architect between 1969-81.

Croydon
Brick by Brick, established by Croydon Council in 2016, is creating around 2000 new homes for the borough by using brownfield plots: old garage sites, car parks, vacant buildings of open space infill sites on council estates.

Barnet

Social Capital

Hampstead Garden Suburb was founded by social reformer Henrietta Barnett and her husband Samuel Augustus Barnett. They also founded Toynbee Hall to bridge the gap between rich and poor citizens.

Clitterhouse Farm
🚶 Clitterhouse Playing Fields, NW2 1AP
🕐 Sat 10am–4pm (max 12) + A story of resilience, survival and resurgence – Clitterhouse Farm Buildings at 11am · A story of resilience, survival and resurgence – Clitterhouse Farm Buildings at 1pm · A story of resilience, survival and resurgence – Clitterhouse Farm Buildings at 3pm. Last entry Sat 3.00pm. **T·R·P·F·D·A**
🚇 Brent Cross, Cricklewood
🚌 102,C11,189
The project aims to restore and bring back into community use the historic Clitterhouse Farm Buildings. Crowdfunded to build a small on-site café and open three of the derelict workshops spaces.

Friends Meeting House
🚶 North Square, NW11 7AD
🕐 Sun 1pm–5pm. Last entry Sun 4.15pm. **B·R·T**
🚇 Golders Green
🚌 460,13,102,H2

Delightful brick and tile building inspired by the famous 1688 Meeting House at Jordans in Buckinghamshire. A simple building in a tranquil setting, reflecting the Quakers' beliefs. Frederick Rowntree, 1913

Golders Green Unitarians
🚶 31-and-a-half Hoop Lane, NW11 8BS
🕐 Sat 10am–5pm/Sun 1pm–5pm. Last entry 4.45pm. **D·T·0**
🚇 Golders Green
🚌 13,H2,102,210,460
Grade II-listed small inter-war building with Arts and Crafts pulpit and mural by Ivon Hitchens in the tradition of Morris & Co. Reginald Farrow, 1925

Hampstead Garden Suburb Free Church
🚶 Central Square, Hampstead Garden Suburb, NW11 7AG
🕐 Sat/Sun 10am–5pm. Last entry 4.15pm. **D·P·R·T·0**
🚇 Golders Green
🚌 H2,102,13,460

• New Ground © Diana Plummer

Grade I-listed Nonconformist church, set in the suburb's integrally planned Central Square to balance St Jude's Church nearby, but with a low concrete dome. Distinctive interior with large Tuscan columns on high brick plinths. Sir Edwin Lutyens, 1911

Hush House
🚶 19A Woodlands Close, NW11 9QP
🕐 Sat Architect-led tours, hourly (11am–3pm, max 10). **A**
❗ Pre-book only: studio@ashtonporter.com
🚇 Brent Cross
🚌 232,240,183,83
A new-build two bedroom house of 90 sqm for a first time homeowner, nestled into a small site at the end of a quiet cul-de-sac in North London. Ashton Porter Architects, 2017

New Ground
🚶 5b Union Street, Chipping, EN5 4DF
🕐 Sat 10am–1pm + Architect-led tour at 10am, 11.30am, 1pm/Sun 1pm–5pm + Architect-led tour at 2pm, 3.30pm, 5pm (max 10, Access to common room and garden. Access to flats during tours only.)
❗ Pre-book only: See Open House website for more information
🚇 High Barnet, New Barnet
🚌 263, 34, 234
25 homes designed with the Older Women's Co-Housing group using PTE's 'fabric first' approach which maximises the benefits of orientation, air-tightness and insulation and following the co-housing model. Pollard Thomas Edwards, 2016

Phoenix Cinema
🚶 52 High Road, N2 9PJ
🕐 Sun 10am–12pm (Access to projection rooms only with pre-booked tours) + ½ hourly tour (10am–11.30am, max 10). Last entry 11.15am. **R·T**
❗ Pre-book only: (Tours) phoenixcinema.co.uk/ PhoenixCinema.dll/Home (Phone: 020 8444 6789)
🚇 East Finchley
🚌 102,143,234,263
One of the oldest cinemas in the country, with a barrel-vaulted ceiling and Art Deco wall reliefs by Mollo and Egan. Grade II-listed. S Birdwood, 1910

St Edward the Confessor Catholic Church, Golders Green
🚶 700 Finchley Road, Golders Green, NW11 7NE
🕐 Sat 11am–5pm + Tour at 11am, 2pm (max 20)/ Sun 2pm–5pm + Tour at 3.30pm, 2pm (max 20). Last entry Sat/Sun 4.30pm. **T·R·D**
🚇 Golders Green
🚌 13,460,102,H2
A handsome and substantial early 20C Gothic church with flushwork decoration to the towers and several internal furnishings of note. Arthur Young, 1914

• Hush house

St Jude on the Hill
🚶 Central Square, NW11 7AH
🕐 Sat 10am–5pm/Sun 12pm–5pm. Last entry 4.45pm. **D·B·P·R·T·O**
🚇 Golders Green
🚌 460,102,13,H2
Eccentric Edwardian church, Grade I-listed. Described by Simon Jenkins as "one of Lutyens' most distinctive creations". Extensive 20C wall paintings by Walter Starmer, memorial to horses of WWI. Local archives display. Sir Edwin Lutyens, 1911

Wrotham Park
🚶 Wrotham Park, Barnet, EN5 4SB
🕐 Sun Hourly tour (10am–4pm, max 20, No tour at 1pm). **P**
❗ Pre-book only: OHL@wrothampark.com
A privately owned Grade II-listed Palladian mansion with grand interiors restored in 1883, set in 300 acres of parkland in the midst of 2,500 acres. Built for Admiral The Hon. John Byng. Isaac Ware, 1754

Walks & Tours

Hampstead Garden Suburb Artisans' Quarter Walk
🚶 Meet: inside St Jude on the Hill, Central Square, NW11 7AH
🕐 Sun 2pm, 2.30pm, 3pm (max 25).
🚇 Golders Green
🚌 460,H2,13,102
Guided walks of "the most nearly perfect example of the 20C Garden Suburb" (Pevsner), designed by Unwin & Parker, Lutyens, Bunney, Baillie Scott and others. Informally laid out terraces and picturesque Arts and Crafts vernacular cottages.

Enfield

Social Capital

Enfield has changed socially and demographically since 1965, witnessing inner-London characteristics moving outwards.

All Saints Church, Edmonton

🕇 Church Street, N9 9PE
🕘 Sat/Sun 10am–5pm. Last entry 4.15pm. **D·T·P·O**
🚇 Edmonton Green
🚌 102,144,149,192,259,279,491,W6,W8

Church dating back to at least early 12C. Charles and Mary Lamb buried in churchyard.

Building BloQs Workshop

🕇 4 Anthony Way, N18 3QT
🕘 Sat/Sun 10am–5pm + The Building BloQs Workshops In Action, hourly (11am-4pm, max 15, Have a nosey around and see crafts and trades people make and build the things we use and buy). Last entry 4.15pm. **D·T·P·R·O**
🚇 Meridian Water, Tottenham Hale
🚌 444,341,192,34

A professionally equipped 15,000 sq ft open access workshop, home to over 350 makers. The space includes a wood workshop, metal workshop, fashion and textiles studio, spray booth, CNC router and laser cutter + on-site café. Meridian Works – 5th Studio, Current Building – Community Designed, 2012. *buildingbloqs.com/open-house*

Chickenshed Theatre

🕇 290 Chase Side, Southgate, N14 4PE
🕘 Sat 10am–5pm + Tour of building, including theatres and backstage, hourly (11am-4pm, max 20) + Community Market. Last entry Sat 4.30pm. **T·R·P·D·O**
🚇 Cockfosters, New Barnet
🚌 298,299,307

Modern, accessible purpose-built theatre, housing the unique, inclusive Chickenshed. Building houses Rayne Theatre auditorium, Studio Theatre, dance studio, restaurant, backstage and wardrobe areas, with amphitheatre and garden outside. Renton Howard Wood Levin Partnership, 1994

Christ Church Southgate and the Minchenden Oak Garden

🕇 Waterfall Road, Southgate, N14 7EG
🕘 Sat/Sun 10am–5pm (Stepped access to Lady Chapel and Chancel) + Sat Tour at 11am, 12pm, 2.30pm, 3.30pm + Sun Hourly tour (2pm-4pm). Last entry 4.15pm. **D·P·R·T·O**
🚇 Arnos Grove, New Southgate
🚌 121,298,299,W6

Grade II-listed church with fine collection of Pre-Raphaelite stained glass windows by Morris & Co. including Burne-Jones and Rossetti. Wall paintings. Mosaic reredos. Minchenden Oak – ancient pollarded oak more than 800 years old. George Gilbert Scott, 1861

Energetik's Arnos Grove Energy Centre

🕇 Millennium Court, 3 Weld Place, N11 1QZ
🕘 Sat Energetik's specialists-led tour, hourly (11am–2pm, max 6, duration 45 mins. Sensible footwear and clothing should be worn. No under 16s).
❗ Pre-book only: info@energetik.london
🚇 Arnos Grove, New Southgate
🚌 221,232

Energetik is Enfield Council's energy company. The Arnos Grove energy centre supplies low-carbon heating and hot water to new homes via a district heat network. Join a tour to learn about decentralised energy and the future of heating.

Enfield Brewery

🕇 Unit 17A Eley road, Edmonton, N18 3BB
🕘 Sat 12pm–6pm/Sun 12.30pm–5.30pm (max 100, access to bar only, full access via tours) + Brewery Tour, every 90 mins (1pm–4pm, max 15). Last entry Sat 5.15pm | Sun 4.45pm. **R·D·T·P**
🚇 Meridian Water, Silver Street
🚌 444,34,192

A modern open-plan building that houses fully functioning and impressive brew house equipment. The exterior looks like a clean modern warehouse-style building but the interior is updated with industrial equipment.

• Bulding Bloqs © Claudia Agati

Forty Hall & Estate
🏃 Forty Hill, Enfield, EN2 9HA
🕐 Sat/Sun 11am–5pm. Last entry 4.30pm. **B·P·R·T·0**
🚇 Turkey Street
🚌 191
Grade I-listed Caroline mansion hall is set in a fine estate. Built as a family home by Sir Nicholas Rainton, Lord Mayor of London 1632–33 and Master of the Haberdasher's Guild.

King George V Pumping Station
🏃 Swan & Pike Road, EN3 6JH
🕐 Sat/Sun Tour every 15 mins (10am–4.15pm). **P**
🚇 Enfield Lock
🚌 121,491
Designed to pump water from the River Lee into the King George V reservoir, the building houses three old disused gas Humphrey pumps, and two electric pumps currently in service. William Booth Bryan, 1913

Meridian Water Train Station
🏃 Angel Edmonton Road, Upper Edmonton, N18 3HF
🕐 Sat/Sun 10am–5pm (max 60, area beyond ticketline only accessible during tours) + Architect-led tour every 90 mins (11am–3pm, max 60). Last entry 4.15pm. **R·D·A**
🚇 Meridian Water
🚌 34,192,341 ,444
A new £47m railway station at the heart of Meridian Water. The landmark design combines 'Civic meets Civil' engineering with stunning architecture. High-quality concrete and dark brick contrast a folded golden soffit. Acanthus, Atkins Global, Karakusevic Carson Architects, 2019

Myddelton House
🏃 Bulls Cross, EN2 9HG
🕐 Sat 11am–4pm (ground floor only). Last entry 3.30pm. **D·P·R·T**
🚇 Turkey Street
🚌 217,317
Former home of the great horticulturist Edward Augustus Bowles. Neoclassical yellow Suffolk stock brick villa. Victorian conservatory to south side. Mid-19C extension to north end. Adam style ceilings to ground floor. George Ferry and John Wallen, 1818

Palmers Green Extension
🏃 111 Powys Lane, N13 4HJ
🕐 Sat 10am–5pm (max 10, downstairs only). Last entry 4.15pm. **A**
🚇 Bounds Green, Palmers Green
🚌 299
Rear extension and full ground-floor refurbishment of an Edwardian house, creating an open-plan home with a simple and minimalist material palette. Exposed brick, timber and polished concrete surfaces create a sharp and modern extension. Collective Works, 2018

Parish Church of St Andrew Enfield
🏃 Market Place, Enfield, EN2 6LL
🕐 Sat 10am–5pm (max 30, no access to bell space) + Short informal guided tours on request (max 20). Last entry 4.15pm. **T·0**
🚇 Enfield Town, Enfield Chase
🚌 121,191,192,231,307
Listed church, much added to, with a recently refurbished organ, which has a fine circa 1750s wooden organ case. There are many fine memorials. The Church has an eight-bell peal – the oldest bell dates from 1680.

Priory Hospital North London
🏃 Grovelands House, The Bourne, N14 6RA
🕐 Sat 10am–1pm (limited access) + Tour at 10am, 11am (max 20). Last entry 12.15pm. **P·R·T**
🚇 Southgate, Winchmore Hill
🚌 121,125,299,W6
Grade I-listed Neoclassical villa designed for Walker Gray. Grounds laid out by Repton. Elegant trompe l'oeil breakfast room. John Nash, 1797

Queen Elizabeth II Stadium
🏃 Donkey Lane, EN1 3PL
🕐 Sat 10am–1pm (max 6) + ½ hourly tour (10am–1pm, max 6). Last entry 12.30pm. **P·T**
🚇 Southbury, Enfield Town
🚌 191,217,317
Two storey concrete sports pavilion in streamlined 1930s style. Building work interrupted by WWII and completed in 1952. Distinctive 'drum' contains stylised staircase leading to glass-walled café and sheltered seating. Frank Lee Borough, 1936

Royal Small Arms Factory
🏃 RSA Island Centre, 49 Island Centre Way, (off A1055 Mollison Avenue), EN3 6GS
🕐 Sat 10am–5pm (Access to clock tower involves climbing ladders. Visitors must wear appropriate footwear and be of reasonable fitness. The keeper reserves the right to refuse admission) + Tour of the clock tower with the Keeper, every 15 mins (11am–4pm, max 2). Last entry 4.15pm. **P·T·0**
🚇 Enfield Lock
🚌 121,491
Grade II-listed arms factory closed to public for 170 years, buildings on site included a church (the original font is displayed at the centre), a police station and a school. Now a mixed-use community and commercial centre. Clock c1783. Board of Ordnance, 1854

Rumi Mosque & Dialogue Centre
🚶 337 Fore Street, Edmonton Green N9 0NU
🕐 Sat/Sun 10am–5pm. Last entry 4.15pm
🚇 Edmonton Green
🚌 144,491,192,341,102,149,279,259,W8,W6
Building was a gurudwara temple until bought by a charity in 2004 and since then it has been home to Rumi's Community, a place of worship and gathering house. Previously used as Passmore Edwards Free Library from 1897. Caroe & Passmore, 1890

Salisbury House
🚶 Bury Street West, N9 9LA
🕐 Sat/Sun 11am–4pm (max 20) + Local Community Horticultural Festival celebrating local growers and crafts. Last entry Sat/Sun 3.30pm. **R·T**
🚇 Edmonton Green, Bush Hill Park
🚌 217,231,192,329,W8
Grade II*-listed gabled and brick Tudor manor house restored by Enfield Council, now used as an Arts Centre. The finest piece of late-Elizabethan architecture left in the borough. Two fine panelled rooms and early painting on plaster.

St Alphege Church, Edmonton
🚶 Rossdale Drive/Hertford Road, Lower Edmonton, N9 7LG
🕐 Sat 10am–5pm. Last entry 4.45pm. **D·T·P·R**
🚇 Southbury, Ponders End, Edmonton Green
🚌 377,191,491,349,279
Grade II-listed combining Modernist Scandinavian and traditional ecclesiastical forms, with good-quality sculptural enrichment; graceful, lofty interiors, with subtle detailing applied consistently throughout. Sir Edward Maufe, 1959

The Drumsheds
🚶 Meridian Water, Argon Road, N18 3BW
🕐 Sat/Sun Hourly tour (12pm–2pm).
🚇 Meridian Water
🚌 Bus routes: 341,192,34,444
Previously a gasworks 1930s–1970s and has remained unused until now. This unique venue will now embrace a new lease of life, in which the former gasworks and outdoor space will be revived as a ground-breaking and multi-purpose event space.

The Lodge
🚶 Hotspur Way, Whitewebbs Lane, EN2 9AP
🕐 Sat 10am–1pm (max 10) + F3 Architectural Tour , ½ hourly (10am-12.30pm, max 10). Last entry 12.15pm. **T·P·D·A**
❗ Pre-book only: cillian.twohig@f3architects.com
🚇 Turkey Street
Private accommodation for Tottenham Hotspur Football Club's first team and academy in a bespoke designed facility. Its creation allows the club to create a controlled, consistent and familiar environment for their players. F3 Architects, 2018. *f3architects.com/work/ thfc-training-centre/*

• The Lodge

Winchmore Hill Friends Meeting House & Burial Ground
🚶 59 Church Hill, N21 1LE
🕐 Sat/Sun 2pm–5pm. Last entry 4.45pm
🚇 Southgate, Winchmore Hill
🚌 125,329,W9
Grade II-listed, built 1790. A central double door under a bracketed cornice hood, large sash windows with delicate glazing bars. Panelled interior. Curved entrance wall allowed carriages to turn in the narrow lane. Notable burial ground.

Walks & Tours

Dujardin Mews Walking Tour
🚶 Meet: Outside Welcome Point Community Centre, 141 South Street, Ponders End, EN3 4PX
🕐 Sat 11am–1pm. **A**
🚇 Ponders End
🚌 349,279,191
Walk with Karakusevic Carson Architects. Dujardin Mews RIBA Award Winner and finalist for Housing Design Awards and others 2017. Nearby Electric Quarter Phase A nearing completion. Karakusevic Carson Architects, 2017

Meridian Water Masterplan Walking Tour
🚶 Meet: Eastern Forecourt of Meridian Water Station, Angel Edmonton Road, N18 3HF
🕐 Sat/Sun 12pm, 2pm (max 30). **T·R·A**
🚇 Meridian Water
🚌 192,341,34,444
The £6bn Meridian Water development will be a distinctive neighbourhood designed to nurture economic, environmental and social sustainability. This tour provides an insight into the masterplan for this bold and unique development.

Haringey

Social Capital

With 24.9% of Haringey's population aged between 0 and 19: this is proportionately higher than both London (24.5%) and England and Wales (24%).

6 Wood Lane

🏃 Highgate, N6 5UB
🕐 Sat 11am–5pm (max 15) + Tour every 45 mins. Last entry 4.15pm.
🚇 Highgate
🚌 263,43,134

A double-height ark floats above a masonry base and entrance footbridge. Off the elevated living area a smokers' balcony overlooks the lush garden below. Above, semi-circular terrace and winter garden nestles within the wooded surrounds. Birds Portchmouth Russum, 2016

Blue House Yard

🏃 5 River Park Road, N22 7TB
🕐 Sat/Sun 10am–5pm (max 25). Last entry 4.15pm. **T·O**
🚇 Wood Green, Alexandra Palace
🚌 W3,329,243,232,123,230,221,184,144,121,67,141,29

A collection of new creative workspaces. Framed by a bright blue refurbished studio complex, nine tall, slender standalone worksheds and a double-decker bus café, the Yard will be a much-needed social space in Wood Green. Jan Kattein Architects, 2017

Breakout Extension

🏃 2 Felix Avenue, Crouch End, N8 9TL
🕐 Sat 1pm–5pm (ground floor flat). Last entry 4.45pm. **A**
🚇 Crouch Hill, Finsbury Park, Hornsey
🚌 W3,W7,41

Two extensions break out from an existing bedroom, responding to, and limited by, the angles of the small garden fences. In a darker corner the roof breaks out, by being prised open and folded back, allowing the daylight in.

Bruce Castle Museum

🏃 Bruce Castle Museum, Lordship Lane, Tottenham, N17 8NU
🕐 Sat/Sun 1pm–5pm (max 25) + Children's Historical Costume Dressing-up at 1pm (max 10). Last entry 4.15pm. **F·D·B·P·R·T·O**
🚇 Bruce Grove
🚌 123,243,318

Tudor manor house built for Sir William Compton in 1514, substantially altered in 17C, 18C and 19C. A museum since 1906 housing local history and community collections, archives, art and exhibitions of Bruce Castle, and Haringey area.

Cut Glass Studio Ltd, Tottenham Hale

🏃 15–16 The High Cross Centre, Fountayne Road, N15 4QN
🕐 Sat/Sun 10am–5pm. Last entry 4.15pm. **T·D**
🚇 Seven Sisters, Tottenham Hale
🚌 230,123,W4,41,76

Industrial unit used as an art studio in a small industrial estate.

Green Rooms

🏃 13–27 Station Road, Wood Green, N22 6UW
🕐 Sun 11am–10pm (Access to the lobby and bar area, max 15) + Access to guest-only areas including the gallery and bedrooms at 1.30pm, 2.30pm (max 20). Last entry 9.45pm. **R·T·O**
❗ Pre-book only: (Tours) info@greenrooms.london
🚇 Wood Green, Alexandra Palace
🚌 184,141,W3,29

Arts-led hotel in a striking late Art Deco building, built in 1935 for The North Metropolitan Power & Electricity Company. Clean modern lines contrast with original architectural features and authentic vintage British craft furniture. SODA, 2015

Grow Tottenham

🏃 Ashley House, Ashley Road, N17 9LZ
🕐 Sat Tour at 4pm. **D·T·R·O**
🚇 Tottenham Hale
🚌 W4,230,192,123,76,41

A meanwhile use project incorporating a community garden, café, bar, event space and studios; built in and around a refurbished ex-mechanics depot. Beep Studio, 2018

Highgate School Chapel, Library, Museum

🏃 Highgate School, North Road, N6 4AY
🕐 Sat 10am–1pm. Last entry 12.30pm. **R·T**
🚇 Highgate, Archway
🚌 143,210,271,214

Highgate is three schools in one. Founded by Sir Roger Cholmeley, Lord Chief Justice of England, in 1565, Highgate is governed as a single charitable foundation. Clarke Kidwell Architects, Junior School Architype 2016, Central Hall Claude Pemberton Leach 1899

Markfield Beam Engine and House

🚶 Markfield Road, South Tottenham, N15 4RB
🕐 Sat Steam Tour, every 90 mins (12.30pm–3.30pm)/
Sun 1pm–5pm + Steam Tour, every 90 mins (12.30pm–
3.30pm). Last entry 4.15pm. **D·B·P·R·T·O**
🚇 Tottenham Hale, South Tottenham
🚌 318,W4,41

Grade II-listed Victorian industrial building set within
a park and next to the River Lea, with the original Wood
Bros beam pumping engine in situ, as originally installed
and operating under steam power.

Outdoor Classroom

🚶 Highgate Primary School, Storey Rd, North Hill,
Highgate, N6 4ED
🕐 Sat/Sun 10am–5pm (max 20, Entrance via Early Years
Playground). Last entry 4.15pm. **F·A**
🚇 Highgate
🚌 143,263

The Outdoor Classroom is a playful structure, made from
CNC-cut plywood, and was developed through workshops
with the school children, funded through a charity
dinner and built by the school caretaker and some
volunteers. Collective Works, 2019

Oxford Road

🚶 27 Oxford Road, Stroud Green, N4 3HA
🕐 Sun 10am–1pm (max 30). Last entry 12.30pm. **T**
🚇 Crouch Hill, Finsbury Park
🚌 W5,210,W3,W7

• Percy House

Rear/infill extension with a sequence of uses, each
defined by changes in ceiling pattern: exposed larch
beams shift orientation from the roof-lit dining space
to window seat/living area, and flow externally to a
sheltered pergola space. Chance de Silva, 2017

Page High Estate

🚶 4 Lymington Avenue, N22 6JQ
🕐 Sat Tenants' Association-led tour at 2pm,
4pm (max 14).
🚇 Wood Green, Alexandra Palace
🚌 230,141,W4,W3,144,243,67,29

Page High is a hidden jewel of post-war London social
housing, a 92-home rooftop village in Wood Green. High
above the hue and cry of the High Road, Page High (Good
Design in Housing award, 1976) is a model for social
housing today. Dry Halasz Dixon Partnership, 1975

Percy House

🚶 796 High Road, Tottenham, N17 0DH
🕐 Sat Architect-led tour of the restoration and
extension, hourly (10am–2pm, max 8). **X·P·D·T·A**
❗ Pre-book only: talya.richman@f3architects.com
🚇 White Hart Lane
🚌 259,279,149

2018 refurbishment and extension of Grade II*-listed
Percy House for the Tottenham Hotspur Foundation.
The property forms part of a listed Georgian terrace,
immediately north of the new THFC Stadium. F3
Architects, 2018. *f3architects.com/work/percy-house/*

Roslyn Road

🚶 81 Roslyn Road, N15 5JB
🕐 Sat/Sun 10am–1pm + Architect-led tour, ½ hourly
(10am–12.30pm, max 10). Last entry 12.45pm. **X·A**
🚇 Seven Sisters, South Tottenham
🚌 41,67

The existing building is a Victorian terrace house made
from London stock brick. The project comprises of a brick
rear extension, zinc loft conversion and complete house
refurbishment, including a new plywood staircase.
Magri Williams, 2018

St Augustine of Canterbury

🚶 Corner Archway Road & Langdon Park Road, N6 5BH
🕐 Sat/Sun 10am–5pm. Last entry 4.15pm. **R·O**
🚇 Highgate, Archway
🚌 43,134,263

Victorian/Arts and Crafts church completed in 20C.
Imposing west front by J Harold Gibbons with statuary
by Dorothy Rope. Lady chapel by Henry Wilson. Stained
glass by Margaret Aldridge Rope. Fine Hunter organ plus
case. JD Sedding, Henry Wilson, J Harold Gibbons, AG
Scott, 1888

The Old Schoolhouse
🏃 136 Tottenham Lane, N8 7EL
🕐 Sat 10.30am–2.30pm/Sun 10am–5pm.
  Last entry Sat 1.45pm | Sun 4.15pm. **T·B·O**
🚆 Turnpike Lane, Hornsey
🚌 91,41,W3
Originally St. Mary's Infants School, later as Holy
Innocents' National School until 1934. It then became
derelict until 1981 when it became headquarters of the
Hornsey Historical Society in 1981 after refurbishment.
Marius Reynolds, John Henry Taylor, 1848

Tower and Churchyard of St Mary's Hornsey
🏃 High Street Hornsey, N8 7NT
🕐 Sun 2pm–5pm + Tour of the Tower, including the roof,
  every 15 mins (max 15). Last entry 4.45pm. **F·R**
🚆 Turnpike Lane, Hornsey
🚌 41,144,W3
Grade II*-listed tower with restored chapel remaining
from Medieval parish church. Tour includes crypt,
ringing chamber and main roof with excellent extensive
views in all directions. Organised by Friends of Hornsey
Church Tower, 1500

Up Side Down House Highgate
🏃 44 Northwood Road, N6 5TP
🕐 Sat/Sun 10am–5pm (max 10). Last entry 4.15pm. **A**
🚆 Highgate
🚌 263,43,134
This Highgate Victorian Terrace was fully refurbished
and extended on three levels. The modern extensions,
elaborate colour scheme, exposed materials and clever
internal planning transformed the derelict terrace into
a modern home. Collective Works, 2019

Walks & Tours

Hale Village
🏃 Meet: outside Tesco Express, N17 9NE
🕐 Sat 10.30am (max 10). **T·D·O**
🚆 Tottenham Hale
🚌 W4,192,230,76,41,123
New high-density waterside development with green
design features including biomass energy system and
green roofs. Includes residential for sale and rent,
student accommodation and range of community
facilities. BDP, 2008

Muswell Hill Walk
🏃 Meet: Queen's Avenue, beside Muswell Hill
  Library, N10 3PE
🕐 Sat 2pm (max 45). **R·T·O**
🚆 East Finchley, Alexandra Palace
🚌 43,102,134,144,234,W7
Tour takes in early and late Victorian, Edwardian and
1930s buildings, and gives an historical interpretation
of how a rural enclave changed into a unique Edwardian
suburb. Finishes North Bank, Pages Lane, with an
illustrated talk.

Tottenham Green Conservation Area
🏃 Meet: outside Old Tottenham Town Hall, Town Hall
  Approach Road, N15 4RY
🕐 Sun 11am. **T·D**
🚆 Seven Sisters, South Tottenham
🚌 123,476,349,341,230,76,149,243,259,279
External tour of buildings including 18C Georgian houses,
19C Jewish Hospital, Prince of Wales Hospital and Holy
Trinity Church, ancient High Cross Monument, Edwardian
Town Hall complex, housing developments and Bernie
Grant Arts Centre. AS Taylor & AR Jemmett, 1904

Tower Gardens Garden Suburb
🏃 Meet: 5 Tower Gardens Road, Tower Gardens, N17 7PX
🕐 Sun Tower Gardens self guided walking tour
  (10am–4pm). **R·T**
🚆 Turnpike Lane, Bruce Grove
🚌 123,144,243,217,444
One of the first garden suburbs in the world, two storey
terraced cottages retaining decorative architectural
features. LCC created 'housing of the working classes'
role for architects' department under Riley, member of
the Art Workers guild. WE Riley, 1905

• Roslyn Road © Nicholas Worley 2018

Barking & Dagenham

Social Capital

In the 1930s, Becontree estate was the largest public housing development in the world. Today, approximately half of all the borough councillors are elected from wards covering the estate.

Barking Abbey with St Margaret's Church
🚶 The Broadway, North Street, IG11 8AS
🕐 Sat 10am–3pm. Last entry 2.15pm. **D·P·R·T·O**
🚇 Barking
🚌 5,62,287,366
666AD Grade I-listed church with a Curfew Tower, Chapel of Holy Rood with 12C Rood Stone among monuments, art and ruins. Artworks by George Jack & Walker Organ (1914). Captain Cook was noted to have been married here.

Eastbury Manor House
🚶 Eastbury Square, IG11 9SN
🕐 Sun 11am–4pm + Hourly tour (11am–3pm). Last entry 3.30pm. **D·R·T**
🚇 Upney, Barking
🚌 62,287,368
Architecturally distinguished and well-preserved, brick-built, Elizabethan Grade I-listed manor house. Contains 17C wall-paintings, wood panelling, a charming walled garden and a fine Tudor turret. Many original features have been restored. Richard Griffiths Architects, 2003

St Patrick's Church
🚶 Blake Avenue, IG11 9SQ
🕐 Sat 10am–5pm + St Patrick's Church First Flower Festival. Last entry 4.15pm. **F·T·R·O**
🚇 Upney, Barking
🚌 EL2,62,287,368,EL1
Built thanks to a generous gift from local benefactress, Mrs Lavinia Keene, St Patrick's was consecrated in July 1940 and is unusual in style. The concrete and brick interior contrasts with the dramatic, colourful reredos. Grade II-listed. AE Wiseman, 1940

The Ice House Quarter (featuring the Granary, Malthouse & Boathouse)
🚶 80 Abbey Road, IG11 7BT
🕐 Sat 10am–1pm (max 40) + Tour (10am–12.15pm, max 40). Last entry 12.15pm. **P·T**
🚇 Barking
🚌 325,366
Home to the Granary and Malthouse, originally built for Randalls Malt Roasters c1860. The restored buildings include a Victorian Granary and adjacent Malthouse located on the River Roding/Barking Creek. 1860

Valence House
🚶 Avenue, Dagenham, RM8 3HT
🕐 Sat 10am–4pm. Last entry 3.45pm. **B·P·T·R·O**
🚇 Becontree, Chadwell Heath
🚌 150,62,128,368
Grade II*-listed 15C manor house with Medieval moat. Recently discovered late 16C wall painting and impressive oak panelling. Evocative museum galleries that bring Barking and Dagenham's past alive.

White House, Becontree Estate
🚶 884 Green Lane, Becontree, RM8 1BX
🕐 Sun 11am–4pm (max 20, No entry to artists' bedrooms unless by permission. Only accessible as part of Becontree Bus Tour). Last entry 3.30pm. **P·D·R·T·O**
❗ Pre-book only: whitehouse@createlondon.org
🚇 Dagenham Heathway, Chadwell Heath
🚌 368,150,128,62
A public space for art and social activity. The White House invites artists to live and work in the house, exploring new ways to collaborate with the local community and hosts a regular programme of events with and for local residents. Apparata, 2016

Walks & Tours

Barking Town Centre Tour

🚶 Meet: outside Barking Town Hall,
1 Town Square, Barking, IG11 7LU

🕐 Sat 10am, 2pm (max 25). **T**

❗ Pre-book only: david.harley@befirst.london

🚇 Barking

🚌 EL2,EL1,62,287,368

Barking town centre has seen significant development over recent years with substantial growth in housing and infrastructure. These guided tours will visit existing award-winning schemes and set out the vision for the future of the town. Allford Hall Monaghan Morris, 2008

Becontree Estate Bus Tour, Dagenham

🚶 Meet: outside CU London (formerly Dagenham Civic Centre), Rainham Road North, RM10 7BN

🕐 Sun 10am (max 52, coach tour with ex-Becontree Housing Manager Bill Jennings. Duration 4hrs and includes visits to Valence House, Kingsley Hall, Eastbury Manor House and two vacant council properties). **R·P·T**

🚇 Dagenham East, Romford

🚌 5,103,128,150

Built by the LCC during the 1920s and early 1930s, the estate was once the largest of its kind in Europe, with over 25,000 houses. Later building programmes extended the estate to house an estimated population of 90,000. G Topham Forrest, 1940

East End Women's Museum – making a museum

🚶 Meet: In front of the gatehouse at St Margaret's Parish Church, The Broadway, IG11 8AS

🕐 Sat Hourly tour (11am–3pm, max 25, a talk about plans for a new museum, currently under construction. The talk will be outside, so please dress appropriately. Each talk will last approx. 30 mins). **D**

🚇 Barking

🚌 368,287,62,5

The East End Women's Museum is set to open in Barking in 2021, to record, share and celebrate the stories of East London women. Join the museum team at its new location – currently a building site – and hear more about their exciting plans.

• Barking Town Centre Tour © Patel Taylor 2014

Bexley

Social Capital

Despite the lack of new affordable housing, private rent for low earners in Bexley is the second most affordable in London.

70 Pier Road

🕴 Erith, DA8 1BA
🕐 Sat/Sun 10am–3pm (max 20, ground floor only). Last entry 2.15pm.
🚇 Erith
🚌 469,428,99,B12,229

This Victorian office building was originally constructed as a branch of London and Provincial Bank but was taken over by merchants. The building is locally listed as it "represents a vibrant period in the commercial development of Erith".

Crossness Southern Outfall

🕴 The Old Works, Thames Water Sewage Treatment Works, Bazalgette Way, SE2 9AQ
🕐 Sun 10.30am–4pm. Last entry 3pm. **F·D·B·P·R·T**
🚇 Abbey Wood
🚌 177,229,401

The southern outfall of the Victorian sewerage system designed by Joseph Bazalgette. Grade I and Grade II-listed buildings contain four of the largest rotative beam steam engines in the world and amazing Victorian decorative ironwork. Charles H Driver, 1832

• 70 Pier Road

Danson House

🕴 Danson Park, Danson Road, Welling, DA6 8HL
🕐 Sun 10am–4pm (max 45, no access to offices on top level). Last entry 3.30pm. **T**
🚇 Bexleyheath, Welling
🚌 89,96,B13,B14,486

A stunning Grade I-listed Georgian villa designed by the architect of the Bank of England. Set in more than 200 acres of magnificent parkland overlooking Danson Lake. Sir Robert Taylor, 1763

Erith Pier

🕴 Erith Town Centre, DA8 2AH
🕐 Sat 11am–9pm + Erith Pier Festival/Sun 10am–5pm. Last entry Sat 8.30pm | Sun 4.15pm. **T·F·D·O**
🚇 Erith
🚌 468,99,469,229

Erith Pier is a large concrete structure that extends into the Thames from Erith town centre. Constructed originally as a working pier, it is now enjoyed by locals for walks, fishing and taking in views of the river. 1957

Hall Place & Gardens

🕴 Bourne Road, DA5 1PQ
🕐 Sat Tour at 10.30am (max 60)/Sun Tour at 10.30am, 2pm (max 60). **D·P·R·T**
❗ Pre-book only: 01322 621238
🚇 Bexley, Bexleyheath
🚌 B12,132,229,492

Once the country residence (1537) of Sir John Champneys, a former Lord Mayor of London. Fine Great Hall with minstrels' gallery and Tudor kitchen. Set in formal gardens on the River Cray with splendid 18C gates.

Lakeside Centre

🏃 Southmere Lake Complex, 2 Bazalgette Way
   (formerly Belvedere Road), Thamesmead, SE2 9AN
🕐 Sat Tour, hourly (1pm–3pm, max 25). **R· O**
❗ Pre-book only: eventbrite.com/e/open-house-bow-
   arts-trust-lakeside-centre-tour-tickets-62136005465
🚇 Abbey Wood
🚌 401,B11,177,229,244

Iconic centre undergoing renovation led by Bow Arts
in partnership with Peabody, supported by the Mayor's
London Regeneration Fund (LEAP). The centre will
reopen as a cultural hub for Thamesmead. Architecture
in partnership with Bow Arts, 2017

Lamorbey House

🏃 Lamorbey Park, Burnt Oak Lane, Sidcup, DA15 9DF
🕐 Sat 10am–3pm (Includes house and grounds) + Hourly
   tour (11am–1pm). Last entry 2.15pm. **R· P· T**
🚇 Sidcup
🚌 51,229,269,286

World-renowned Rose Bruford drama college with recent
additions and landscaping to provide contemporary state
of the art facilities. Site also includes Grade II-listed
Lamorbey Park Mansion – a rare survivor of Sidcup's
Georgian houses. Rivington Street Studio, 1744

Red House

🏃 Red House Lane, Bexleyheath, DA6 8JF
🕐 Sat/Sun 11am–5pm (max 50).
   Last entry 4.15pm. **B· R· T**
🚇 Bexleyheath
🚌 89,96,422,486,269

The only house commissioned, created and lived
in by William Morris, founder of the Arts and Crafts
movement. Much original detail survives, decorated
by the pre-Raphaelites, and of extraordinary
architectural and social significance. Philip Webb
& William Morris, 1860

St John the Evangelist

🏃 Church Road, Sidcup, DA14 6BX
🕐 Sat 9am–5pm/Sun 12pm–4pm.
   Last entry Sat 4.45pm | Sun 3.45pm. **D· T· O**
🚇 Sidcup
🚌 269,229,R11,492,321,233,51

A large High Victorian nave, high church chancel
and choir. Stained glass, much by Comper. 17C pulpit
and reredos with many wall tablets. George Fellowes-
Prynne, 1904

Thamesmead Information Hub

🏃 The Information Hub, 214 Yarnton Way,
   Thamesmead, DA18 4DR
🕐 Sat 11am–4pm + 20th Century Society and Peabody
   led tour at 12pm (max 25). Last entry 3.45pm. **T· R· O**
🚇 Abbey Wood
🚌 401,180,B11

Created to provide a new community shared space
to showcase the regeneration projects happening in
Thamesmead and provide an exhibition space. Robert
Rigg, 1967

The Old Library, Erith

🏃 The Old Library, Walnut Tree Road, Erith, DA8 1RS
🕐 Sat/Sun 10am–5pm (Ground floor and lower ground
   floor are accessible) + History and what's happening
   in the future tour, every 90 mins (11am–4pm, max
   20). Last entry 4.15pm. **F· T· R· O**
❗ Pre-book only: (Tours) eventbrite.co.uk/e/open-
   house-eriths-old-library-tickets-58938384294
🚇 Erith
🚌 469,99,229

The first library in Bexley, designed by William
Egerton and funded by Andrew Carnegie. After a
period of closure, this building reopened in 2019
after a first-phase of repair and renewal work led by
Robin Lee Architects. William Egerton, 1906

Walks & Tours

Lesnes Abbey Tour

🏃 Meet: Lesnes Abbey Coffee Kiosk,
   Lesnes Abbey Lodge, Abbey Road, SE2 0QJ
🕐 Sat 2pm (max 20, wear sensible shoes.). **R· T· O**
❗ Pre-book only: 020 3045 3369
🚇 Abbey Wood
🚌 229,469,B11,99,301

Bexley Archivist Oliver Wooller leads a tour on the
history of Lesnes Abbey. Norman architecture, 1178

Greenwich

ROYAL *borough of*
GREENWICH

visit**greenwich**
time after time

Social Capital

Where once architect and entrepreneur Eric Lyons had to battle fiercely with Greenwich Council over developing in Blackheath Park, his Span estates are now lauded in the Greenwich Conservation Area.

Charlton House
🏃 Charlton Road, Charlton, SE7 8RE
🕐 Sat 10am–4pm + Historical Guided Tours at 11am, 2pm (max 25). Last entry 3.30pm. **D·P·R·T·O**
🚇 North Greenwich, Charlton
🚌 486,53,54,422
London's only surviving great Jacobean mansion, set in Charlton Park, red brick with white stone dressings and classic Jacobean styles. Each room has a unique fireplace coupled with beautiful strap work ceilings and original features.

Devonport Mausoleum
🏃 National Maritime Museum, Romney Road, SE10 9NF
🕐 Sat/Sun 11am–4pm (max 15) + Hourly tour (max 15). Last entry 3.00pm.
🚇 Greenwich, Cutty Sark
🚌 177,180,188,199,286
Handsome mausoleum in former Royal Navy cemetery, restored in 1999 by the University of Greenwich. Many interesting plaques. Thomas Ripley, 1750

Greenwich Pumping Station
🏃 Greenwich High Rd, SE10 8JL
🕐 Sat Hourly tour (11am–3pm, max 15, Pre-Book Only). **T**
❗ Pre-book only: greenwichpumpingstation2019. eventbrite.co.uk
🚇 Deptford Bridge, Deptford
🚌 177,53,453
Greenwich Pumping Station was built between 1859 and 1865 by the Metropolitan Board of Works. Built by Sir Joseph Bazalgette, this Grade II-listed building was built in London Stock Brick in an Italianate style. Joseph Bazalgette, 1859

• Greenwich Pumping Station

Greenwich Yacht Club
🏃 1 Peartree Way, SE10 0BW
🕐 Sat/Sun Guided tour (2.30pm–4.15pm). **T**
🚇 Westcombe Park, North Greenwich
🚌 486,472,161,132,108,129
Contemporary timber and aluminium building using existing pier, offering unique views of the river, The O_2 and Thames Barrier. Frankl + Luty, 2000

Old Royal Naval College
🏃 Main entry West Gate (King William Walk), or East Gate (Park Row) and Romney Road crossing. Entry also from pier via Cutty Sark Gardens, SE10 9NN
🕐 Sat/Sun Hourly tour (11.30am–3.30pm, max 20, Meet on Grand Square to collect tickets and start/finish tours). **T**
🚇 Maze Hill, Cutty Sark
🚌 177,180,188,199,286

Chapel, Visitor Centre, Jacobean Undercroft, and Admiral's House
🏃 Sat/Sun 10am–5pm + Jacobean Undercroft tours, hourly (11am–4pm, max 15, Access by stairs only) · Architect-led tour of King William Undercroft, hourly (Sat: 2.30pm- 3.30pm/Sun: 11.30am–3.30pm, max 15). Last entry Sat/Sun 4.15pm. **D·A·B·R·T**
❗ Pre-book only: (Tours) ornc.org
Sir Christopher Wren's riverside masterpiece in Greenwich. Sir James Thornhill, Sir Christopher Wren, Nicholas Hawksmoor, 1696

Old Royal Naval College – King William Court
Wren-designed building completed under the direction of Hawksmoor and Vanbrugh, 1698–1712. Original wood panelling, refurbished by Dannatt Johnson in 2001 for University of Greenwich. Sir Christopher Wren, Nicholas Hawksmoor, Sir John Vanbrugh, 1698

Old Royal Naval College – Queen Anne Court
Wren and Hawksmoor building, completed 1749 when Thomas Ripley built the pavilions facing the river. Highlights include council boardroom, grand staircase and restored Portland stonework. Refurbished in 2000 for University of Greenwich. Sir Christopher Wren, Nicholas Hawksmoor, 1689

Old Royal Naval College – Queen Mary Court
Last major building on the site (1751). Original layout, timber panelling, barrel vaulting and Portland stone. Refurbished in 2000 by Dannatt Johnson for University of Greenwich. Sir Christopher Wren, Thomas Ripley, 1694

Ravensbourne
🚶 6 Penrose Way, Greenwich Peninsula, SE10 0EW
🕐 Sat Hourly tour (11am–4pm, max 30). **T·O**
🚇 North Greenwich
🚌 132,188,108,129,161,486
This stunning location on the Greenwich Peninsula is home to an inspirational learning environment. It features a series of interlinked floors around an impressive central atrium. BREEAM Excellent status. RIBA Award Winner 2011. Foreign Office Architects, 2010

• Eltham High Street 2017

Royal Museums Greenwich:
The Altazimuth Pavilion
🚶 Royal Observatory, Greenwich Park, SE10 8XJ
🕐 Sat/Sun Tour, ½ hourly (2pm–4pm, max 10, Duration 25 mins). **T·P·R·B**
❗ Pre-book only: Bookings@rmg.co.uk or 0208 312 6608
🚇 Greenwich, Cutty Sark
🚌 129,177,180,188,199
Normally closed to the public, the exterior of this charming 19C dome features terracotta mouldings with the interior housing a new suite of modern, astrographic telescopes. William Crisp, 1899

Severndroog Castle
🚶 Castle Wood, Shooters Hill, SE18 3RT
🕐 Sun 11am–4pm (max 30, ticketed on a first come basis) + Autumn Fayre. Last entry 2pm. **P·R·T·Q**
🚇 Charlton, North Greenwich, Eltham, Falconwood
🚌 B16,89,122,161,244,486
Grade II*-listed triangular brick Georgian tower sited in Oxleas Woods. Standing 63ft tall, it offers spectacular panoramic views across the capital. It was built in 1784 by Lady Anne James in memory of her husband Sir William James. Richard Jupp, 1784

Shrewsbury House
🚶 Bushmoor Crescent, SE18 3EG
🕐 Sat/Sun 10am–5pm + Historian-led Tour at 11am, 3pm (Duration 90 mins). Last entry 4.15pm. **F·D·T·R·O**
🚇 Blackheath, Woolwich Arsenal – then bus
🚌 486,89,244
Built in 1923, to replace its 18C namesake, Grade ll listed Shrewsbury House is the focus of the Shrewsbury Park Estate conservation area, built 1934–1936 by John Laing and Sons. Two civil defence centres are within the grounds. Fred Hulse and Sons, 1923

St Alfege Church, Greenwich
🚶 Greenwich Church Street, SE10 9BJ
🕐 Sat/Sun 11am–4pm. Last entry 3.45pm. **D·T·O**
🚇 Cutty Sark, Greenwich
🚌 177,180,188,199,286
Magnificent English Baroque church, Grade I-listed, gutted by fire in 1941 and restored by Sir Albert Richardson to original design. Many original features. Burial site of Thomas Tallis, organist/choirmaster (1505–85). Nicholas Hawksmoor, 1714

Thames Barrier View Café & Information Centre
🚶 1 Unity Way, SE18 5NJ
🕐 Sat/Sun 10.30am–4.30pm (max 40, no access to Thames Barrier structure). Last entry 4pm. **P·R·T**
🚇 North Greenwich, Charlton
🚌 472,180,177,161
Information Centre has a working model of the Barrier, films showing inside the Barrier, machinery and its construction. Boards on the Environment Agency, flooding and past, present and future of the Thames Barrier and flood defences. Rendel, Palmer and Tritton, 1984

The Conservatoire, Blackheath
🚶 19–21 Lee Road, SE3 9RQ
🕐 Sun 10am–5pm + Tour at 12.30pm (max 20, the tour is led by local architect Jo Townshend. Jo's studio in the Arts Building is open 12pm–2pm. The tour is 15–20 minutes long and space is limited. Last entry 4.15pm. **A·R·T**
❗ Pre-book only: (Tours) conservatoire.org.uk/events
🚇 Blackheath
🚌 54,89,108,202,386
Part of the oldest surviving purpose-built cultural complex in London, founded by the community through the purchase of bonds in 1881. Arguably the finest in London, the main art studio is spacious with a magnificent north light. John Edmeston and Edward Gabriel, 1896

The Fan Museum

🚶 12 Crooms Hill, SE10 8ER
🕐 Sat 11am–5pm. Last entry 4.30pm. **D·B·R·T**
🚇 Greenwich, Cutty Sark
🚌 177,180,188,286,386
Carefully restored Grade II*-listed Georgian town houses, retaining many principal architectural features, including elegant façades and panelled rooms. Now houses the UK's only museum devoted to the history of fans and craft of fan-making. John Savery, 1721

The Tide

🚶 Peninsula Square, Greenwich Peninsula, SE10 0SQ
🕐 Sat/Sun 10am–5pm + Design Tour at 11am,
1pm (max 15). Last entry 4.15pm. **T·R·P·D·O**
🚇 North Greenwich
🚌 132,486,422,161,108,472
A new cultural linear park running alongside the Thames on Greenwich Peninsula. Offering an evolving collection of free-to-view public art along a landscaped route for running, walking and meditation, The Tide is open to all. NEIHEISER ARGYROS, DS+R, Diller Scofidio + Renfro, 2019

University of Greenwich, Stockwell Street

🚶 Stockwell Street, SE10 9BD
🕐 Sat/Sun Hourly tour (11am–3pm, max 20). **T**
🚇 Cutty Sark, Greenwich
🚌 286,177,180,188
The building features a limestone exterior designed to 'complement but not mimic' the surrounding historical architecture, while behind the façade is a four storey composition of steel, glass and exposed concrete. Heneghan Peng Architects, 2014

Walks & Tours

Eltham High Street

🚶 Meet: Passey Place next to Delicio's café SE9 1TD
🕐 Sat 10am/Sun 1pm. **O**
🚇 Eltham
🚌 162,132,321,314,286,233,160,126,124,B16,B15
This public realm scheme sought to support the diversity of the High Street economy by linking up its different parts, aiming to improve the High Street in all its diversity, smoothing traffic and enhancing character at all scales. EAST Architects, 2017

Emirates Air Line Tour

🚶 Meet: Unit 1–4, Edmund Halley Way, SE10 0FR
🕐 Sat/Sun 10am, 11am, 12pm (max 20, pre-book only). **Q**
❗ Pre-book only: ealgroups@macemacro.com
🚇 North Greenwich, Charlton
🚌 161,486,472,129,188
Tour exploring the civil engineering achievements of the construction of the cable car. Led by the Emirates Air Line engineers and front-of-house team. Wilkinson Eyre Architects, 2011

• The Tide Greenwich Peninsula 2019

Hackney

Social Capital

In 1948 Hackney Council declared it would no longer build above three storeys. This act only lasted until the early 1950s when demand for housing became too high.

Hackney

24 St John's Church Road

E9 6EJ
Sat 1pm–5pm/Sun 10am–5pm (max 20) + Architect-led talk including presentation of heating system, ½ hourly (1pm–4.30pm, max 20, Tea and coffee available). Last entry 4.45pm. **A·R·T**
Hackney Central, Hackney Downs
488,425,48,38,277

Gracefully refurbished Victorian terrace introducing the UK's first heated clay ceiling. Natural and reclaimed materials complement original features throughout. Modern, light filled extension with sedum roof. Silke Stevens, 2014

A House with a Slide

41 Groombridge Road, E9 7DP
Sat Architect-led Tour, hourly (2pm–4pm, max 10). **A**
! Pre-book only: eventbrite.co.uk/e/open-house-a-house-with-a-slide-architect-led-tour-tickets-62843549749
Homerton, London Fields
388,277,425,26

House with a Slide has a fun puzzle-like layout. It has a slide from the kitchen to the basement, a double-height atrium with large internal window. The five storey (originally 3) property is an end-of-terrace house built around 1866. Sean and Stephen, 2018

Abney Park Cemetery – Mortuary Chapel

215 Stoke Newington High St, Stoke Newington, N16 0LH
Sat 10am–5pm/Sun History tour of the Chapel and Park at 2pm (max 20. Start at the main entrance of the Park). Last entry 4.15pm. **B**
Stoke Newington
73,276,149,393,476

Abney Park Chapel, is a Grade II-listed chapel, designed by William Hosking and built by John Jay that is situated in Europe's first wholly non-denominational cemetery, Abney Park Cemetery, London. William Hosking, 1840

Arcola Theatre

24 Ashwin Street, E8 3DL
Sat 10am–1pm. Last entry 12.30pm. **R·T·O**
Dalston Junction, Dalston (Kingsland)
149,242,38,277,243

Multi-award-winning professional theatre housed in the Reeves and Sons 1868 Artist's Colour Works. Renovation focused on sustainability and features include minimal intervention, large-scale materials reuse and renewable energy technology. Edward Henry Horne, 1868

Black Stone House

155 Wilberforce Rd, N4 2SX
Sat Architect-led Tour, ½ hourly (10am–4.30pm, max 12, Break for lunch 1pm–2pm). **T**
! Pre-book only: open-house-6a-black-stone-building-2019.eventbrite.co.uk
Arsenal, Finsbury Park
4,19,236,106,141

The concrete framed structure of this apartment building adjusts to its irregularly shaped corner plot. Exposed beams and columns support lime-washed interiors and a scratched stucco façade forms an abstract expression to the street. 6a Architects, 2017

Block House

43 Lavers Road, N16 0DU
Sat 10am–5pm (max 15, downstairs only) + Architect-led tour, hourly (11am–4pm, max 15). Last entry 4.30pm. **A·R**
Stoke Newington, Rectory Road
476,393,73,76,276,243,149,67

A bold and unusual wrap around extension focused around a double-height internal courtyard; the project employs a palette of richly coloured and textured materials to create a unique, unusual family home. Nimtim Architects, 2018

Bruno Court, The German Hospital

10 Fassett Square, E8 1BF
Sun 10am–1pm (max 30). Last entry 12.15pm. **T**
Dalston Junction, Hackney Downs
38,242,277,30,56

Modernist extension to Hackney's German Hospital, closed 1987 and converted into flats in 1999. Burnet, Tait and Lorne, 1935

• Gascoyne Estate (and neighbouring council housing)1947

By Beck Road 19
🚶 E8 4RE
🕐 Sat/Sun 10am–6pm. Last entry 5.30pm
🚇 Bethnal Green, London Fields, Hackney Central, Cambridge Heath
🚌 388,254,106,55,48,26
For nearly 50 years, Beck Road has been home to a large number of resident artists. This exhibition will present art made in houses and studios, and the practices of artists, from the 1970s until now in a series of studios, domestic rooms and in the street itself. Visit Open House website for more information on exhibitors and special events.

Calouste Gulbenkian Foundation
🚶 50 Hoxton Square, N1 6PB
🕐 Sat 10am–5pm (max 50, kitchen and main office will be closed to visitors). Last entry 4.30pm. T·D
🚇 Shoreditch High Street, Old Street
🚌 243,55,48,35,47
The Foundation's artistic and social interests are at the heart of the design. A dramatic intervention to the first floor allows natural light to permeate to the ground floor. Theis + Khan, 2009

Chats Palace
🚶 42-44 Brooksbys Walk, E9 6DF
🕐 Sat 10am–5pm/Sun 2pm–5pm (max 20) + Colin O'Brien Exhibition (max 10) Last entry 4.15pm. D·T·R
🚇 Homerton
🚌 488,394,W15,236,276,242,308
Homerton Library (Chats Palace) is one of the UK's 660 Carnegie libraries. Designed for "betterment of the people of the East End" its glass roof, leaded lights, marble floor and pillared frontage testify to the architect's eye for detail. Sir Thomas Edwin Cooper, 1913

Clissold House
🚶 Clissold Park, Stoke Newington Church Street, N16 9HJ
🕐 Sun 10am–5pm + Clissold Park User Group Talk + Presentation at 11am (max 25) + Talk by Amir on the History of Clissold House at 11am (max 25). Last entry 4.15pm. T·R·D
🚇 Manor House, Stoke Newington
🚌 141,341,106,393,73
Recently restored elegant late 18C brick villa with six-column Doric veranda on the west façade, set in parkland and a rare survivor of its type. Built for Jonathan Hoare by his nephew. Richard Griffiths Architects, 1793

Coal House
🚶 West & Coal House entrance: new River path via Lordship Road, N16 5HQ
🕐 Sat/Sun 10am–5pm (access to roof terrace weather dependent) + Sat Wonderful Wildlife Weekend at 1pm (drop-in event 1pm–3pm). Last entry 4.15pm. F·D·R·T·O
🚇 Manor House, Stamford Hill
🚌 106,253,254,29,141,341
A haven for wildlife and people in Hackney: reed-fringed ponds and dykes with a heritage café. Allen Scott Associates and Kaner Ollette, 1833

Dalston Eastern Curve Garden
🚶 Dalston Lane, E8 3DF
🕐 Sat/Sun 11am–10pm. Last entry 9.30pm. D·R·T·O
🚇 Dalston Junction, Dalston (Kingsland)
🚌 30,56,277,38,242
Popular community garden in area lacking in green public space, created on abandoned railway land. Wooden pavilion and 'Pineapple House' structures. Hackney Design Award Winner, Landscape Institute President's Award 2011. J&L Gibbons, EXYZT, Muf Art and Architecture, 2010

De Beauvoir Block
🚶 92–96 De Beauvoir Road, N1 4EN
🕐 Sat 1pm–3.30pm (max 20, regular Architect-led tours). Last entry 2.45pm. A·T
🚇 Dalston Junction, Haggerston
🚌 76,242,141,21,243,149
A new development of inspirational workspaces, designed for businesses in the creative industry. Characterful Victorian warehouses with recent addition of rooftop studio/offices and external central courtyard. Henley Halebrown, 2017

Frampton Park Baptist Church & Housing
🚶 Frampton Park Road, E9 7PQ
🕐 Sat 10am–5pm (max 20) / Sun 10am–1pm (max 10). Last entry Sat 4.15pm | Sun 12.15pm. D·T·O
🚇 London Fields, Hackney Central
🚌 254,277,388,106,425,55,26
New church and community facilities with three new residential blocks on a post-war council estate. Matthew Lloyd Architects LLP, 2015

Garden House
🚶 27 Buckingham Road, N1 4DG
🕐 Sat/Sun 11am–5pm (max 40) + New & Archive works by Whitaker Malem on display (max 40). Last entry 4.15pm. **A**
🚇 Dalston (Kingsland), Dalston Junction
🚌 67,76,149,242,243
Artist's studio/home/gallery in a land-locked site in Hackney. Features cantilevered steel stair and a bespoke terraced garden to the roof. Hayhurst and Co., 2015

Gascoyne Estate (and neighbouring council housing)
🚶 Gascoyne Community Centre, Gascoyne Road, E9 7FA
🕐 Sun Tour by John Boughton, leading expert on the history and development of social housing at 2pm (max 20).
🚇 Homerton
🚌 425,277,26,30,388
Typical 1930s five storey walk-up balcony-access tenement blocks, with some Art Deco design. Later phase two addition, 10-storey high-rise system-built blocks with low-rise infill of various types. London County Council, 1948

Geffrye Museum
🚶 136 Kingsland Road, E2 8EA
🕐 Sat 11am–5pm (Access to restored Almshouse) + tours of the new Museum of the Home with Wright & Wright Architects and ZMMA hourly (12pm–4pm, max 10, hard hat tours last 45 minutes. Suitable for families with children over 12) + The Restored Almshouse (max 16, Explore the 18th-Century home of London's poor and elderly with our expert guides). Last entry 4.30pm. **A·T**
🕐 Pre-book only: (Tours) geffrye-museum.org.uk/whatson/events/special-events
🚇 Hoxton
🚌 149,242,243,394
Grade I-listed 18C almshouse, converted to a museum in 1914. Wright & Wright Architects are leading a major transformation, due to reopen in 2020, featuring Café, Studio, Learning Pavilion, and galleries exploring multiple meanings of home. Richard Halsaul and Robert Burford, 1714. *geffrye-museum.org.uk*

Hackney Extension
🚶 Lower Ground Floor Flat, 126 Amhurst Road, E8 2AG
🕐 Sat Architect-led, ½ hourly (1pm–4.30pm, max 20). **A**
🚇 Hackney Central, Hackney Downs
🚌 276,38,55,106,254
A modern rear extension and refurbishment to a Victorian lower ground floor flat in Hackney, East London. A new garden pavilion with anodised aluminium slimline glazing transforms the internal relationship with the large rear garden. Proctor and Shaw, 2018

Hackney New Primary School
🚶 333 Kingsland Road, E8 4DR
🕐 Sat 1pm–3.30pm (max 20). Last entry 2.45pm. **A·T**
🚇 Haggerston
🚌 149,242,243
333 Kingsland Road is a mixed-use scheme combining a courtyard primary school and an apartment building, located on the site of a former fire station on an arterial road in the London Borough of Hackney's Kingsland Road Conservation Area. Henley Halebrown, 2019

Hackney Town Hall
🚶 Mare Street, E8 1EA
🕐 Sun Hourly tour (11am–4pm, max 35). **D·T·O**
🚇 Hackney Downs, Bethnal Green
🚌 48,55,106,38,277,253,D6,30,236,276,W15
Grade II-listed Neoclassical building of Art Deco style. Lanchester & Lodge, 1934

Here East
🚶 Press Centre off Waterden Road, Queen Elizabeth Olympic Park, E20 3BS
🕐 Sat 10am–5pm + Hourly tour (11am–4pm). Last entry 4.15pm. **D·A·T**
🚇 Stratford, Hackney Wick
🚌 388
A 1.2 million square foot technology and creativity campus, includes work spaces, large-scale studios and large event venue. Explore communal spaces and on-site businesses such as The Trampery on the Gantry, Plexal and Scope. Hawkins/Brown, 2017

Hoxton Hall
🚶 130 Hoxton Street, N1 6SH
🕐 Sat 10am–5pm. Last entry 4.30pm. **F·D·R·T·O**
🚇 Hoxton
🚌 48,55,394,149,243,242
Unique Grade II*-listed Victorian saloon-style music hall dating from 1863. Additional rooms added to the building by Quakers in 1910, with the current frontage added in 1980. Restoration by Foster Wilson Architect in 2013–2015. Lovegrove & Papworth, 1863

Kings Crescent Estate
🚶 Murrain Road, N4 2BN
🕐 Sat 10am–4pm (Access to pedestrian street and shared areas, including internal spaces and residential courtyards) + Tour of estate, hourly (max 25). Last entry 3pm. **D·A**
🚇 Finsbury Park, Stoke Newington
🚌 106,341,141
Three new courtyard blocks completed in 2018 integrated with refurbished 1970s housing blocks around three landscaped communal gardens. This award-winning scheme comprises nearly 300 new homes and over 100 refurbished homes. Karakusevic Carson Architects, Muf Art and Architecture, Henley Halebrown, 2018

Kingsland Basin Moorings (CHUG)
🚶 Kingsland Basin Moorings (via towpath), N1 5BB
🕐 Sun 1pm–5pm (max 50, participating boats are marked with a green flag). Last entry 4.15pm. **R·T·O**
🚇 Haggerston
🚌 149,242,243,394
Small is beautiful: 6ft narrowboats provide individual design solutions for living and working in confined conditions. The self-managed moorings are a unique community with shared open spaces, offering a glimpse of alternative urban living.

Mossbourne Community Academy
🚶 100 Downs Park Road, E5 8JY
🕐 Sat 10am–1pm (max 50) + Student Art Exhibition (max 25). Last entry 12.15pm. **D·A·R·T**
🚇 Hackney Central, Hackney Downs
🚌 56,276
One of the largest timber-framed buildings in the UK, configured as a broad 'V' with access from a covered cloister. Its focus is the generous external space to the North. RIBA Award Winner 2005 and Civic Trust Awards Winner 2006. Rogers Stirk Harbour + Partners, 2004

Pankhurst Mews
🚶 1 Pankhurst Mews, Finsbury Park Road, N4 2JZ
🕐 Sat 12pm–5.30pm (max 10). Last entry 4.45pm
🚇 Finsbury Park
🚌 254,253,106,29,19,4
New-build house replacing a former garage on the plot. Due to the tight garden site, the design of the house has to navigate complex planning and infrastructural restrictions, resulting in the compact stained timber clad design. Nissen Richards Studio, 2019

• Hackney Extension © Ben Blossom 2018

PEER
🚶 Peer UK, 97-99 Hoxton Street, N1 6QL
🕐 Sat 12pm–6pm + PEER Notices (a showcase of work embracing everyday resourcefulness). Last entry Sat 5.45pm. **T·D·O**
🚇 Old Street, Hoxton
🚌 394,243,242,149
PEER is a gallery with a 10-metre wide glass façade, bringing art straight onto the street. With its community garden, and Chris Ofilli's 'Black Hands' outdoor clock, PEER is also a welcoming and open public space. Trevor Horne Architects, 2016

Pembury Circus
🚶 Pembury Road, E8 1JG
🕐 Sat Architect-led tour, hourly (10am–4pm, max 20). **A**
🚇 Hackney Central, Hackney Downs
🚌 254,253,242,106,55,48,38,30
Award-winning car free mixed-use development of 268 high-quality homes for all ages. Including older people's accommodation, a vibrant community centre and commercial space, a new public square and play area. Fraser Brown MacKenna, 2015

Pitwell Mews
🚶 4 Pitwell Mews, (r/o 42 Wilton Way), E8 1FH
🕐 Sun 10am–5pm (max 30, House No 4 and the Yard). Last entry 3.30pm. **A**
🚇 Dalston Junction, Hackney Central
🚌 277,38
A secluded, sustainable mixed-use mews, consisting of three houses and a small office building. Wilton Studio, 2013

Rivington Place
🚶 EC2A 3BA
🕐 Sat 12pm–6pm. Last entry 5.15pm. **D·B·T·O**
🚇 Old Street, Shoreditch High Street
🚌 135,48,55,149,205,242,243
First permanent visual arts space dedicated to global diversity, inspired by African art and architecture as well as contemporary art and music. RIBA Award Winner 2008. Adjaye Associates, 2007

Round Chapel
🚶 Lower Clapton Road (junction with Glenarm Road), E5 0NP
🕐 Sun 11am–5pm. Last entry 4.15pm. **D·T·R·B**
🚇 Hackney Downs, Clapton, Hackney Central
🚌 38,48,55,106,253,242,254,394,488
Grade II*-listed Nonconformist chapel for 1,000 people. Described by Pevsner as"'one of the finest Nonconfirmist buildings in London". Horseshoe plan, innovative cast-iron columns and tracery, restored as a centre for the performing arts. Henry Fuller & James Cubitt, 1871

Shoreditch Town Hall
🚶 380 Old Street, EC1V 9LT
🕐 Sat/Sun 10am–5pm (max 20, no access to the
Council Chamber). Last entry 4pm. **B·R·T**
🚇 Shoreditch High Street, Old Street
🚌 26,35,47,48,55,78,135,149,242,243
A magnificent Grade II-listed building housing many
contrasting spaces from the grand assembly hall to the
untouched rabbit warren of basement rooms. Caesar
Augustus Long, 1866

St Augustine's Tower
🚶 Mare Street, E8 1HR
🕐 Sat/Sun 11am–5pm (max 50).
Last entry 4.30pm. **B·R·0**
🚇 Hackney Central, Hackney Downs
🚌 30,38,48,55,106,236,242,253,254,276,277,394,D6
Grade I-listed, remaining tower of Medieval parish
church, with working late 16C clock. New exhibition
of Hackney's history. Extensive views from roof.
Organised by Hackney Historic Buildings Trust.

St Leonards Church, Shoreditch
🚶 119 Shoreditch High Street, E1 6JN
🕐 Sat 11am–4pm/Sun 12pm–7pm + 'Burbage,
Shakespeare and The Theatre': an exhibition of the
Shoreditch scene · Family Day at 11am + Sun Blue
Badge Guided Tour, hourly (2pm–5pm, max 20, 45
mins duration) · Sun 'There is a river': music and
poetry workshop with composer Deborah Pritchard at
4pm · Sun 'Sun at Night' sound service at 6pm · Tudor
Lutemob – an Elizabethan music flashmob at 2pm.
Last entry 3.45pm. **T·R·F·D·0**
🚇 Shoreditch High Street, Old Street
🚌 243,242,149,78,55,48,35,26
Site of the Medieval 'Actors' Church' of the Burbage
family, Shakespeare's players and 'the bells of
Shoreditch', the Georgian building was designed by
George Dance the Elder, opening in 1740. Restoration
supported by Heritage Fund. George Dance the Elder,
1740. *twitter.com/ShoreditchChurc*

St Mary of Eton Church Mixed Use Development
🚶 95 Eastway, Hackney Wick, E9 5JA
🕐 Sat 12pm–4pm (no access to housing).
Last entry 3.30pm. **D·T·0**
🚇 Hackney Wick
🚌 488,26,30,236,276,388
Refurbished Grade II*-listed church with new
community facilities, new housing. 2015 RIBA Award,
New London Architecture Award, Housing Design Award.
Bodley & Garner, 1892

Suleymaniye Mosque
🚶 212 Kingsland Road, E2 8AX
🕐 Sat/Sun 10am–6pm. Last entry 5.45pm.
B·A·P·R·T·0
🚇 Haggerston, Hoxton
🚌 394,243,242,149
Six storey building featuring a Western exterior and
traditional Islamic interior, modelled on the Blue Mosque
in Istanbul. Has dome and minaret tower. Networld
Project Management, 1996

The Print Studio
🚶 32 Cassland Road, E9 7AN
🕐 Sat 11am–4.30pm (max 8) + Architect-led tour of the
studio, hourly (11am–4pm, max 8). Last entry 4pm. **A**
🚇 London Fields, Homerton
🚌 388,26,277,425
Situated behind a grand terrace of Grade II-listed
Georgian townhouses, at the end of a long garden and
hidden by mature planting – the Print Studio is both
workspace and sanctuary for the artist occupier and
long-term Hackney resident. Studio RO.ST, 2018

Tower Theatre
🚶 16 Northwold Road, Stoke Newington, N16 7HR
🕐 Sat 10am–5pm + ½ hourly tour (max 15, the ground
floor is fully accessible). Last entry Sat 4.15pm. **T·R**
🚇 Stoke Newington
🚌 476,393,276,243,149,106,73,67,76
Built as a chapel in 1875, this octagonal brick building
has also served as a synagogue, an office and a gym.
Now this local landmark has been brought back into
use as a theatre for the Tower Theatre Company.

Vex
🚶 85 Maury Road, N16 7BT
🕐 Sat 10am–5pm (max 30). Last entry 4.30pm. **T·Q**
🚇 Stoke Newington, Rectory Road
🚌 73,106,393,276
A new curving fluted concrete house with sound/music
by 'Scanner'. Chance de Silva, 2016

Havering

Social Capital

Havering is the second-largest
London authority, with half of its
land area within the green belt.

Havering
LONDON BOROUGH

64 Heath Drive
🚶 Gidea Park, Romford, RM2 5QR
🕐 Sat/Sun 2.30pm–5pm (max 12, Guided tours of
whole house). Last entry 4.15pm. **P·T·Q**
🚇 Gidea Park
🚌 498,174
Model Modernist villa completely refurbished 2003,
with modern garden by Dan Pearson. Grade II-listed.
Unsuitable for children under 7. Lubetkin & Tecton, 1934

Bower House
🚶 Orange Tree Hill, Havering-atte-Bower,
Romford, RM4 1PB
🕐 Sat 10am–3pm (no access to basement and to the
second floor, limited access to the first floor).
Last entry 2.15pm. **B·P·R·T**
🚇 Hainault, Romford – then bus
🚌 375
Grade I-listed country house commanding the most
extensive southerly views over Essex. Staircase mural
by Sir James Thornhill, a painter notable for the 'Painted
Hall' at the Royal Naval Hospital at Greenwich. Set in
grounds with a pond. Henry Flitcroft, 1729

Havering Museum
🚶 19–21 High Street, Romford, RM1 1JU
🕐 Sat 11am–5pm (max 40). Last entry 4pm. **X·D·B·T**
🚇 Romford
🚌 365,66,175,248,496
A cultural centre in part of the old Romford Brewery
building near to the historic market place. Permanent
and temporary exhibition displays tell the story of the
London Borough of Havering from Bronze Age to present
day. TTSP Architects, 2010

Ingrebourne Valley Visitor Centre
🚶 Hornchurch Country Park, Squadrons Approach,
RM12 6DF
🕐 Sat/Sun 10am–5pm. Last entry 4.15pm. **D·B·P·R·T·O**
🚇 Hornchurch, Elm Park
🚌 252,256
Ingrebourne Valley Visitor Centre, at Hornchurch
Country Park, the Former RAF Hornchurch Airfield.
Tim Ronalds Architects, 2015

Rainham Hall
🚶 The Broadway, Rainham, RM13 9YN
🕐 Sat 10.30am–5pm (max 15, see website for full
access statement). Last entry 4.15pm. **B·R·T**
🚇 Rainham (Essex)
🚌 103,165,287,372
Grade II*-listed 18C house and garden built for a
merchant. The Hall features fine wrought-iron gates,
carved porch, and interior panelling. Opened fully in
2015 following renovation project, with a new café and
exhibition programme. Julian Harrap Architects, 2016

Rainham Parish Church of St Helen and St Giles
🚶 The Broadway, Rainham, RM13 9YW
🕐 Sat 10am–5pm. Last entry 4.30pm. **T**
🚇 Rainham (Essex)
🚌 372,103,165,287
Grade I-listed Norman church with notable chancel arch
with chevron and nailhead ornament, built by Richard
De Lucy. Richard de Lucy, 1170

Thames Chase Forest Centre
🚶 Broadfields Farm, Pike Lane, Upminster, RM14 3NS
🕐 Sat/Sun 10am–5pm. Last entry 4.30pm.
F·D·B·P·R·T·O
🚇 Upminster
🚌 370,347,346,248
Distinctive award-winning visitor centre of modern
timber sustainable construction forming an A-frame
building roofed with cedar shingles, attached to 17C
listed barn – one of the best preserved in the London
area. Laurie Wood Architects, 2005

The Round House
🚶 Broxhill Road, Havering-atte-Bower,
Romford, RM4 1QH
🕐 Sat/Sun Tour at 10.30am, 12pm, 2.30pm (max 15). **P·T**
❗ Pre-book only: michaelheap26@gmail.com,
eventbrite.co.uk/e/open-house-london-2019-guided-
tour-of-the-round-house-tickets-62508625983
🚇 Romford – then bus
🚌 375
Grade II*-listed late Georgian elliptical three storey
stuccoed villa. Attributed John Plaw, 1792

Upminster Tithe Barn Museum

🚶 Hall Lane, Upminster, RM14 1AU
🕐 Sat/Sun 10am–4pm. Last entry 3.15pm. **D·P·O**
🚇 Upminster
🚌 347,248

15C box-framed, nine-bay, aisled barn, weatherboarded with crown-post, collar-tie reed-thatched roof. The Barn is scheduled as an Ancient monument. Kent Barn Builders, 1450

Upminster Windmill Visitor Centre

🚶 Mill Field, St Mary's Lane, Upminster, RM14 2QL
🕐 Sat/Sun 1pm–4pm
🚇 Upminster
🚌 248,370

Modern visitor centre with a living green roof. The visitor centre was built over the old mill house which was demolished in 1960s. Rees Bolter, 2016

Walks & Tours

Gidea Park Garden Suburb Walk

🚶 Meet: entrance to Balgores Square car park, (immediately north of Gidea Park Station), RM2 6AU
🕐 Sat 10.15am. **T·R**
❗ Pre-book only: 01277 219892
🚇 Gidea Park
🚌 294,496

The first Gidea Park Garden Suburb houses were built as a result of an open competition in 1910 for architects. Tour takes in Gidea Park exhibition houses and Hare Street buildings. William Curtis Green, Parker & Unwin, 1910

• Ingrebourne Valley Visitor Centre

Lewisham

Social Capital

Forty-six per cent of Lewisham residents are of black and minority ethnic heritage, but this rises to just over 76% among school children.

Ash House
🚶 124 Manor Park, SE13 5RH
🕐 Sat Architect-led tour, ½ hourly (11am–4pm, max 8, no shoes inside). **X·D·A**
🚇 Hither Green
🚌 273
Transformation of a Victorian house with a side extension opening out into three gardens along river Quaggy. R2 Studio Architects, 2018

Blackheath Quaker Meeting House
🚶 Lawn Terrace, Blackheath, SE3 9LL
🕐 Sat 10am–4pm + Tour every 10 mins. Last entry 3.45pm. **T·R**
🚇 Blackheath
🚌 54,89,108,202,380,386
A calm space for Quakers and others in octagonal meeting room lit naturally from high central roof lantern and side 'turrets'. Civic Trust Award 1973. Concrete Society Commendation 1974. Now Grade II-listed. Trevor Dannatt, 1972

Boone's Chapel
🚶 Lee High Road, SE13 5PQ
🕐 Sat/Sun 1pm–5pm (max 30, excludes access to adjacent almshouse garden) + The almshouses of South East London. Last entry 4.30pm. **D·A·O**
🚇 Blackheath, Lewisham
🚌 321,178,261,122
Grade I-listed former almshouse chapel (1682) restored in 2008 as a studio and exhibition space. Brick and Portland stone chapel with contemporary service building and small garden in grounds of the Merchant Taylors' Almshouses. Possibly by Robert Hooke, 1682

Brockley House
🚶 7 Braxfield Road, SE4 2AW
🕐 Sat 10am–1pm (max 15, access to Ground floor only). Last entry Sat 12.45pm. **A**
🚇 Brockley
🚌 484,172,171
Black charred larch cladding by Shou-Sugi-Ban was used to clad the extension as well as Critall doors distinguishing the addition from its Victorian context. When your design is truly bespoke even the cat gets its own door to the garden. SAM Architects, 2018

David & Elena's House
🚶 24, Arthurdon Road, SE4 1JU
🕐 Sat/Sun 11am–2pm (Downstairs only). Last entry 1.45pm. **A**
🚇 Ladywell, Crofton Park
🚌 122,284,P4
Side extension to a Victorian house to create a new kitchen, dining room and courtyard garden. The extension is clad in black timber, a striking modern addition to the London stock brickwork of the house. Matthew and David – Design Ltd, 2017

End House
🚶 87a Manwood Road, SE4 1SA
🕐 Sat 9.30am–12.30pm (max 10). Last entry 12pm. **D**
🚇 Ladywell, Crofton Park
🚌 284,P4,171,172,122
A fresh, contemporary end-of-terrace house that makes clever use of a small site by using a simple form to offer privacy combined with open-plan living. Sustainable features include recycled newspaper insulation and breathable walls. Edgley Design, 2010

Forest Mews
🚶 Rockbourne Mews, SE23 2AT
🕐 Sun 10am–1pm (max 25). Last entry 12.15pm. **A**
🚇 Forest Hill
🚌 122,185,197
Three bespoke houses, each with a studio and courtyard, set around a communal courtyard. Inspired by views of ivy growing over trees in wintertime – all three houses are clad with striking green walls, trained to a geometric pattern. Stolon Studio, Robert and Jessica Barker, 2014

Harefield Road East
🚶 10 Harefield Road, SE4 1LR
🕐 Sat 10am–1pm (max 15, access only to the ground floor and new extension). Last entry 12.15pm. **A**
🚇 Brockley
🚌 172,171,484
This rear extension by Gruff Architects combines an oak timber statement pitched roof, exposed grey brickwork and pockets of glazing. Its central planted courtyard brings light and soft planting to the heart of the living space. Gruff Architects, 2019

Hive House

🚶 32 Hawkesfield Road, SE23 2TL

🕐 Sat 10am–5pm (max 15, downstairs only.
Remove shoes) + Architect-led tour or extension,
hourly (11am–4pm) Last entry 4.15pm. **A**

🚇 Forest Hill, Lower Sydenham, Catford

🚌 202,181,75

A simple, effective stepped rear extension driven
by the principles of simplicity and honesty. Budget
informed structure and materials to create a light-filled
and unique design that has a transformative effect on
everyday family life.

JAWS (James and Wakana's Studio)

🚶 Sienna Place, SE23 1DZ

🕐 Sat/Sun 11am–4pm. Last entry 3.45pm. **T·A**

🚇 Honor Oak Park

🚌 172,P12,171,122,P4

A purpose-built pottery studio located within a private
mews in South East London, tucked away behind a
typical Victorian terrace on a parcel of land just 4.2 x 6.4
metres. Matthew and David – Design Ltd, 2017

Ladywell Self-Build Community Hub

🚶 Church Grove, SE13 7UU

🕐 Sat 12pm–4pm. Last entry 3.30pm. **T·D·A**

🚇 Ladywell

🚌 P4,484,284,122

New community space with self-build volunteers to
create a knowledge hub for community-led housing.
Designed as a demountable structure utilising reclaimed
materials, the project was crowdfunded and will open
autumn 2019. Rural Urban Synthesis Society, 2019

Lewisham Arthouse

🚶 140 Lewisham Way, SE14 6PD

🕐 Sat 12pm–8pm/Sun 1pm–5pm + Tour at 4pm, 2pm +
Open Studios and Exhibition. Last entry Sat 7.15pm |
Sun 4.15pm. **F·D·T·R·O**

🚇 New Cross

🚌 172,171,21,436,136,321

Formerly Deptford Central Library, Grade II-listed.
A good example of classic Renaissance architecture,
the building is Berkshire brick with a Portland stone
façade in the Ionic order with many original features
remaining. Sir Alfred Brumwell Thomas, 1914

Manor House Gardens Ice House

🚶 Old Road, SE13 5SY

🕐 Sat/Sun 12pm–5pm (max 8). Last entry 4.15pm. **O**

🚇 Hither Green

🚌 178,122,261,321

Grade II-listed ice well and underground chambers
(1770) in Manor House Gardens park, which provided
ice for nearby Manor House. Cited in 2002 Civic Trust
Awards.

Mulberry House

🚶 8A Eliot Park, Blackheath, SE13 7EG

🕐 Sat/Sun 10am–5pm (max 20). Last entry 4.15pm.
T·D·A

🚇 Lewisham

🚌 89,54,321,21,380,273,199,180

A new addition to the Blackheath Conservation Area,
this family dwelling is designed with sustainability in
mind as well as using natural materials and integrated
flora to create a harmonious relationship with its
surroundings. Apex Architecture Consultancy Limited,
David Hurcombe, Joe Hurcombe, Jibreel Shaikh, 2019
apexarchitecture.com

Pitched Black

🚶 8a Tyrwhitt Road, SE4 1QG

🕐 Sat 10am–5pm (max 15). Last entry 4.15pm. **A**

🚇 St.John's, Lewisham

🚌 436,321,136,21

Gruff Architects' founder's new home, Pitched Black
responds to a challenging site within a conservation
area: this black-clad new-build house leans at 10 degrees
towards a tree-lined railway cutting, and away from
neighbouring gardens. Gruff Architects, 2019

R & S house

🚶 30 Lampmead Road, SE12 8QL

🕐 Sat Architect-led tour, every 45 mins
(10am–4pm, max 10). **X·A**

🚇 Blackheath, Hither Green

🚌 321,261,180,178,122

Stylish contemporary refurbishment, loft conversion
and rear extension in a conservation area which includes
an elegantly crafted zinc-clad roof dormer, a new
extended kitchen, Crittall screens and a feature double-
height slot window. PLANSTUDIO, 2017. *planstudio.uk*

Seager Place, Distillery Tower

🚶 1 Mill Lane Deptford, SE8 4HN

🕐 Sat/Sun 10am–5pm. Last entry 4.15pm.

🚇 Deptford Bridge, Deptford

🚌 453,225,177,53,47

Regeneration project by Galliard Homes on the site
of a former Seager distillery, includes refurb of a 19C
warehouse, conversion of former 19C Holland House, a
new Crescent building, Pavilion and 27-storey residential
tower with viewing gallery. BUJ Architects, 2005

South East London Combined Heat & Power Energy Recovery Facility

🚶 Landmann Way, off Surrey Canal Road, SE14 5RS

🕐 Sun 10am–3pm. Last entry 2.00pm. **R·T**

🚇 South Bermondsey, New Cross Gate

🚌 47,188,199,225,P12

Energy Recovery Facility providing long-term
sustainable solution for waste treatment, producing
National Grid electricity and heat for Southwark
residents. Designed to minimise visual impact while
remaining a high-quality landmark building. Alan J
Smith Partnership, 1993

St Margaret's Church, Lee

🚶 Lee Terrace, SE13 5DN
🕐 Sun 1pm–5pm (max 20). Last entry 4.15pm. **T·P·D**
🚇 Lewisham, Blackheath
🚌 108,89,54

The Church was built in 1839–41 as a white 'Hall-Church'. The 1870s Gothic Revivalism was overseen by James Brooks and helped by 10 top craftsmen of the day. We also have a WWI Memorial by Violet Pinwill. John Brown of Norwich/James Brooks, 1841

The Fellowship Inn

🚶 Randlesdown Road, SE6 3BT
🕐 Sat 10am–5pm + Audio guided tour, every 90 mins (11am–3pm, max 6) + Q&A with the Architect. Last entry 4.30pm. **T·D·A**
🚇 Bellingham
🚌 199,208,54

A rare example of a 1920s 'improved public house' built as part of the Homes for Heroes Bellingham Estate. Restored as a community venue including bar, cinema and café by Phoenix Community Housing with National Lottery Heritage Fund support. FG Newnham, 1923

The Mansion, Homesteads and lake at Beckenham Place Park

🚶 Beckenham Place Park, Beckenham Hill Road, BR3 1SY
🕐 Sun 11am–5pm. Meet the designer - walking tour 1pm, 2.30pm, 4pm (max 30) · Homesteads restoration talk, hourly (12pm–4pm, max 30, meet in the Homesteads courtyard) + Artists' Open Studios (max 30). Last entry 4.15pm. **P·D·A·R·T·O**
🕐 Pre-book only: cityoflondon.gov.uk/openhouse
🚇 Beckenham Hill, Beckenham Junction
🚌 54,352,354

Georgian mansion house, newly-restored stable yard, formal gardens and parkland, including restored lake. Opportunities to view the mansion attic and to meet the designers of the lake, landscape and building restorations.

The Master Shipwright's House

🚶 Watergate Street, SE8 3JF
🕐 Sat 10am–5pm/Sun 10am–1pm. Last entry Sat 4.45pm | Sun 12.45pm. **R**
🚇 Deptford
🚌 188,47,199

The oldest upstanding building of the former Deptford Royal Dockyard – home and office of the master shipwright since 1513 – remodelled in early 18C. Gardens & river frontage. "Hidden London at its delightful best" – The Telegraph.

Tidemill Academy and Deptford Lounge

🚶 9 Giffin Street, SE8 4RJ
🕐 Sat 11am–4pm. Last entry 3.30pm
🚇 Deptford, Deptford Bridge, New Cross
🚌 47

Award-winning civic centre in the heart of Deptford. A model of co-location, combining a brand new 448 pupil place primary school; state of the art district library; community centre; artist's studios; 38 affordable homes and a market square. Pollard Thomas Edwards, 2011

Walter Segal Self-build Houses

🚶 Multiple houses, Walters Way, Honor Oak Park, SE23 3LH
🕐 Sat 1pm–7pm (max 20, Access to downstairs only for most properties. NB two steps to each house). Last entry 6.45pm. **R·T**
🚇 Honor Oak Park
🚌 P4,P12,171,63

A close of 13 self-built houses. Each is unique, built using a method developed by Walter Segal, who led the project in the 1980s. Houses have been extended and renovated. Sustainable features including solar electric, water and space heating. Walter Segal, 1987

Walks & Tours

Blackheath SE3

🚶 Meet: on the Heath outside Eastnor House, on the corner of Tranquil Vale and Lloyds Place, Eastnor House, Lloyds Place, SE3 0QD
🕐 Sun 11am (max 30).
❗ Pre-book only: self-addressed envelope to Blackheath Society, 11 Blackheath Village, SE3 9LA (No comfort stops, no small children)
🚇 Blackheath
🚌 386,380,54,89,108,202

Guided walk on part of the south side of Blackheath from Lloyds Place, Grotes Buildings to Blackheath Vale and back to Hare & Billet Row. Architectural interest from the 1750s to the mid-late 19C and some more modern examples.

• The Fellowship Inn © Phoenix Community Housing 2015

Newham

Social Capital

There were approximately 118,100 dwellings in Newham as of the end of May 2019, nearly 6000 more than in April 2017.

105 Barking Road
🚶 E16 4HQ
🕐 Sat 10am–5pm. Last entry Sat 4.15pm. **D·T·R·O**
🚇 Canning Town
🚌 474,69,115,5,276,330,300
Victorian public hall with links to East London's suffragette and labour movements. Keir Hardie and Sylvia Pankhurst both spoke here. Features include a mosaic terrazzo floor and stained glass windows. Now home to charity Community Links. Lewis Angell , 1894

32 Grosvenor Road
🚶 Leyton, E10 6LQ
🕐 Sat 10am–1pm/Sun 1pm–5pm.
Last entry Sat 12.15pm | Sun 4.15pm. **A**
🚇 Leyton Midland Road, Leytonstone
🚌 W16,69,97
Grosvenor Road is an extension and rationalisation of a Victorian terrace, providing additional living and bedroom accommodation for a young family. Additions to the interior have been made in environmentally friendly OSB smartply. Studio Bark, 2017

Abbey Mills Pumping Station
🚶 Abbey Lane, E15 2RN
🕐 Sat/Sun Hourly tour (10am–4pm, max 15, Pre-Book Only). **T**
❗ Pre-book only: abbeymills2019.eventbrite.co.uk
🚇 West Ham
Abbey Mills pumping station 'A', built by engineer Joseph Bazalgette, Edmund Cooper and architect Charles Driver. Built between 1865 and 1868 it has been described as the cathedral of sewage. Joseph Bazalgette, Charles H Driver, 1900

Cody Dock
🚶 11c South Crescent, Canning Town, E16 4TL
🕐 Sat/Sun 10am–5pm. Last entry 4.15pm. **F·R·T·O**
🚇 Star Lane (DLR)
🚌 323,276
One of London's most exciting creative spaces, Cody Dock provides a gateway to the Lea River Park and is home to a gallery, gardens, café & bar that make this the perfect pit stop for exploring The Line Sculpture trail and Lower Lea River. Constructed for Harper Twelvetrees as part of Imperial Chemical Works, 1871

House Mill
🚶 Three Mill Lane, Bromley by Bow, E3 3DU
🕐 Sat/Sun Hourly Tours, 11am–4pm (max 18). Last entry 3.15pm. **B·P·R·T**
🚇 Bromley By Bow
🚌 25,D8,323,488
The world's largest tidal mill. 5-storey, timber-framed, brick-clad timber watermill with four waterwheels, originally built 1776 to mill grain for distillery trade. Operational until 1940. On historic 3 Mills Site, Clock Mill adjacent.

Millennium Mills
🚶 Rayleigh Rd, Royal Docks, London, E16 1UR
🕐 Sat/Sun Hourly tour (10am–3pm, max 10, Meet Point: Rayleigh Road Entrance).
❗ Pre-book only: royaldocks.london
🚇 Custom House, Pontoon Dock (DLR)
🚌 474,147,241,325
Built in the early 20C by flour company Spillers, the Art Deco landmark has stood vacant since the decline of the docks as a working port in the 1980s.

Royal Docks Pumping Station
🚶 Shackleton Way, Royal Docks, E16 2JQ
🕐 Sat/Sun 10am–4pm. Last entry 3.30pm. **R**
🚇 Gallions Reach
🚌 262,474
Built in 1912, this Pump House based in London's Royal Docks has a lot of character, an industrial feel and is still operational in maintaining water levels in what was once the largest stretch of enclosed water in the world.

Salmen House
🚶 53a Salmen Road, Plaistow, E13 0DT
🕐 Sat 10am–5pm (max 10) + Architect-led tours, ½ hourly. Last entry 4.30pm. **A**
🚇 Plaistow
🚌 69,241,262,473
A new build, three bed house, of pink textured render with green terrazzo details. It contains generous vertical spaces, such as double-height bedrooms, exposed beam ceilings, and a triple-height staircase, on a constrained corner site. Office S&M, 2017

• Millennium Mills © James O'Jenkins 2018

St Mary Magdalene Church & Nature Reserve
🏃 High Street South/Norman Road, E6 3PG
🕐 Sat 10am–5pm + Hourly tour (max 10). Last entry Sat 4.15pm. **D·R·T·O**
🚊 Beckton, East Ham
🚌 101,104,474
Grade I-listed 12C church, with London's largest churchyard and one of the best-preserved Norman archways in the country, as well as other interesting features, including 750-year-old wall paintings.

St Mary the Virgin
🏃 Church Road, Manor Park, Little Ilford, E12 6HA
🕐 Sat 10am–5pm/Sun 1pm–5pm (no access to crypt). Last entry 4.45pm. **T·O**
🚊 Woodgrange Park, East Ham, Manor Park
🚌 25,86,101,104,147,474
Small Grade I-listed 12C chapel in lovely churchyard setting, it retains original architectural features and has interesting brasses, monuments and stained glass windows.

The City of London Cemetery and Crematorium at Aldersbrook
🏃 Aldersbrook Road, E12 5DQ
🕐 Sat/Sun 10am–1pm + Tours (10am–1pm, max 35, regular tours). Last entry Sat/Sun 12.15pm. **P·R·T**
❗ Pre-book only: 020 8530 2151
🚊 Manor Park, Woodgrange Park
🚌 474,101,104,W19
A stunning Grade I-listed 200-acre landscape designed and landscaped in 1856 to deal with the environmental/health/space issues of London's cramped and over-used churchyards. Rich in architecture from the Victorian era. William Haywood & William Davidson, 1855

Workable
🏃 1 Westfield Avenue – level 19, E20 1HZ
🕐 Sun 11am–4pm (max 120).
❗ Pre-book only: eventbrite.co.uk/e/workable-open-house-2019-tickets-63854077264
🚊 Stratford, Stratford International
Situated within the Rogers Stirk Harbour + Partners designed buildings at IQL, Workable is a new approach to flexible working in Stratford that combines panoramic views over London with stylish interior design. Fletcher Priest Architects, 2018

Walks & Tours

ICE Engineering Highlights Cycle Tour of the Queen Elizabeth Olympic Park
🏃 Meet: outside the Timber Lodge Café, Honour Lea Avenue, Queen Elizabeth Olympic Park, E20 3BB
🕐 Sun 2pm (max 30, Please check the Open House for up-to-date timings). **A**
❗ Pre-book only: london@ice.org.uk
🚊 Stratford, Stratford International
Tour will explore the Olympic Park's enabling works and the construction of the venues, through to the utilities and their supporting infrastructure. Organised by the Institution of Civil Engineers. Various architects, 2012

Jubilee Line Night Tour
🏃 Meet: West Ham Station Ticket Hall, West Ham Underground Station, Manor Road, E15 3BN
🕐 Sat 12pm (max 20, Tour starts at 12am midnight on Friday night). **O**
❗ Pre-book only: See Open House website for more information
🚊 West Ham
🚌 276
With a focus on the architecture and the operations of the Jubilee line extension stations, this tour takes advantage of the Night Tube to showcase the award-winning built environment along this line's 1999 extension, 20 years after its opening.

Olympic Legacy Masterplan
🏃 Meet: on the approach from Westfield before the Aquatics Centre, Information Point Queen Elizabeth Olympic Park, Stratford Walk, E15 2DU
🕐 Sat 11am (max 30). **D·O**
❗ Pre-book only: press@alliesandmorrison.com
🚊 Stratford, Hackney Wick
London's 2012 Games provided a catalyst for regeneration in the Lower Lea Valley. Guided by the Legacy Masterplan, thousands of new homes and jobs are now being created, stitching together existing communities across the former floodplain. Allies and Morrison with Aecom, 2012

Redbridge

Social Capital

Ilford as a town is synonymous with photography having lent its name to the famous roll-film brand manufactured there until the 1980s.

Bancroft's School

🚶 611–627 High Road, Woodford Green, IG8 0RF
🕐 Sat 12.30pm–2.30pm (Access to Quad, Chapel & Tower only). Last entry 2.15pm. **P**
🚇 Woodford, Chingford
🚌 20,179,W13,397

A dignified and impressive design with later additions. Spiral staircase leads to the top of the tower, giving excellent views. Formerly a Drapers' Company charitable school in Mile End Road, Bancroft's moved to its present site in 1889. Sir Arthur Blomfield, 1889

Christ Church

🚶 Wanstead Place, E11 2SW
🕐 Sat 10am–1pm/Sun 1pm–5pm.
🚇 Wanstead, Snaresbrook
🚌 W12, 66, 101, 145, 308, W13, W14

Grade II*-listed church with ragstone tower, spire, good stained glass by Kempe and newly restored William Hill organ. A characteristic work of Scott. It is Gothic Revival in the style of the 13C. Sir George Gilbert Scott, 1861

Fullwell Cross Library

🚶 140 High Street, Barkingside, Ilford, IG6 2EA
🕐 Sat 9.30am–4pm. Last entry 3.30pm. **T·O**
🚇 Barkingside, Fairlop
🚌 128,150,167,169,247

The library was built on an open site in Barkingside High Street. Circular library design copies nearby roundabout. Complex is set back from the pavement, to form a new local civic centre with a public space. Refurbished 1990 and 2011. Coombes & Partners, Frederick Gibberd, HC Connell, 1958

Quaker Meeting House, Wanstead

🚶 Bush Road, E11 5AU
🕐 Sun 1pm–5pm. Last entry 4.45pm. **P·T**
🚇 Leytonstone, Leytonstone High Road
🚌 101,308,257,145,W19

Four hexagon Modernist building within an Epping Forest setting. A sunny meeting room for Quaker worship faces onto a wooded burial ground of simple headstones, including those of Elizabeth Fry, William Mead and Norman Frith. Norman Frith, 1968

Repton Park (former Claybury Asylum)

🚶 Manor Road, Woodford Bridge, IG8 8GG
🕐 Sat/Sun Tour at 10am, 11.30am (max 30). **R·Q**
🚇 Woodford, Chigwell
🚌 275,W14

Former mental asylum includes 17C Claybury Hall with Adam staircase. Original asylum (Hall, Chapel, Water Towers, Gate Lodges, Ward Blocks, Airing Shelters) all Grade II-listed. Private parkland originally designed by Sir Humphrey Repton. George T Hine, 1889

St Mary The Virgin Wanstead

Overton Drive, E11 2LW
🚶 Sat/Sun 10am–5pm. Last entry 4.15pm
🚇 Wanstead
🚌 145, 66

One of the finest examples of Georgian architecture. It has been hardly altered since built. The church is a rectangle building of Portland stone, with a projecting chancel. Two external walls have been restored in 2019 by Thomas Heatherwick.

Sukkat Shalom Reform Synagogue

🚶 1 Victory Road, Wanstead, E11 1UL
🕐 Sun 10am–4pm + General Historical update. Last entry 3.45pm. **D·P·R·T**
🚇 Snaresbrook
🚌 W12,W13

Grade II*-listed, originally the Merchant Seaman's Orphan Asylum, bought by the synagogue in 1995 and restored with Lottery Fund grant. Timber work and windows from a synagogue which was inside the Tottenham Home for Incurables. Somers Clarke, 1863

The Hospital Chapel of St Mary & St Thomas

🚶 48 Ilford Hill, Ilford, IG1 2AT
🕐 Sat 10am–4pm/Sun 1pm–4.30pm (Access to Chapel and courtyard.) Last entry Sat 3.45pm | Sun 4.15pm. **D·B·R·T·O**
🚇 Ilford
🚌 145,147,425,296,169,25,86,123,179,128,167,EL1

Founded c1145 by the Abbess of Barking as a hospice for 13 old and infirm men, the present building is 12C and 19C. Grade II*-listed with many interesting monuments, including Burne-Jones windows. Abbess of Barking, 1145

• Valentines Mansion Gardens © Paul Riddle 2008

Valentines Mansion & Gardens
🚶 Emerson Road, Ilford, IG1 4XA
🕐 Sun 11am–4pm. Last entry 3.30pm. **T·D·0**
🚇 Gants Hill, Ilford
🚌 150,167,296,123,179,128,396

Large, late 17C Grade II*-listed house with fine staircase and Venetian window and Georgian additions, used as a family dwelling until the early 1900s. Reopened to the public in Feb 2009 following extensive restoration works. Richard Griffiths Architects, 1696

Woodford County High School for Girls
🚶 High Road, Woodford Green, IG8 9LA
🕐 Sun 1pm–5pm + Tour every 15 mins + 100 years in the life of our school (1919–2019). Last entry 4.30pm. **T·R**
🚇 Woodford
🚌 20,179,275,W13

Formerly Highams Manor, an elegant Georgian manor house built for the Warner family with grounds by Repton. William Newton, 1768

Walks & Tours

Wanstead Heritage Walk
🚶 Meet: outside Wanstead Station,
    21 The Green, E11 2NT
🕐 Sun 10am (max 35).
❗ Pre-book only: eppingforest.eventbrite.com
🚇 Wanstead
🚌 66,101,145,308,W13,W14

A guided walk, Wanstead Station to the Temple, Wanstead Park, taking in the history and architectural heritage of Wanstead House. The walk finishes at the Temple and will include an optional private tour of its displays.

Tower Hamlets

TOWER HAMLETS

Social Capital

Boundary Estate was the world's first council estate, created by the LCC on the demolished site of a notorious slum, Old Nichol.

Balfron Tower
🚶 Balfron Tower, St Leonard's Road, E14 0QR
🕐 Sat 10am–1pm (max 6, access to the show apartment). Last entry 12.15pm. **Q**
❗ Pre-book only: melina@londonewcastle.co.uk
🚇 All Saints, Langdon Park
🚌 108,15,115,D8,309
Designed by architect Ernö Goldfinger, the Grade II*-listed residential tower is one of the last Brutalist landmarks in the UK, and is currently undergoing extensive restoration to reinstate key elements of Goldfinger's original design. Ernö Goldfinger, 1967

Bethnal Green Mission Church
🚶 305 Cambridge Heath Road, E2 9LH
🕐 Sat 10am–5pm (max 20, no access to roof or residential areas)/Sun 1pm–5pm. Last entry 4.15pm. **T·R·A**
🚇 Cambridge Heath, Bethnal Green
🚌 8,106,254,388,D8
Mixed-use building comprising a church, community centre, café/gallery and offices with apartments above. In appearance it takes its cues from the local conservation area, formed of pale brick framed by a light pre-cast concrete grid. Gatti Routh Rhodes Architects, 2018

Binary House
🚶 101 Finis Street, E2 0DX
🕐 Sat Architect-led tour, ½ hourly (10am–4.30pm, max 15, overshoes will be provided). **A**
🚇 Bethnal Green
🚌 106,254
A surprising but subtle two storey front extension and a glass box rear extension, containing a special mirco-louvred brass mesh, have been added to this otherwise dull house, providing much-needed space and elegance. Space Group Architects, 2018

Bow Church - St Mary
🚶 230 Bow Road, E3 3AH
🕐 Sat 10am–5pm/Sun 12pm–5pm (Step free access to the main church) + Tour at 1pm, 3pm (max 20) + Children's self-led tour (max 20). Last entry 4.45pm. **T·R·B·O**
🚇 Bow Church, Bow Road
🚌 25,8,D8,425,205,276,108,488

Medieval village church, restored in late 19C and after bomb damage in WWII. 15C font and memorials from five centuries. Grade II*-listed. Refurbished for 700th anniversary in 2011; the bell tower and cupola were restored in 2017–18. H. Lewis Curtis, CR Ashbee, HS Goodhart-Rendel, 1311

Béton Brit
🚶 5 East Arbour St, E1 0PU
🕐 Sun Architect-led tour of Picture Frame House and Béton Brit at 1pm, 2.30pm, 4pm (max 20, tours start at Béton Brit). **A**
🚇 Limehouse, Shadwell
🚌 15,115,135
Béton Brit is a ground-floor side and rear extension with internal refurbishment of a terraced house in the Albert Gardens Conservation Area of Stepney Green, East London. Archer & Braun, 2018

Bow Garden Square and St Paul's Way Foundation Primary School
🚶 32 St Paul's Way, E3 4AL
🕐 Sat 11am–5pm. Last entry 4pm
🚇 Limehouse, Mile End
🚌 309
This imaginative, award-winning co-location project combines a new primary school with a mosque, houses and apartments. The school is set around a landscaped courtyard, with classrooms linked by a cloister providing informal break-out space, below 100 new mixed tenure homes. Pollard Thomas Edwards Architects, 2019

Craft Central at The Forge
🚶 397–411 Westferry Road, E14 3AE
🕐 Sat 11am–5pm/Sun 11am–4pm. Last entry Sat 4.15pm | Sun 3.15pm. **R·T·O**
🚇 Island Gardens, Mudchute
🚌 135,D7,277
1860 Grade II-listed forge, many historic features, converted in 2017 to provide working and meeting spaces for craftspeople and other creative professionals, and an exhibition hall. 1860

Crossrail Place Roof Garden
🚶 (Accessed from Adams Plaza on North Colonade or Upper Bank Street), Canary Wharf, E14 5AR
🕐 Sat 10am–5pm/Sun 10am–5pm. Landscape Architect-led tour of roof garden, hourly (10am–1pm). The tours will begin in the performance space (adjacent to Giant Robot). Last entry 4.15pm. **T·O**
🚇 Canary Wharf
🚌 277,135,D8,D7,D3
The Crossrail Place Roof Garden sits atop Crossrail Place, the first building to open for the new Elizabeth Line. The roof garden displays unusual plants from across the globe, encased beneath an intricate lattice roof. Foster + Partners, 2015

Darbishire Place (Peabody Whitechapel Estate)
🚶 John Fisher Street, E1 8HA
🕐 Sat Tour at 10am, 11am, 12pm. **A**
🚇 Tower Gateway, Fenchurch Street
🚌 100,78,42,15,343
New block of 13 homes which completes an ensemble of six housing blocks surrounding an internal courtyard. The façade complements the existing Victorian buildings by Henry Astley Darbishire. RIBA Award Winner & Stirling Prize shortlist 2015. Niall McLaughlin Architects, 2014

Dennis Severs House
🚶 18 Folgate Street, E1 6BX
🕐 Sat 12pm–4pm (max 30). Last entry 3.15pm. **Q**
🚇 Liverpool Street, Shoreditch High Street
🚌 8,26,388,35,48
Originally part of the St John's and Tillards Estate, when Folgate Street was known as White Lion Street. The house retains its panelled interior and staircase of 1724, and was altered in the early 19C. 1724

English National Ballet
🚶 41 Hopewell Square, E14 0SY
🕐 Sat/Sun 10am–5pm (max 20) + Tours to be confirmed. Please see Open House website for further details. Last entry 4.30pm. **T·R**
❗ Pre-book only: (Tours) unityartsfestival.com
🚇 Canning Town
🚌 D3
The ENB stands as a translucent, lightweight structure where the masonry blocks appear to creak open to reveal a striking glimpse of the island core, wrapped by six colourful and eye catching GHA buildings. Glenn Howells, 2018

Four Corners
🚶 121 Roman Road, E2 0QN
🕐 Sat 10am–5pm + Hourly tour (10.30am–4.30pm). Last entry 4.15pm. **R·T**
🚇 Bethnal Green
🚌 309,D6,8

• Gin Distillery, Whitechapel ©The Modern House 2018

Refurbished extended building, a centre for film and photography. Central courtyard integrated 'hub' allows light and air to filter through. Loft conversion to create studio and work space. Sustainable features include sedum roof. JaK Studio, 2007

Gin Distillery, Whitechapel
🚶 221 Jubilee Street, E1 3BS
🕐 Sat, Tours hourly (10am–3pm, max 10). **R·A**
❗ Pre-book only: eventbrite.co.uk/e/tour-of-gin-distillery-whitechapel-open-house-london-2019-tickets-61921887031
🚇 Bethnal Green, Whitechapel
🚌 205,25
Conversion of a Victorian gin distillery into a bright and contemporary family home. The project was longlisted for RIBA House of the Year 2018. Rupert Scott, Open Practice Architecture, 2017

Half Moon Theatre
🚶 43 White Horse Road,, E1 0ND
🕐 Sat/Sun 10.30am–4pm (max 100) + ½ hourly tour (max 20) + Children's art cart · Half Moon Theatre Archive. Last entry 3.30pm. **T·R·F·D·B·O**
🚇 Limehouse
🚌 135,115,15,D3,D7
Half Moon Theatre is a highly decorated stucco-rendered building in the York Square conservation area which was renovated 2012–15. The building was originally constructed as Limehouse District Board of Works in 1864. CR Dunch, 1864

Hermitage Community Moorings
🚶 16 Wapping High Street, E1W 1NG
🕐 Sat/Sun 10am–5pm. Last entry Sat/Sun 4.15pm. **R·T**
🚇 Tower Hill, Wapping
🚌 100,42,78,343
A development of residential and recreational moorings for historic vessels on the Thames. The unique Pier House, built to a high specification, provides a floating community centre just downstream from Tower Bridge. Anna Versteeg & Ollie Price, 2010

Java House
🚶 Hope Street, E14 0LG
🕐 Sat/Sun 10am–5pm (No access to residential areas) + UNITY art exhibition. Last entry 4.15pm. **T·R·O**
🚇 Canning Town
🚌 D3
Designed by Glenn Howells Architects for Ecoworld Ballymore. It provides two new public venues, Trinity Art Gallery and Arebyte Gallery. An exhibition of locally sourced artworks will be exhibited here over Open House Weekend. Glenn Howells Architects, 2015

Lanterna, Fish Island Village
🚶 Wyke Rd, Fish Island, London, E3 2PL
🕐 Sat Architect-led tour of exterior, hourly (10am–3pm, max 8). **D·A**
🚇 Hackney Wick
🚌 276,339,488
This highly contextualised residential-led block is a unique addition to London's creative heartland, and part of an innovative development from Peabody and Hill. Lyndon Goode Architects, 2018

Limehouse Town Hall
🚶 646 Commercial Road, E14 7HA
🕐 Sat 12pm–5pm/Sun 12pm–5pm. Sat Tower Hamlets Wheelers bicycle maintenance workshop (Finishes 3pm.) Last entry 4.45pm. **T**
🚇 Westferry, Limehouse
🚌 135,15,115,D3
Former town hall now in arts and community use. Palazzo style with stone dressings, vast arched windows to the upper Hall, and grand Portland stone and iron staircase. A & C Harston, 1881

Monier Road
🚶 Meet: on the corner of Monier Road and Roach Road, Hackney Wick, E3 2PS
🕐 Sat Architect-led tour, ½ hourly (10am–12.30pm, max 10). **A**
❗ Pre-book only: monierroadtours.eventbrite.co.uk, limited turn up on the day places available
🚇 Hackney Wick
🚌 30,8,488,339,276
A new-build development for Peabody in partnership with Hill of 71 homes, with ground floor commercial workspace. Each of the three blocks has its own identity and palette of materials, arranged around a shared central courtyard. Pitman Tozer Architects, 2018

Museum of London Docklands
🚶 No. 1 Warehouse, West India Quay (off Hertsmere Road), E14 4AL
🕐 Sat/Sun 10am–5.45pm + ½ hourly tour (11am–4.30pm, max 30, Family tours starting at 12:30 & 14:00). Last entry 5.30pm. **F·D·B·R·T·O**
🚇 Westferry, Canary Wharf
🚌 135,277,D3,D7,D8
Grade I-listed, late Georgian sugar warehouse now housing the Museum of London Docklands. Sensitively restored, the new multi-media displays coexist with the massive timber and brick structures of the original building. George Gwilt & Son, 1802

One Bishops Square
🚶 E1 6AD
🕐 Sun 10am–5pm. Last entry 4.15pm. **D·R·T**
🚇 Shoreditch High Street, Liverpool Street
🚌 205,149,135,78,48,47,8,26,35,42
'Intelligent' building with sustainable features, including London's largest office-based solar installation & inbuilt computer system aimed at efficiency and energy conservation. Lights and air conditioning operate only when area is populated. Foster + Partners, 2006

One Canada Square, Canary Wharf Group (CWG) Marketing Suite and Level39
🚶 Meet: South Lobby, One Canada Square, Canary Wharf, E14 5AB
🕐 Sat 10am–5pm (max 20, access to CWG Marketing Suite and Level39 only). Last entry 4pm. **T**
❗ Pre-book only: openhouse@canarywharf.com (Supply names/email addresses of all attendees and preferred time. Max 4 guests per booking.)
🚇 Heron Quays, Canary Wharf
🚌 D3,D7,D8,135,277
CWG has overseen the largest urban regeneration project ever undertaken in Europe. Canary Wharf houses Europe's most influential FinTech scaler, Level39, and will soon welcome its first residents with the development of Wood Wharf. Cesar Pelli, 1991

Oxford House in Bethnal Green
🚶 Derbyshire Street, Bethnal Green, E2 6HG
🕐 Sat/Sun 10am–1pm (Roof terrace accessible by stairs only). Last entry 12.15pm. **D·A·T·O**
🚇 Bethnal Green
🚌 D3,8,254,106,388
First 'University Settlement' to open Sept 1884. Arts, community and heritage space. Grade II and on Buildings at Risk Register. Heritage refurbishment in 2019 includes new entrance/café, repairs and lighting to chapel and new roof terrace. Sir Arthur Blomfield, 1892

Picture Frame House
🚶 10 Dunelm Street, E1 0QQ
🕐 Sat 1pm–5pm/Sun 11am–1pm (Limited bedroom
  access). Last entry Sat 4.15pm | Sun 12.15pm. **A**
🚇 Whitechapel, Shadwell
🚌 339,135,115,15
Picture Frame House is a ground-floor extension and
full internal refurbishment of a terraced house in the
Albert Gardens Conservation Area of Stepney Green,
(East London). Archer & Braun, 2016

Republic: The Import Building & Public Realm
🚶 2 Clove Crescent, East India, E14 2BE
🕐 Sat/Sun 9am–6.15pm (The atrium).
  Last entry 6.00pm. **T·R·D·O**
🚇 East India
🚌 15,115,D3
The Import Building has been refurbished and
reimagined with the insertion of a lightweight modular
engineered timber frame. Externally, a major bus route
was re-routed to enable the creation of an inspired
public realm and water gardens. Studio RHE Ltd., 2018

Royal College of Pathologists
🚶 6 Alie Street, E1 8DD
🕐 Sat 10am–5pm (max 60). Last entry 4.30pm. **T·D·A·O**
🚇 Tower Gateway, Aldgate East
🚌 25,42,78,115,135,205,242,254,34
Designed by Bennetts Associates, the new 4,500 sqm
building in East London marks the final step in the
College's move from a traditional Grade I-listed building
in St James to sustainable, contemporary purpose-built
premises. Bennetts Associates, 2018

• Republic: The Import Building & Public Realm
© Dirk Linder 2018

Royal Pharmaceutical Society Museum
🚶 66 East Smithfield, E1W 1AW
🕐 Sat 11am–4pm (Ground floor only) + Guided tour
  of museum displays, ½ hourly (max 10) + drop-in
  viewing of library early printed collection with
  Librarian at 1.30pm. Last entry 3pm. **D·T·O**
🚇 Tower Gateway, Tower Hill
🚌 100
The RPS museum collections cover all aspects of
British pharmacy history, from the 1400s up to the
present day. The library's early printed collection
includes pharmaceutical texts dating back to 1485.
Kristen Liedl, Interior Design Associate at BDP
(Building Design Partnership Ltd), 2015

Sandys Row Synagogue
🚶 4a Sandys Row, E1 7HW
🕐 Sun 11am–4pm (max 60) + Talks about the history of
  the synagoque, every 90 mins (11.30am–3pm, max
  60, by author Rachel Lichtenstein) · Tours hourly
  (12pm–3pm, max 20) + Our Hidden Histories (max
  10). Last entry 3.30pm. **B·R·T**
🚇 Shoreditch High Street, Liverpool Street
🚌 135,78,42,100,205
Hidden gem in the heart of London. Built originally as
a Huguenot chapel in 1763, this extraordinary building
has been in continuous use as a synagogue since 1860.
Oldest Ashkenazi synagogue in London and the third
oldest in the country. 1763

Society for the Protection of Ancient Buildings
(SPAB)
🚶 37 Spital Square, E1 6DY
🕐 Sat 10am–5pm (No access to top floor) + Craft display.
  Last entry 4.15pm. **B**
🚇 Liverpool Street, Shoreditch High Street
🚌 8,26,35,47,48,78,149,344
The only Georgian building left on Spital Square, the
headquarters of the Society for the Protection of Ancient
Buildings. It is likely that it was built in 1740 by Peter
Ogier, a Huguenot silk merchant.

St Anne's Church, Limehouse
🚶 Newell Street, E14 7HP
🕐 Sun 1pm–5pm (Access to main church and crypt
  room only) + Open House Guest Service at 10.30am.
  Last entry 4.30pm. **R·T**
🚇 Limehouse, Westferry
🚌 15,115,135,D3
St Anne's Limehouse is an imposing Hawksmoor Church
in brick and Portland stone. It is home to an active
church congregation today. Nicholas Hawksmoor, 1730

St Bonifatius RC German Church
🚶 47 Adler Street, E1 1EE
🕐 Sat 10am–5pm + Organ Concert by resident organist
  P. Dichtl at 4pm. Last entry 4.15pm. **T·R·D·O**
🚇 Aldgate East
🚌 25,205,254,15,115,135

• Balfron Tower © Nick Rochowski

St. Margaret's House
🚶 21 Old Ford Road, E2 9PL
🕐 Sat 10am–4pm (max 10) + Tours, ½ hourly
(10.30am–3.30pm, max 10) + Reminiscence Tea
Party at 2pm (max 30). Last entry 3.15pm. **F·T·O**
❗ Pre-book only: (Tea party) eventbrite.co.uk/e/
reminiscence-tea-party-tickets-62306724089
🚇 Bethnal Green, Cambridge Heath
🚌 D3,388,309,254,106,8
St. Margaret's House is a group of buildings centred
around a three storey Georgian terrace. Victorian
additions were made in the building of a Chapel
(consecrated 1904) and Mulberry Rooms. The buildings
host several community projects. Anthony Natt, 1753

Plain modern church serving the German-speaking
Catholic community in London. Landmark tower
featuring four bells, artwork and organ by artists and
craftsmen from Germany. Donald Plaskett Marshall
& Partners, 1960

St Dunstan and All Saints Church
🚶 Stepney High Street, E1 0NR
🕐 Sat 10am–5pm + Who was St Dunstan? At 3pm +
Annual Art Show · Have a Go at Calligraphy! At
11am (max 6) · Take a Line for a Walk at 2pm (max 6,
Children 6+)/Sun 1pm–5pm + Who was St Dunstan? At
4pm + Annual Art Show. Last entry 4.15pm. **F·R·T·O**
🚇 Stepney Green, Limehouse
🚌 15,25,115,309,339,205
Grade I-listed early Medieval parish church (site in use
from 952, pre-dating Tower of London). Fine interior:
Anglo-Saxon Rood, Norman font, Medieval 'squint',
memorials, stained glass, brasses. Many founders of
Trinity House buried here. St Dunstan, 1100

St Matthias Old Church – Community Centre
🚶 113 Poplar High Street, E14 0AE
🕐 Sat 10am–5pm/Sun 1pm–5pm. Last entry 4.15pm.
D·P·R·T·O
🚇 Poplar, All Saints
🚌 15,115,D6,D7,D8
Oldest building in Docklands built in the Gothic and
Classical styles, with original 17C stonework and fine
mosaics. One of only three churches built during the
Civil War, it was originally the East India Company
Chapel. John Tanner, 1649

St Paul's Bow Common
🚶 Corner of Burdett Road/St Paul's Way, E3 4AR
🕐 Sat 10am–5pm/Sun 1pm–5pm + ½ hourly tour.
Last entry 4.45pm. **P·R·T·O**
🚇 Mile End, Limehouse
🚌 309,277,D6,D7
Described as 'the most significant church built after the
WWII in Britain' – Brutalist, inclusive and influential
signpost for future church design. Robert McGuire &
Keith Murray, 1960

Steampunk House
🚶 3 East Arbour Street, E1 0PU
🕐 Sat 10am–5pm (max 12). Last entry 4pm. **A**
🚇 Whitechapel, Limehouse
🚌 115,15,399,309,135
A Georgian townhouse re-examined. With a 'more-is-
more' brief, this beautiful locally listed property in
Stepney incorporates arch glazing, pivot windows,
bright steels and a reclaimed palette to blend Bauhaus,
Art Deco and Steampunk. Bradley Van der Straeten
Architects, 1819

Thames River Police
🚶 98 Wapping High Street, E1W 2NE
🕐 Sat/Sun 11am–5pm. Last entry 4.45pm. **R·O**
🚇 Wapping
🚌 100
A unique ex-carpenters' workshop (1910), contained
within a working police station. The workshop space
now displays a history of Thames River Police. John
Dixon Butler, 1910

Town Hall Hotel & Apartments
🚶 Patriot Square, E2 9NF
🕐 Sun 10am–5pm. Last entry 4.15pm. **D·R·T·O**
🚇 Cambridge Heath, Bethnal Green
🚌 254,106,D6,388,48,55,26
Beautiful redevelopment of a Grade II-listed town hall
incorporating contemporary design complementing the
original Edwardian/Art Deco features. Percy Robinson &
W Alban Jones, 1909

Toynbee Hall

🚶 28 Commercial Street, E1 6LS

🕐 Sat/Sun 10.30am–4.30pm (Ground floor historic rooms, extension and exhibition spaces) + The History of Toynbee Hall at 11am, 1pm, 3pm (max 20). Last entry Sat/Sun 3.45pm. **D·T·O**

❗ Pre-book only:

🚇 Aldgate East

🚌 25,115,15, 242,254

The world's founding university settlement. Built to provide educational & social spaces for East Londoners. Neo-Tudor Grade II-listed with notable room decorated by Arts and Crafts designer CR Ashbee. Restoration completed in 2018. C R Ashbee, Elijah Hoole, 1884

Toynbee Studios

🚶 28 Commercial Street, E1 6AB

🕐 Sat/Sun 10am–4.30pm + regular tours. Last entry 3.30pm. **T·R·D**

🚇 Aldgate East

🚌 25,15,115, 242, 254

Toynbee Studios is Artsadmin's centre for the development and presentation of artists' work. There is a 280-seat 1930s theatre, an old juvenile court room, rehearsal studios, a roof-top dance studio, café and offices for arts organisations. Alister MacDonald, 1938

Tree House

🚶 200 Jubilee Street, E1 3BP

🕐 Sat Architect-led tour, hourly (10am–4pm, max 8, no shoes inside). **T**

❗ Pre-book only: open-house-6a-tree-house-2019. eventbrite.co.uk

🚇 Whitechapel

🚌 254,205,106,25

Treehouse sits within the overgrown garden of two tiny cottages, curving around a central sumac tree. Its ramped interior connects old buildings to new, re-orienting the house around the garden to create an accessible family home. 6a Architects, 2013

Trinity Buoy Wharf/Container City

🚶 64 Orchard Place, E14 0JW

🕐 Sat/Sun 12pm–5pm + Sat tour at 12.30pm. Last entry 4.15pm. **T**

🚇 Canning Town

🚌 D3

Home to London's only lighthouse, fine stock buildings and examples of the innovative Container City buildings. This former buoy manufacturing site is now a centre for the creative industries with various sculptures and installations. Container City, Lacey and Partners, ABK Architects, Eric Reynolds, James Douglass, 1822

West India Dock Impounding Station

🚶 Western end of Marsh Wall, E14 8JT

🕐 Sat/Sun 10am–5pm + West India Dock Impounding Station Tour at 11am. Last entry 4.15pm.

🚇 Canary Wharf, Heron Quays

🚌 277,D7,D8,135

The recently automated impounding station controls the water level in the docks using the original Worthington Simpson pumps driven by Lancashire dynamo. 1929

Wilton's Music Hall

🚶 Graces Alley, E1 8JB

🕐 Sat 10am–1pm (The ground floor (including the stalls of the theatre) is wheelchair accessible). Last entry 12.15pm. **D·R·T·O**

🚇 Tower Gateway, Fenchurch Street, Tower Hill

🚌 100

Wilton's Music hall is the oldest Grand Music Hall in the world. Its importance as an historic venue, both in terms of architecture and a monument to social history, is unprecedented. Jacob Maggs, 1859

Walks & Tours

London City Island

🚶 Meet: the Red Bridge at Canning Town Station by Bow Creek, Kent Building, 45 Hope St, Leamouth Peninsula, E14 0QG

🕐 Sat/Sun 11am, 2pm (max 60, Tour of London City Island down to Trinity Buoy Wharf). **T·R·O**

❗ Pre-book only: unityartsfestival.com)

🚇 Canning Town

🚌 D3

From Canning Town Station our walk begins by crossing the Red Bridge over the River Lea. Following the river path the walk opens out into the gardens of London City Island. The walk can then continue into neighbouring Trinity Buoy wharf. Glenn Howells Architects, 2015

Tower Hamlets Cemetery Park

🚶 Meet: in front of the Soanes Centre. On the right once you've entered via the main gates on Southern Grove E3, Soanes Centre. Mile End, E3 4PX

🕐 Sun Heritage Tour, 10am, 12pm · Nature Tour, 2pm. **D·P·R·T·O**

🚇 Mile End, Bow Road

🚌 205,25,277,D6,D7,425,323

One of the magnificent 7 cemeteries. Burials ceased 1966, now 31 acres of woodland, meadows & ponds including the Soanes Centre (Robson Kelly 1993). Of outstanding importance for flora and fauna, set among funereal monuments, some listed. Thomas Wyatt & David Brandon, 1841

Waltham Forest

Social Capital

The eastern edge of the borough is covered nearly in its entirety by Epping Forest, the largest public open space in the London area. And this year Waltham Forest is London's first Borough of Culture.

All Saints Church (The Old Church)
🚶 Old Church Road, Chingford, E4 8BU
🕐 Sat 10am–5pm/Sun 12pm–4pm. Last entry Sat 4.30pm | Sun 3.45pm. **D·T·R·O**
🚇 Highams Park, Chingford
🚌 397,215,97
Original parish church of Chingford, with Norman foundations and interesting monuments. Tudor porch.

Blackhorse Workshop
🚶 1-2 Sutherland Road Path, E17 6BX
🕐 Sat 10am–5pm (Downstairs only. No access to private studios upstairs). Last entry 4.15pm. **D·R·T**
🚇 Blackhorse Road, St.James' Street
🚌 158,123,230,W15
A makerspace offering open access to a fully equipped wood and metal workshop with bench space, tools and machinery. Includes outdoor working area, education space, community café and 40 studios for creative businesses. Assemble, 2014

Colby Lodge
🚶 1c, The Drive, E17 3BN
🕐 Sun 10am–1pm. Last entry 12.30pm. **D·T**
🚇 Walthamstow Central
🚌 W16,212
Inspirational Development completed March 2018, designed for local older people, incorporating principles from the HAPPI report, good light, ventilation, space, balconies, storage, adaptable to changing needs, impressive views over London. Pollard Thomas Edwards, 2017

Leytonstone and Wanstead Synagogue
🚶 2 Fillebrook Road, Leytonstone, E11 4AT
🕐 Sun Community-led tour, ½ hourly (11am–4pm, max 15) + Exhibition of Historical Photos and Film footage (max 15). **T·R·X·D·O**
❗ Pre-book only: lawsynagogue.org/open_house.html
🚇 Leytonstone High Road, Leytonstone
🚌 W19,W16,W15,W14,W13,339,257,145,66
Stemming from a minyan started in 1924, Leytonstone & Wanstead Synagogue is one of the last East London synagogues holding regular services. The current building in Fillebrook Road opened in 1954 and still retains many post-war features. Norman Cohen, 1953

Monoux Almshouses
🚶 Church End, E17 9RL
🕐 Sun 10am–1pm (Monoux Hall only). Last entry 12.15pm. **T**
🚇 Walthamstow Central, Walthamstow Queens Road
🚌 212,W12
A row of 13 dwellings plus a hall used as a committee room and offices, constructed as one block on two floors. The building is divided by a jettied cross range. Grade II-listed. Sir George Monoux, 1527

Queen Elizabeth's Hunting Lodge
🚶 6 Rangers Road, Chingford, E4 7QH
🕐 Sat/Sun 10am–5pm + Tudor dressing-up for all ages (Stair access to upper floors.). Last entry 4.45pm. **F·T·P·O**
🚇 Chingford
🚌 397,97,179,212,313
Tudor timber-framed hunt standing/grandstand (1543), Henry VIII Tudor food display, Tudor dressing up. Gateway to 6,000 acres ancient Epping Forest, once Royal hunting ground, protected since 1878 by City of London Corporation, Grade II*.

St Peter & Paul Church
🚶 The Green, Chingford, E4 7ER
🕐 Sat 10am–5pm. Last entry 4.15pm. **T·R·D·O**
🚇 Chingford
🚌 179,212,97,313
Nave (1844) by Lewis Vulliamy, chancel (1903) by Sir Arthur Blomfield. Stained glass windows by Christopher Webb and by Clayton & Bell. Norman font brought from the Old Church. Grade II*-listed. Lewis Vulliamy (1844); Sir Arthur Blomfield (1903), 1844

• Colby Lodge © Pollard Thomas Edwards Architects 2018

• Blackhorse Workshop © Ben Quinton 2014

• Leytonstone and Wanstead Synagogue © Bernard Stern 2018

St Michael and All Angels Church

🏃 Northcote Road, Walthamstow, E17 6PQ

🕐 Sat/Sun 1pm–5pm (max 50, Ground floor accessible) + Tour of hidden neo-Gothic gem, every 90 mins (10.30am–4pm, max 10). Last entry 4.15pm. **T·R·D·O**

🚇 Walthamstow Central, Blackhorse Road

🚌 W15,W11

Jame Maltby Bignell (1827–1885) worked in the practice of Sir George Gilbert Scott, the architect of St Pancras Station. The style of St Micheal's is late Gothic Revival, in its size and height reminiscent of Nothern European churches. James Maltby Bignell, 1885

St. Mary's Church, Walthamstow Village

🏃 Church End (top of Church Hill), Walthamstow, E17 9RL

🕐 Sat 11am–5pm + Tower Tours, every 45 mins (12pm–4.30pm, max 8, pre-book only, no children under 8, no disabled access)/Sun 12.30pm–5.30pm + Tower Tours, every 45 mins (1pm–4.45pm, max 8, pre-book only, no children under 8, no disabled access). Last entry Sat 4.45pm | Sun 5.15pm. **T·R·F·D·O**

❗ Pre-booking only: (Tours) eventbrite.co.uk/e/open-house-weekend-tower-tours-tickets-61576818923

🚇 Wood Street, Walthamstow Central

🚌 W16,W12,212

Grade II*-listed church dating from 12C with Medieval, Tudor, Georgian and Victorian features.

The Magistrates

🏃 Waltham Forest Town Hall Complex, 1 Farnan Avenue, E17 4NX

🕐 Sat 10am–5pm (max 25). Last entry 4pm. **D·T·P**

🚇 Blackhorse Road, Walthamstow Central

🚌 215,357,34,97,123,275

Remodelled 1972 Brutalist former Magistrates Court. The refurbishment, completed in early 2018, saw the building stripped back to its core structure, opened up and now provides facilities for 350 plus council staff over 3000sqm. Gort Scott, 2018

The Science Lab

🏃 134 Trumpington Road, E7 9EQ

🕐 Sat Owner/Designer led tour, every 45 mins (10am–4pm, max 30). **A**

❗ Pre-book only: thesciencelab.eventbrite.co.uk

🚇 Leytonstone, Forest Gate, Wanstead Park

🚌 308,58

A two storey 1935 former school canteen, science lab and art department that was later used as recording studio. It has now been converted into a 200 sqm 4-bed residence with green roof/terrace, steel windows and original parquet flooring. Made with Volume, 2017

The View Visitor Centre

🏃 6 Rangers Road, Chingford, E4 7QH

🕐 Sat/Sun 10am–5pm + Drawing from our displays (drop in, self-led, drawing activity for all ages.). Last entry 4.45pm. **F·T·P·B·O**

🚇 Chingford

🚌 397

The View, Epping Forest's central visitor centre and museum, was developed from an early 20C stable complex. It offers exhibition space, a Forest viewing balcony and shop. Paths lead directly into 6000 acres of Forest trails. Freeland Rees Roberts Architects, 2012

Turning Earth Ceramics E10

🏃 11 Argall Avenue, E10 7QE

🕐 Sat/Sun 10.30am–5pm (max 15) + Studio Tour, hourly. Last entry 4.15pm. **D·T·O**

🚇 Lea Bridge

🚌 56,55,48,W19

New ceramics centre for the Lee Valley, covering the entire top floor of an old hardware factory. Three rooms, providing just over 8000 sq ft of floor space; the main room is capped by its original saw-tooth glass roof feature.

Vestry House Museum
🚶 Vestry Road, E17 9NH
🕐 Sat Tour of Vestry House at 1pm (max 30). **B·T·O**
🚇 Walthamstow Queens Road, Walthamstow Central
🚌 W12,W16
Built as a workhouse in 1730, the date plaque warns "if any should not work neither should he eat". It became a police station, then a private house, and from 1931 the Museum for Waltham Forest.

Walthamstow Pumphouse Museum
🚶 10 South Access Road, E17 8AX
🕐 Sat/Sun Museum Tour, hourly
   (11am–3.30pm, max 10). **D·B·R·T·O**
🚇 Blackhorse Road, St.James' Street
🚌 58,158,230,W19
Grade II-listed Victorian engine house remodelled to take a pair of 1895 Marshall steam engines, still in working order. A museum celebrating the rich Boroughs and the Lea Valley Region Industrial Heritage. George Jerram, 1885

Walthamstow School for Girls
🚶 58–60 Church Hill, Walthamstow, E17 9RZ
🕐 Sat 10am–1pm + ½ hourly tour (10am–12.15pm).
   Last entry 12.15pm. **T**
🚇 Walthamstow Central, Walthamstow Queens Road
🚌 212, W12
Founded 1890, moving to present site in 1913, retaining St Mary's Vicarage (1902). Grade II-listed frontage, in a red brick English Baroque style. Won a BCSE Design Award in 2011. Greek Theatre, 1925, within the grounds. CJ Dawson, 1911

Walthamstow Town Hall
🚶 Waltham Forest Town Hall Complex, Forest Road,
   701 Forest Road, E17 4JF
🕐 Sat 10am–5pm (max 25, No access to the roof).
   Last entry 4.15pm. **F·D·T**
🚇 Walthamstow Central, Blackhorse Road
🚌 34,97,215,123,275
Impressive civic centre, built in Portland stone with a classical layout in Swedish influenced popular inter-war style. Art Deco internal design. PD Hepworth, 1937

William Morris Gallery
🚶 Lloyd Park, Forest Road, E17 4PP
🕐 Sat Tour at 11am, 2pm. **D·T·P·R·B·O**
🚇 Walthamstow Central, Blackhorse Road
🚌 123
A behind-the-scenes tour of the William Morris Gallery, revealing the history of this Grade II*-listed Georgian building and access to the Gallery's object store. 1740

Walks & Tours

Epping Forest Heritage Walk: Hollow Ponds and surroundings
🚶 Meet: Leytonstone Station, outside Church Lane
   entrance, Church Lane, E11 1HE
🕐 Sun 10am (max 35).
❗ Pre-book only: eventbrite.co.uk/o/epping-
   forest-9768889881
🚇 Leytonstone, Leytonstone High Road
🚌 W19,W16,W14,W13,339,257,145,66
Guided walk from Leytonstone Station linking local heritage buildings, Alfred Hitchcock and Epping Forest's Hollow Ponds. Discover how public campaigns led to the Forest being saved in 1878 and its 141 years as a City of London open space.

Walthamstow Wetlands
🚶 Meet: Marine Engine House, 2 Forest Road, N17 9NH
🕐 Sun Tour every 90 mins (11am–3pm, max 15).
   D·A·T·P·R·B·O
❗ Pre-book only: walthamstowwetlands.com/whats-on
🚌 W4,123,230
Join us for a tour of the refurbished Marine Engine House with our architects Kinnear Landscape Architects and Witherford Watson Mann Architects.

• Walthamstow town hall © Anthony Coleman

Bromley

Social Capital

The eastern part of the borough includes large amounts of farmland and most residents see themselves living in Kent rather than in London. Only a tiny part of the borough is within the London postal districts.

'Not Forgotten' – The story of the V2 rocket attack on the Crooked Billet in 1944

🕇 The Garden Room, St Augustine's Church, Southborough Lane, Bromley, BR2 8AT

🕐 Sat V2 Rocket Attack Talk at 10.30am (A talk about the V2 rocket attack on this public house 75 years ago). **T·R·D·B·P**

🚇 Bickley, Petts Wood

🚌 336,R7,208

Hear the story of what happened when the Crooked Billet, packed with people, was struck by a V2 rocket and how over 66 years later those who were killed and injured were to be commemorated by a blue plaque on the rebuilt pub. Nowell Parr & Son, 1937

2 Ferndale

🕇 Bromley, BR1 2RX

🕐 Sat 10am–5pm (max 10, ground floor extension and garden). Last entry 4.30pm. **A**

🚇 Bickley, Bromley North

🚌 162, 229

The creation of a space that is a focus of a vibrant family life. The project transforms the existing house and garden, and with it how the home is lived in. Conibere Phillips Architects, 2016

• 2 Ferndale © Peter Landers 2017

Bromley and Sheppard's College

🕇 London Road (entrance via Wren Gates, no vehicle entry), BR1 1PE

🕐 Sat College Tour at 10am, 12pm, 2pm (max 25). **R·B·T**

❗ Pre-book only: 020 8460 4712

🚇 Bromley South, Bromley North

🚌 208,358

Founded to house the widows of clergymen, the original building consisted of 20 houses built around a classically-styled quadrangle. Captain Richard Ryder – one of Sir Christopher Wren's surveyors – was in charge of design and construction. Captain Richard Ryder, 1666

Crystal Palace Bowl

🕇 Crystal Palace Park, Thicket Road, SE19 2GA

🕐 Sat 10am–5pm. Last entry 4.15pm.

❗ Pre-book only: (Tours) eventbrite.co.uk/o/crystal-palace-museum-16655603775

🚇 Crystal Palace

🚌 417,410,358,322,249,227,157,3

A landmark of South London's historic Crystal Palace Park, this sculptural corten steel stage by Ian Ritchie Architects was a nominee for the 1998 Stirling Prize. A rare opportunity to access the structure ahead of a restoration project. Ian Ritchie Architects, 1997

Crystal Palace Museum

🕇 Anerley Hill, London, SE19 2BA

🕐 Sat/Sun 11am–4.30pm + Water tower (now demolished) every 20 mins. Last entry 4.00pm. **X·O**

🚇 Crystal Palace

🚌 450,432,417,410,363,358,322,227,249,202,157,122,3

The Museum tells the story of both the Hyde Park and Sydenham Crystal Palaces. Housed in the only surviving building constructed by the Crystal Palace Company it was a lecture room for the Company's School of Practical Engineering.

Crystal Palace Subway

🕇 West-side pavement of Crystal Palace Parade, SE19

🕐 Sun 10am–5pm. Last entry 4.15pm. **O·Q**

🚇 Crystal Palace

🚌 3,322,410,450,227

Magnificent subway under Crystal Palace Parade like a vaulted crypt – connected the High Level Station (Charles Barry Junior 1865; demolished 1961) to the Crystal Palace – Joseph Paxton 1854; fire (1936); new gate (2016); new paving (2019). Charles Barry Junior, 1865

• Crystal Palace Bowl

Keston Windmill
🚶 108 Heathfield Road,, Keston, BR2 6BF
🕐 Sat 11am–4.30pm (max 8) + Guided tour of the
windmill, every 20 mins (11am–4pm, max 8, access
to Roundhouse but steep steps inside the main body;
no high -heeled shoes allowed). Last entry 3.30pm.
R·F·Q
🚆 Bromley South, Hayes (Kent)
🚌 246,146,320
Keston Windmill is a preserved post mill dated 1716 in
complete mechanical and structural condition. As such,
it is arguably the finest surviving example of its kind in
the South East of the country.

St Nicholas Church, Chislehurst
🚶 Church Lane, Chislehurst, BR7 5PE
🕐 Sat 10am–5pm + Tower/Clock Tour at 11am, 2pm
(max 6, suitable shoes; fitness to climb) · Churchyard
Tour, hourly (11am–4pm, max 15, no tour at 13.00.
Duration 45 mins)/Sun 12pm–5pm + Churchyard
Tour at 3pm, 12pm (max 15, duration 45 mins.) ·
Tower/Clock Tour at 2pm (max 6, suitable shoes;
fitness to climb). Last entry 4.15pm. **P·R·T·O**
🚆 Chislehurst
🚌 269,273,61,160,161,162
Medieval Parish Church, 15C, enlarged and rebuilt in
19C. Shingle spire 1857, by Wollaston. Chancel by Ferrey,
lengthened with East wall by Bodley & Garner. Scadbury
Chapel (Walsingham tombs), with rood screen. Clock by
Dent, 1858.

The Old Palace, Bromley Civic Centre
🚶 Stockwell Close, Bromley, BR1 3UH
🕐 Sun 11am–3pm (Regular tours available).
Last entry 2.30pm. **T**
🚆 Bromley South, Bromley North
🚌 61,119,126,138,162,146,208,246,261,314,320,336
Old Palace was the official residence of the Bishops of
Rochester. Present building dates from 1775, although
there have been manor houses on the site since 10C.
Richard Norman Shaw, Ernest Newton, 1775

The Royal Bell
🚶 High Street, BR1 1NN
🕐 Sat 2pm–5pm (max 50, Ground floor and first floor
only) + Display panels showing history, architect's
drawings and proposals and future events. Last
entry Sat 4.30pm. **A**
🚆 Bromley South, Bromley North
🚌 162,269,354,320,227,358,208
The Royal Bell is a Grade II-listed hotel that has lain
empty for about 10 years. Designed by Ernest Newton in
1898, it was one of three coaching inns in Bromley and
an important centre of Victorian and Edwardian culture.
Ernest Newton, 1898

Walks & Tours

HG Wells walk
🚶 Meet: In front of the main entrance to Primark,
Market Square, BR1 1HE
🕐 Sat 10.30am (max 40, A tour of HG Wells' Bromley –
in his own words).
🚆 Bromley North, Bromley South
🚌 208,358,227,320,354,269,162
A walk around the streetscapes that the young
Herbert George Wells knew when he was growing up,
experiencing the built environment that would later
shape his novels. Ernest Newton, Berney and Son, 1898

In Ziggy's Footsteps – The walking tour of
David Bowie's Beckenham
🚶 Meet: outside main entrance, Beckenham Junction
Train Station, Station Approach, Beckenham,
BR3 1HY
🕐 Sat 2pm (max 18, Duration 2.5 hours). **T**
❗ Pre-book only: bowiewalkingtour@
inziggysfootsteps.com
🚆 Beckenham Junction
🚌 54,227,354,162
Bowie moved to Beckenham in 1969 and lived there
for over 4 years, leaving as an international star. This
guided walk visits the main architectural locations
where Bowie and the Spiders lived, performed and
spent their day to day lives.

Self-guided Architecture of Chislehurst Walk
🚶 Meet: start at Church of the Annunciation of the
Blessed Virgin Mary, 42 High St, Chislehurst BR7 5AQ,
Organised by the Chislehurst Society
🚆 Elmstead Woods, Chislehurst
🚌 61,269,162
A look at some of the large houses built in the late
nineteenth and early twentieth century by Ernest
Newton, CHB Quenell and other noted architects.
Download from chislehurst-society.org.uk/CATTWALK.
pdf. Ernest Newton, EJ May, 1890

Croydon

CROYDON
www.croydon.gov.uk

Social Capital

Brick by Brick, established by Croydon Council in 2016, is creating around 2000 new homes for the borough by using brownfield plots: old garage sites, car parks, vacant buildings of open space infill sites on council estates.

Airport House
🏃 Purley Way, Croydon, CRO 0XZ
🕐 Sat/Sun 11am–4pm (max 48, no disabled access to the top floor, Control Tower) + ½ hourly tour (11am–3pm, max 15). Last entry 3.pm. **D·B·P·T·O**
🚇 Waddon, South Croydon
🚌 119,289
Unique Grade II*-listed 1928 Government building constructed in a restrained Neoclassical style. Britain's first airport terminal. Landmark building incorporating the world's oldest Air Traffic Control Tower. Upgraded to Grade II* in 2017. Air Ministry – Directorate of Works and buildings, 1926

Bernard Weatherill House
🏃 8 Mint Walk, (corporate reception off Fell Road), CRO 1EA
🕐 Sat 9am–12pm (max 50, access to reception, 8th floor common areas and terraces). Last entry 11.30am. **T**
🚇 East Croydon, West Croydon
🚌 468,466,455,412,407,405,403,312,264,250,197,166
300,000 sq ft of BREEAM Excellent accredited modern commercial accommodation spread over 12 storeys with a public access facility on the ground floor at the heart of the building. EPR Architects, 2013

Brick by Brick Shop and Offices
🏃 62 George Street, Croydon, CRO 1PD
🕐 Sat/Sun 10am–5pm (max 20). Last entry Sat/Sun 4.15pm. **T·A·O**
🚇 West Croydon, East Croydon
🚌 468,466,455,412,407,405,403,312,264,250,197,166
The recently refurbished offices and shop for local developer Brick by Brick and Common Ground Architecture. Set over five floors, this Victorian property has been completely transformed to create a joyful new work space. Common Ground Architecture, 2019

Church of St Mary the Blessed Virgin
🏃 Addington Village Road, Addington, CRO 5AS
🕐 Sat 10am–5pm/Sun 1pm–5pm. Last entry 4.15pm. **P·R·T·O**
🚇 East Croydon then tram to Addington Village
🚌 64,130,353,466
Founded in 11C, with Jacobean memorial c1615. Burial site of five Archbishops of Canterbury.

Croydon Town Hall and Clocktower Complex
🏃 Katharine Street, Croydon, CR9 1ET
🕐 Sat 10am–1pm (max 20, no access to the Bell Tower) + Family event (This event runs from 11am–4pm and is suitable for 5–11 year olds). Last entry 12.15pm. **D·F·R·T·O**
🚇 East Croydon, West Croydon
Guided tours of the original Town Hall, including council chamber and meeting rooms. Clocktower complex and Museum of Croydon open to the public throughout the day. Charles Henman, 1895

Fairfields' Hall
🏃 Park Lane, CRO 1DG
🕐 Sat/Sun 10am–5pm (Access to public spaces only) + Windrush: Portrait Of A Generation Photography Exhibition (Jim Grover) · An Audience with Janet Street-Porter at 1pm · London Concert Orchestra In Rehearsal at 2pm (max 30) · London Concert Orchestra In Rehearsal at 3pm (max 30) / Sun events: (Access to public spaces only) + Windrush: Portrait Of A Generation Photography Exhibition (Jim Grover) · Paraorchestra at 3.30pm (free) · Paraorchestra at 5.30pm (free). Last entry Sat/Sun 4.15pm. **D·T·O**
❗ Pre-book only: fairfield.co.uk
🚇 West Croydon, East Croydon
After an extensive refurbishment, The Fairfield Halls has been returned to its original mid-century architectural magnificence, retaining the renowned concert hall and theatre while creating new performance spaces for the 21C. Robert Atkinson & Partners, 1962. *fairfield.co.uk*

Heavers Farm Primary School
🏃 58 Dinsdale Gardens, South Norwood, SE25 6LT
🕐 Sat/Sun 10am–1pm + regular tours. Last entry 12.15pm. **T·R**
🚇 Selhurst, Norwood Junction
🚌 157,75,410
Opened in 1972 and rebuilt in 1997, the glass and steel building is designed in the form of an open book. Civic Trust Award Winner 1998. ADP, hnw architects, 2013

Old Palace, Croydon
🚶 Old Palace Road, Old Town, Croydon, CR0 1AX
🕐 Sat Tour at 2pm (max 30). **T**
❗ Pre-book only: 020 8680 8499 or 020 8256 1594
🚇 East Croydon, West Croydon

Grade I-listed manor house, former summer residence of Archbishops of Canterbury 13–18C. Elizabeth I and other monarchs regularly visited. Contains one of the finest great halls with its original roof from the 1440s.

Pump House
🚶 24 Station Road, South Norwood, SE25 5AH
🕐 Sat/Sun Architect-led tour at 11am (max 15). **A**
❗ Pre-book only: eventbrite.co.uk/o/brick-by-brick-21940003437
🚇 Norwood Junction
🚌 410,312,197,196,157,130,75

The first new residential development to be designed by Common Ground Architecture for developer Brick by Brick. The building is due for completion later this year and will provide 14 new homes and a new library space. Common Ground Architecture, 2019

• Windmill Place © Pillar Visuals 2019

Shirley Windmill
🚶 Postmill Close, Upper Shirley Road, CR0 5DY
🕐 Sun Guided regular tours by the FoSW, (11am–4pm, max 12). Tour led by one of our volunteers.
D·R·T·O·Q
🚇 East Croydon
🚌 466,130,119,194,198

The present brick tower windmill was built 1854 to replace a post mill destroyed by fire. Now renovated to near-working condition, it is the only surviving windmill in Croydon.

The Stanley Halls
🚶 12 South Norwood Hill, SE25 6AB
🕐 Sun Tour every 90 mins (11am–4pm, max 20). **R·T**
❗ Pre-book only: stanleyhalls.org.uk/whats-on
🚇 Norwood Junction
🚌 75,157,196,197,410

A public hall, theatre and gallery in grand Edwardian style. Grade II-listed, Stanley made fun of the Victorian style with grand ornamentation. It reflects Stanley's interest in science, the arts and public cultural improvement. William Ford Robinson Stanley, 1903

Thornton Heath Library
🚶 190 Brigstock Road, Thornton Heath, CR7 7JB
🕐 Sat 10am–5pm (max 20) + Tour at 11am, 12.30pm, 2pm (max 10). Last entry 4pm. **X·D·T·O**
🚇 Thornton Heath
🚌 198,250,450

Carnegie Library with original features, refurbished with dramatic façade making a statement on the high street. White concrete and glass pavilion reading area is complemented by rich oak flooring. Rejuvenated children's library and garden. FAT, 2010

Whitgift Almshouses
🚶 North End, CR9 1SS
🕐 Sat Tour at 10.30am, 11.45am, 3.15pm, 2pm (max 30). **T**
❗ Pre-book only: 020 8680 8499 or 020 8256 1594
🚇 West Croydon, East Croydon

Tudor almshouses dating from 1596 and founded by the Archbishop of Canterbury John Whitgift. Chapel and Courtyard with original 16C clock. 1596

Windmill Place
🚶 Coulsdon, CR5 1ET
🕐 Sat/Sun Architect & Developer-led tour at 3pm (max 30). **A**
❗ Pre-book only: eventbrite.co.uk/o/brick-by-brick-21940003437
🚇 Coulsdon South
🚌 404,60,466

Windmill Place is one of the first new residential developments to be completed for developer Brick by Brick. The development will create 24 new homes just off Coulsdon Common. Pitman Tozer Architects, 2019

Kingston upon Thames

THE ROYAL BOROUGH OF
KINGSTON
UPON THAMES

Social Capital

Contemporary Kingston expanded rapidly during the nineteenth century after the construction of a new bridge across the Thames in 1828 and the growth of the railway.

All Saints' Church
🚶 Market Place, KT1 1JP
🕐 Sat 10am–5pm + Tour at 11am/Sun 10am–5pm. Last entry 4.15pm. **R·T·O**
🚇 Kingston
Large church on site dating back 1000 years, where the first seven Kings of England were crowned.

Clover House
🚶 Kingston Hill, KT2 7JP
🕐 Sat 10am–5pm (max 10) + ½ hourly tour (10am–4.30pm, max 10). Last entry 4.15pm. **X·A**
🚇 Norbiton
🚌 85,K3
Extension to and renovation of 1964 house by Robert Stille. New two storey wing containing kitchen and master bedroom, bedroom added over living room. Internal re-arrangement plus refurbishment to create a warm and light-filled five-bedroom home. Richard Pain, Architect, 2011

Coombe Conduit
🚶 Coombe Lane West, Kingston upon Thames, KT2 7HF
🕐 Sun 12pm–4pm (max 10) + Volunteer-led tours, every 15 mins (12pm-3.15pm, max 10). Last entry 3.45pm. **O**
🚇 Raynes Park, Norbiton
🚌 57
Coombe Conduit is one of Kingston's most important ancient monuments. It was built around 1540 as part of a system to collect fresh water from springs on Kingston Hill and channel it to Hampton Court Palace. 1540

Dorich House Museum
🚶 67 Kingston Vale, SW15 3RN
🕐 Sat 11am–5pm. Last entry 4.30pm. **P·T**
🚇 Norbiton, Putney
🚌 85,K3,265
The former studio home of the Russian sculptor Dora Gordine and her husband the Hon. Richard Hare, a scholar of Russian art and literature. 1930s house over four floors including a flat roof terrace and views of Richmond Park. Dora Gordine & Richard Hare, 1936

Frederick W Paine Funeral Directors
🚶 24 Old London Road, KT2 6QG
🕐 Sat 10am–5pm/Sun 1pm–5pm (downstairs only). Last entry 4.15pm. **R·O**
🚇 Kingston

The town's oldest firm of funeral directors has conducted funerals from these premises since 1908. The original interior is Grade II-listed. The building also contains the Frederick W Paine Museum and the firm's archive.

Hillcroft College
🚶 South Bank, Surbiton, KT6 6DF
🕐 Sun 10am–1pm (max 20, supervised access to downstairs only). Last entry 12.45pm. **P·T**
🚇 Surbiton
🚌 281,406,K2
A Victorian mansion house built in 1877 for Wilberforce Bryant of Bryant and May Matches. The building is very typical of its time and retains many of its original features. Rowland Plumbe, 1877

Ivy Conduit
🚶 Holy Cross Preparatory School George Road, KT2 7NU
🕐 Sun 11am–2pm. Last entry 1.15pm. **P**
🚇 Norbiton
🚌 85,K3
Ancient conduit house built around the beginning of the 16C. Constructed by Cardinal Wolsey to help supply fresh water to Hampton Court Palace.

• Ivy Conduit 2019

• Kingston Walking Tour © Mike Gibbs 2018

John Lewis, Kingston
🚶 John Lewis Kingston, Wood Street, KT1 1TE
🕐 Sat/Sun 11am–3pm (max 20, Tour of the shop, roof terrace and Medieval ruins by the riverside). Last entry 2.15pm. **P·T·O**
🚇 Kingston

Modern department store opened September 1990. It offers hypnotic views of the river, an open glass terrace design, new road system as well as uncovering Medieval ruins. Ahrends Burton Koralek, 1990

Kingston Guildhall and History Centre
🚶 High Street, KT1 1EU
🕐 Sat 10am–5pm (Access to History Centre all day. Access to Mayor's Parlour 13.00–14.30 only) + Tour at 12pm. Last entry 4.15pm. **T·O**
🚇 Kingston

Built in the Georgian style, the Guildhall brought together Kingston's administrative functions. Purpose-built Magistrates Courts were included in the building, part of which are now home to Kingston History Centre. Maurice Webb, 1935

Kingston Library, Museum and Art Gallery
🚶 Wheatfield Way, KT1 2PS
🕐 Sat Tour and history of the buildings at 3pm. **B·T·O**
🚇 Kingston

Adjoining Grade II-listed Carnegie-funded library, museum and art gallery. Museum holdings range from ceramics to topographical drawings, including the collection left by Eadweard Muybridge, a native of Kingston and photographic pioneer. Alfred Cox, 1903

Lovekyn Chapel
🚶 London Road, KT2 6PY
🕐 Sun 10am–2pm (Access to Chapel interior only). Last entry 1.45pm. **T·D**
🚇 Kingston

Lovekyn Chapel is a Grade II*-listed Medieval chantry chapel and a Scheduled Ancient Monument. Built in 1309, it is the oldest complete building in Kingston upon Thames and the only remaining free-standing chantry chapel in England.

St Raphael's Church
🚶 Portsmouth Road, KT1 2NA
🕐 Sat 12pm–4pm (max 30). Last entry 3.45pm. **T·P·O**
🚇 Surbiton, Kingston
🚌 465

Grade II* 1847–48 by Charles Parker. Ashlar, with pantiled roof. Three bay nave with aisles, shorter chancel. Tower of three stages, to north and south are two wings, each three bays wide, two storeys high. Charles Parker, 1846

Walks & Tours

Kingston Walking Tour
🚶 Meet: outside the Market House under the golden queen, Market Place, KT1 1JH
🕐 Sat/Sun 11am (max 20). **D·O**
❗ Pre-book only: kingstontourguides.org.uk
🚇 Kingston

Guided walk around Historic Kingston with knowledgeable guides and stories about the fascinating characters who lived here. Maurice Webb, 1930

Merton

merton

Social Capital

English, Polish and Tamil are the three most spoken languages in Merton and more than a half of the population are Christian and over one fifth have no religion.

Baitul Futuh Mosque

🏃 Ahmadiyya Muslim Association,
181 London Road, Morden, SM4 5PT
🕐 Sat/Sun 10am–5pm. Last entry 4.15pm. **D·B·P·R·T·O**
🚇 Morden, Morden South
🚌 93,154,80

Largest purpose-built mosque in Western Europe accommodating 13,000 worshippers. The building is a blend of Islamic and modern British architecture and incorporates much of the structure of an old dairy site. Sutton Griffin Architects, 2003. *baitulfutuh.org*

Buddhapadipa Temple

🏃 14 Calonne Road, Wimbledon Parkside, SW19 5HJ
🕐 Sat/Sun 10am–5pm (max 100). Last entry 4.30pm.
P·T·B·R·O
🚇 Wimbledon
🚌 493,200,93

Complex of buildings on 4 acres of land with Buddhist Theravada Temple in Thai style – one of only two outside Asia. Interior walls with excellent mural paintings by Thai artists, depicting aspects of the Buddha's life. Sidney Kaye Firmin Partnership, 1980

Cannizaro Studios

🏃 The Old Potting sheds, Cannizaro Park, SW19 4UW
🕐 Sat 11am–5pm/Sun 11am–5pm + Guided tour at 2pm (max 25; the tour leaves outside studio 3). Last entry 4.30pm. **D·T**
🚇 Wimbledon
🚌 93,200,493

Victorian Potting sheds converted to artists' studios set within the grounds of Grade II-listed Cannizaro Park.

Lessons House

🏃 61 Denison Road, Colliers Wood, SW19 2DJ
🕐 Sat 10am–5pm (max 12) + Lessons House – A Story to Tell, every 120 mins (10.30am–4pm, max 12). Last entry 4.15pm. **X·A**
🚇 Colliers Wood, Haydons Road
🚌 200,57,131,219

Lessons House showcases where lessons were learned during the renovation process. The result honours the builders & is the crystallisation of a journey of humanity and lessons on mutual respect, and a place that we warmly call 'home'. Cyril Shing & Melissa Mak, 2019

New Wimbledon Theatre

🏃 93 The Broadway, SW19 1QG
🕐 Sat 10am–5pm (Stalls and Studio only). Last entry 4.15pm. **F·R·T**
🚇 South Wimbledon, Wimbledon
🚌 57,131,93,219,493

Striking Edwardian theatre with beautiful main auditorium in classic three-tier design, seating 1652. Recent major refurbishment. Cecil Masey & Roy Young, 1910

Queensmere Road

🏃 3 Queensmere Road, SW19 5PZ
🕐 Sat 10am–5pm (max 10). Last entry 4.15pm.
🚇 Wimbledon Park, Wimbledon
🚌 93

A typical 1980s purpose-built semi-detached property with poorly-lit living space was transformed with this single-storey full-width rear extension. The extension is clad with weathering steel (corten) to create a contemporary aesthetic. Gazey Architects, 2015

St Luke's, Wimbledon Park

🏃 St. Lukes Church, Ryfold Road, SW19 8BZ
🕐 Sat 10am–5pm (max 50). Last entry 4pm. **T·R·B·O**
🚇 Earlsfield, Wimbledon Park
🚌 156

Architecturally consists of a nave with a gallery at the west end, chancel, north and south aisles. A chapel and south transept with a tower to the north. Three stained glass windows. TG Jackson, 1909

The Chapter House, Merton Priory

🏃 Merton Abbey Mills, Merantun Way, SW19 2RD
🕐 Sat/Sun 10am–5pm (max 40). Last entry 4.45pm.
P·B·O
🚇 Colliers Wood, Wimbledon
🚌 470,57,131,152,200,219

Fascinating excavated foundations of the Chapter House of Merton Priory c1100–1200, one of the most important of all Augustinian monasteries prior to its destruction in 1538 by Henry VIII. The remains lie under Merantun Way (A24).

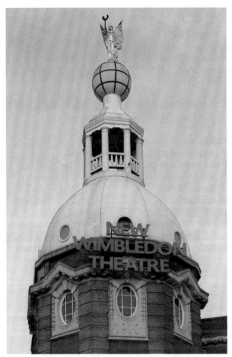

• New Wimbledon Theatre © Peter Dazley

• Wimbledon Windmill

The Wheelhouse
🕺 Merton Abbey Mills, Merantun Way, SW19 2RD
🕐 Sat/Sun 10am–5pm (max 10). Last entry 4.45pm.
  D·T·P·B·0
🚇 Colliers Wood, Wimbledon
🚌 470,57,131,152,200,219
Listed building with unique seven-spoke Victorian
waterwheel, the only daily working example in South
London, originally used by Liberty's for rinsing printed
silk, and now the home of a craft pottery.

Wimbledon Windmill
🕺 Windmill Road, Wimbledon Common, SW19 5NR
🕐 Sat 2pm–5pm/Sun 11am–5pm. Last entry 4.45pm.
  A·B·P·R·T·0
🚇 Wimbledon, Putney
🚌 93
Rare example of a hollow post mill (1817). Grade II*-
listed, it now contains a museum depicting the history
and development of windmills in Britain. Many working
models, windmill machinery, equipment and tools.
Charles March, 1817

Sutton

Sutton

Social Capital

During the 1960s, Sutton built more social housing than many outer boroughs, and is also home to the UK's largest mixed use, carbon neutral development at BedZED.

All Saints Carshalton

🚶 High Street, Carshalton, SM5 3AQ
🕐 Sat 10.30am–5pm/Sun 11.30am–5pm.
  Last entry 4.30pm. **F·D·R·T·O**
🚇 Carshalton
🚌 X26,127,157,407

12C south aisle and former chancel. Blomfield nave, chancel, baptistry. Kempe glass, Bodley reredos and screen, spectacular Comper decorations, monuments and brasses, award-winning lighting scheme, fine modern benches. A & R Blomfield, 1893

BedZED

🚶 24 Helios Road, SM6 7BZ
🕐 Sat BedZED 45 minute outdoor tour, hourly
  (10am–1pm). **T**
🚇 Hackbridge
🚌 S1,127,151

UK's first large-scale, mixed-use eco-village and sustainable community. Completed in 2002, BedZED is an inspiration for low-carbon neighbourhoods promoting One Planet Living. Developed in partnership with Peabody, ZEDfactory, Bioregional. Bill Dunster Zedfactory Architects, 2002

Carew Manor and Dovecote

🚶 Church Road, Beddington, SM6 7NN
🕐 Sun Hourly tour (10am–1pm, Meet at Dovecote). **P**
❗ Pre-book only: sarah.wheeldon@sutton.gov.uk
🚇 Hackbridge
🚌 X26,455,407,410,463

Origin c1510, Grade I-listed Great Hall with its timber hammerbeam roof built for Richard Carew about 1510. 18C and Victorian alterations. Site of important Elizabethan garden created by Sir Francis Carew. 1510

Carshalton Water Tower and Historic Gardens

🚶 West Street, Carshalton, SM5 2QG
🕐 Sat/Sun 1pm–5pm + Tours
  (2pm–4pm, max 20, Available on demand).
  Last entry 4.15pm. **D·B·R·T**
🚇 Carshalton
🚌 S3,157,127,407,X26,154

Early 18C Grade II-listed building incorporating plunge bath with Delft tiles, orangery, saloon and pump chamber with part-restored water wheel. Hermitage and sham bridge in grounds. 1717

Honeywood Museum

🚶 Honeywood Walk, Carshalton, SM5 3NX
🕐 Sat 10am–5pm/Sun 10am–5pm + Sat Living in
  Honeywood at 2.30pm (1 hr duration). Last entry
  4.45pm. **B·R·T**
🚇 Carshalton
🚌 S3,127,157,407,X26

Chalk and flint house dating to 17C with additions including extensions of 1896 and 1903 when owned by John Pattinson Kirk. Rich in period detail and the interior restored and stairs opened up with funding from the Heritage Lottery Fund.

Little Holland House

🚶 40 Beeches Avenue, Carshalton, SM5 3LW
🕐 Sun 10am–5pm. Last entry 4.45pm. **B·T**
🚇 Carshalton Beeches
🚌 154

Grade II-listed building inspired by the ideals of John Ruskin and William Morris and contains Dickinson's paintings, hand-made furniture, furnishings, metalwork and friezes, in Arts and Crafts style. Frank Dickinson, 1902

Nonsuch Gallery and Service Wing at Nonsuch Mansion

🚶 Nonsuch Park, Ewell Road, Cheam, SM3 8AP
🕐 Sun 1pm–5pm + 32 minute film of the archaeological
  dig at Nonsuch Park on the footprint of Nonsuch
  Palace in 1959 (max 12). Last entry 4.30pm.
  B·P·R·T·O
🚇 Cheam
🚌 470,213,151,293,X26,407

Gothic-style Georgian mansion built for Samuel Farmer. Restored Service Wing includes dairy, kitchen, scullery, larders and laundries. Gallery has a model of Henry VIII's Nonsuch Palace, 1959 archaeological dig artefacts and mansion stained glass. Jeffrey Wyatt, 1806

Russettings

🚶 25 Worcester Road, Sutton, SM2 6PR
🕐 Sun 10am–1pm (max 20). Last entry 12.15pm. **T**
🚇 Sutton (Surrey)
🚌 80,280,S1

A double-fronted red brick upper-middle-class house, and one of a few Victorian villas to survive in Sutton. The well-preserved interior includes an entrance hall with a mosaic tiled floor, an oak galleried staircase and fireplaces. Frederick Wheeler, 1899

• The Link Primary School © Luca Miserocchi 2017

St Nicholas Church
🏃 St Nicholas Way, Sutton, SM1 1ST
🕐 Sat 12pm–4pm/Sun 8.30am–2pm + The hidden monuments and lost windows (guide will be on hand to lead ad-hoc tours) + People Power – Individuals' stories and a legacy of art in glass. Last entry Sat 3.45pm | Sun 1.45pm. **R·T·O**
🚉 Sutton (Surrey)
🚌 213,80,151,164,280,407,413,470
Built in the Gothic style with dressed flint and stone dressings. There are monuments to Joseph Glover (1628), Lady Dorothy Brownlow (1699), William Earl Talbot (1782) and Isaac Littlebury (1740). The churchyard has five5 Grade II tombs. Edwin Nash, 1864

Subsea 7
🏃 40 Brighton Road, Sutton, SM2 5BN
🕐 Sun Tour every 75 mins (10am–12.30pm, max 15). **D·T**
❗ Pre-book only: sally.halsey@subsea7.com
🚉 Sutton (Surrey)
A BREEAM 'Excellent' high-quality, contemporary and flexible office building with central atrium, exhibition space, restaurant, café, gym and terraces providing a dynamic and exciting workplace environment for staff and visitors. ESA, 2016

The Link Primary School
🏃 138 Croydon Road, CR0 4PG
🕐 Sat 9am–12pm (max 30). Last entry 1.15pm
🚉 Waddon
🚌 407,410,455
Comprising a learning centre with occupational therapy, DSDHA's approach to the Link Primary School is both resolutely contemporary yet in dialogue with its mid-century surroundings. DSDHA, 2016

Whitehall
🏃 1 Malden Road, Cheam, SM3 8QD
🕐 Sat/Sun 10am–5pm + Sat Living in Whitehall at 11am (1 hour duration) + Children's Explorer Packs. Last entry 4.45pm. **F·T·R·B**
🚉 Cheam
🚌 470,X26,151,213
Originally a farmer's house dating to 1500, with jettied upper storey. Later additions reflect the changing lifestyles of the owners, including the Killicks for over two centuries. Now houses scale model of Henry VIII's Nonsuch Palace.

Walks & Tours

Carshalton Walking Tour
🏃 Meet: at the entrance to Carshalton Train Station, Station Approach, SM5 2HW
🕐 Sun 9.30am (max 30).
❗ Pre-book only: 020 8770 4297
🚉 Carshalton
🚌 127,157
4.5 mile circular walk. The day will prove what an attractive and surprisingly rural place Carshalton is, truly one of London's finest villages. Carew Manor and Dovecote, All Saints Church, Carshalton Water Tower and Honeywood Museum.

Sutton High Street
🏃 Meet: Sutton Green Café, 347 High Street, SM1 1LW
🕐 Sun 10am.
❗ Pre-book only: sutton.gov.uk/culturalservices
🚉 Sutton Common
🚌 S1,164,154,151
A guided linear walk with John Philips and Andrew Skelton looking at the 19 and 20C shop fronts in Sutton High Street.

Sutton's Social Suburbia
🏃 Meet: Russettings, 25 Worcester Road, SM2 6PR
🕐 Sun 1pm.
❗ Pre-book only: sutton.gov.uk/culturalservices
🚉 Sutton (Surrey)
🚌 80,280,S1
A guided linear walk with John Phillips and Andrew Skelton looking at the development of Sutton's suburbia in the Victorian period.

Wandsworth

Social Capital

Housing and development have been features of the borough since its creation, such as the Doddington and Roehampton estates.

Architecturally Redesigned Townhouse & Studio

🚶 201 Battersea Church Road, Battersea, SW11 3ND
🕐 Sat 10am–5pm (max 6). Last entry Sat 4.15pm. **A**
🚇 South Kensington, Clapham Junction
🚌 345,319,19,49,170

Flooded with natural light, this four storey town house on a restricted fan shaped site provides a live-work space complete with courtyard garden and rooftop terrace for an interior architect and art director couple and their family. spacetime, 2016. *spacetime.london*

Blackbook Winery

🚶 Arch 41, London Stone Business Estate, Broughton Street, SW8 3QR
🕐 Sat 10am–5pm/Sun 11am–5pm + Meet the winemaker, hourly (max 20). Last entry 4.15pm. **D**
🚇 Wandsworth Road, Queenstown Road (Battersea)
🚌 452,156,137

Blackbook Winery is in a converted Victorian railway arch. It is open plan, with all equipment required to process, ferment and age wine on site – press, tanks, barrels etc. Our grapes come from English growers within 2 hours of London. 1850

• U.S. Embassy London

Buzz Bingo Hall (former Granada Cinema)

🚶 50 Mitcham Road, Tooting, SW17 9NA
🕐 Sun 9am–12pm + Guided building tour at 9.15am. Last entry 11.30am. **P·T·O**
🚇 Tooting Broadway, Tooting
🚌 44,57,77,127,133,264,270,280,355

Exceptional example of the 'super cinema style' of the 1930s with outstanding Gothic interior by Theodore Komisarjevsky. The first Grade I-listed cinema. Cecil Masey and Reginald Uren, 1931

Emanuel School

🚶 Battersea Rise (entrance via bridge over the railway on Spencer Park), SW11 1HS
🕐 Sat 2pm–5.30pm (max 200) + Tour of the buildings & site at 2.30pm, 4pm (max 35). Last entry 5.15pm. **P·T**
🚇 Clapham Junction
🚌 49,77,219,337

Former Royal Patriotic orphanage, converted to school 1883, with 1896 additions and 20C developments. High Victorian style with stained glass by Moira Forsyth. Set in 12 acres. Henry Saxon Snell, 1871

Foster + Partners

🚶 Riverside, 22 Hester Road, SW11 4AN
🕐 Sat 12pm–5pm / Sun 10am–5pm. Last entry 4.15pm. **R·T**
🚇 Clapham Junction, Sloane Square
🚌 19,49,170,319,345

The main studio is entered via steps through a top-lit galleried space and forms a 60-metre-long, double-height volume. Along its southern edge a mezzanine contains presentation spaces, while below is a state-of-the-art modelshop. Foster + Partners, 1990

Quaker Meeting House, Wandsworth

🚶 59 Wandsworth High Street, Wandsworth, SW18 2PT
🕐 Sat 1pm–5pm (max 50, access to Meeting Rooms & Burial Garden) + ½ hourly tour. Last entry 4.45pm. **F·D·R·T·B**
🚇 East Putney, Wandsworth Town
🚌 220,270,44,28,39,87,156,337

Grade II-listed, this is the oldest Quaker meeting house in Greater London, with original panelling and a ministers' gallery. Secluded burial ground and garden.

• RCA Battersea Dyson + Woo Buildings © Richard Haughton 2015

RCA Battersea: Dyson and Woo Buildings
🏃 Dyson Building, 1 Hester Road, SW11 4AN
🕐 Sat/Sun 12pm–4pm (max 20) + Hourly tour.
   Last entry 3.15pm. **R·D·T**
🚇 South Kensington, Clapham Junction
🚌 19,49,319,345,170
The architect's concept is that of a large Art Factory, where three or four disciplines are visible on any one journey. As students learn by looking at each other's work, the interconnected spaces create a place where ideas can flourish. Haworth Tompkins, 2012

Roehampton University - Mount Claire Temple
🏃 Mount Clare, Minstead Gardens, SW15 4EE
🕐 Sat 10am–1pm (max 10). Last entry 12.45pm. **P**
🚇 East Putney, Putney, Barnes
🚌 170,430
The Mount Clare Temple, The Temple of Fortune, is a Neoclassical garden temple originally standing in the grounds of the second Earl of Bessboroughs House in Roehampton before being moved to Mount Clare in 1913. James 'Athenian' Stuart, or Nicholas Revett, 1762

Roehampton University Library
🏃 Roehampton Lane, SW15 5SZ
🕐 Sat/Sun 10am–5pm (Visitors are asked to respect noise zones). Last entry 4.15pm. **R·D·T**
🚇 Putney, Barnes, East Putney
🚌 265,493
Academic Library at Roehampton University by Feilden Clegg Bradley Studios, opened in 2017. The building is conceived to be a mature, sophisticated space to encourage good behaviour and academic attitude. Feilden Clegg Bradley Studios, 2017

Royal Hospital for Neuro-disability
🏃 West Hill, SW15 3SW
🕐 Sun 10am–5pm + Hourly tour + Exhibitions of the hospital's archive. Last entry 4.15pm. **T·R·P·D**
🚇 East Putney, Putney
🚌 85,39,14,170
The original Grade II-listed house was a former Georgian villa. There were three extensions added through the Victorian period which reflect the style of the era. Subsequent additions reflect medical practices and thinking through the decades. Jesse Gibson, 1788

Sisters Avenue
🏃 78 Sisters Avenue, SW11 5SN
🕐 Sat 10am–5pm (max 20). Last entry 4.30pm. **A**
🚇 Clapham South, Clapham Junction, Clapham Common
🚌 37,35,137
The original building is a post-war end-of-terrace house. The home has been completely refurbished and extended with a contemporary loft and a modern rear extension by its architect owner. Proctor and Shaw, 2017

St John's Hill
🏃 SW11 1TY
🕐 Sat 10am–2pm (No access to flats) + Architect-led tour of development. Last entry 1.30pm. **A**
🚇 Clapham Junction
🚌 295,156,87,39,37,C3,170,337
Regeneration of a 1930s Peabody estate in three phases. The 351 existing homes are being replaced with 599 new ones. A new pedestrian avenue links Clapham Junction to Wandsworth Common. HawkinsBrown, 2014

St Mary's Church, Battersea

🚶 Battersea Church Road, SW11 3NA

🕐 Sat/Sun 1pm–5pm. Last entry Sat/Sun 4.45pm.
D·R·T·O

🚇 South Kensington, Clapham Junction

🚌 19,49,170,319,345

Classic Grade I-listed Georgian church with outstanding interior and monuments. Renovation will be taking place in September. Fair in churchyard on Saturday. Joseph Dixon, 1775

Tara Theatre

🚶 356 Garratt Lane, Earlsfield, SW18 4ES

🕐 Sat 11am–4pm (max 20) + Illustrated talk by Artistic Director at 3pm (max 80)/Sun 11am–3pm (max 20) + Illustrated talk by Artistic Director at 2pm (max 80). Last entry Sat 3.15pm | Sun 2.15pm. **R·T·O**

🚇 Earlsfield

🚌 44,77,270

An architectural fusion of East & West. 100-seat auditorium, with an earth stage floor, a rehearsal studio and an outdoor patio garden. Opened in September 2016 by Mayor of London Sadiq Khan, Tara Theatre is connecting worlds of stories. Aedas, 2016

Tooting Bec Lido

🚶 Tooting Bec Road, SW16 1RU

🕐 Sat/Sun 7am–5pm (max 40) + Architect-led tour at 11am (max 40) · Lido History Tour at 3pm (max 40) + Art event – paint the Lido at 10.30am (max 30, art event for children and their adults – all materials provided.). Last entry 4.30pm. **F·D·A·R·T**

🚇 Streatham, Tooting Bec

🚌 315,249,319

Outdoor pool 100x33 yards. One million gallons of unheated water. Iconic outdoor cubicle doors, fountain and café added in the 1930s, with Art Deco-style entrance. Sports hall pavilion added in 2016. LCC Parks Dept, 1906

U.S. Embassy London

🚶 33 Nine Elms Lane, SW11 7US

🕐 Sat 10.30am–1pm (max 200, limited access to the building will take place on the tour. The Consular entrance, lobby and main public space. The architects will host a lecture. No under 16s). Last entry 12.15pm. **R·D·A·T·Q**

❗ Pre-book only: openhouselondon.open-city.org.uk/ballots/11/entries/new

🚇 Vauxhall, Battersea Park

🚌 436,344,156

The new U.S. Embassy in Nine Elms reflects the best of modern design, incorporates the latest in energy-efficient building techniques, and celebrates the values of freedom and democracy. KieranTimberlake, 2018

Wandsworth Prison Museum

🚶 North Gate Car Park, HMP Wandsworth, Heathfield Road, SW18 3HR

🕐 Sat/Sun 10am–5pm (Closed 12.00–14.00. General access is to Museum only) + Architectural tour of the prison at 12.30pm (max 20, Entry by ballot only). Last entry Sat/Sun 4.15pm.

❗ Pre-book only: wandsworthprisonmuseum@justice.org.uk (Pre-book (ballot) for tours, not needed for general access)

🚇 Wandsworth Common, Tooting Bec

🚌 77,219

Victorian grand design, radial pattern of wings and landings from central point and impressive gatehouse where Governor and Chaplain resided, sometimes viewing arrival of prisoners passing through gate. New museum with over 400 items. Daniel Rowlandson Hill, 1851

Roehampton University, Chadwick Hall

🚶 Meet: outside entrance Roehampton Lane, Roehampton Lane, SW15 4HT

🕐 Sat ½ hourly tour (10am–1pm). **T**

🚇 Putney, Barnes, East Putney

🚌 265,493Commissioned by University of Roehampton, three student residences situated in the grounds of Grade II*-listed 18C Georgian villa Downshire House and Alton West Estate. The design co-opts the garden to make a convivial plan for the student community. Henley Halebrown, 2016

● Foster + Partners

Brent

Brent was the first authority in the UK to have a non-white majority population. By the time of the 2011 census, 64 per cent of Brent residents were from black and minority ethnic communities.

Ace Café London
🚶 Ace Corner, North Circular Road, NW10 7UD
🕐 Sat 8am–11pm/Sun 8am–10.30pm. Last entry Sat 10.15pm | Sun 9.45pm. **D·T·R·O**
🚇 Stonebridge Park
🚌 440,112,18
Established in 1938, Ace Café London has become 'the home' for petrolheads and is known as the world's most famous motor café, based on a shared passion for the rich traditions of motorcycles, cars and rock 'n' roll. 1938

BAPS Shri Swaminarayan Mandir
🚶 105–119 Brentfield Road, Neasden, NW10 8LD
🕐 Sat/Sun 10am–5pm + Guided Tour, ½ hourly (10am–4.30pm). Last entry Sat/Sun 4.15pm. **D·B·P·R·T·O**
🚇 Stonebridge Park, Harlesden
🚌 224,206
Europe's first traditional Hindu temple is a masterpiece of exquisite Indian craftsmanship. Using 5,000 tonnes of Italian and Indian marble and the finest Bulgarian limestone, it was hand-carved in India before being assembled in London. CB Sompura, 1995

Birch & Clay Refugio
🚶 36A Wendover Road, NW10 4RT
🕐 Sat/Sun 10am–5pm (max 10) + Architect-led tour at 11am. Last entry 4.15pm. **A**
❗ Pre-book only: (Tours) mail@risedesignstudio.co.uk
🚇 Willesden Junction
🚌 18,187
This project is a Ground Floor Flat for husband + wife and their two daughters and cat.The project capitalises on taking advantage of natural light and materiality, generating both visual and tactile experiences for this family oasis. RISE Design Studio, 2017
risedesignstudio.co.uk/projects/index.php/birch-clay-refugio

Capital City Academy
🚶 Doyle Gardens, Willesden, NW10 3ST
🕐 Sat Guided Tour, hourly (1pm–4pm, max 8) / Sun Guided Tour, hourly (10am–1pm, max 8). **P·T**
🚇 Willesden Green, Kensal Rise
🚌 206,266
Foster + Partners' first school; first new build City Academy; glass/stainless steel, slightly curved following slope of the grounds surrounded by sports fields and park. Unique with its clean, curved lines reflecting sky and surrounds. Foster + Partners, 2003

Harvist Road Glazed Envelope
🚶 56A Harvist Road, NW6 6SH
🕐 Sat/Sun 10am–1pm. Last entry 12.15pm. **A**
🚇 Kensal Rise, Queen's Park
🚌 187,452,28
This project is the renovation of a ground floor flat by RISE Design Studio that combines modern features with traditional interior finishes to create an elegant home with a minimalist feeling. RISE Design Studio, 2018

John Lewis and Partners OPDC
🚶 Unit 4 Rainsford Road, NW10 7FW
🕐 Sat 10am–3pm regular Site Manager-led tour (max. 20, no under 12s, must be accompanied by an adult)
❗ Pre-book only: see Open House website for details
🚇 Park Royal, Hanger Lane
🚌 224, 112
Modern multi-purpose John Lewis Customer Deliver Hub (CDH). Facilitates two man delivery in London. On site studio.

• Clay Refugio © Ståle Eriksen 2018

Park Royal Fire Station

🚶 Waxlow Road, NW10 7NU

🕐 Sat 11am–3pm (max 10) + Fire Station Tour, ½ hourly (11am–2.45pm, max 10). Last entry 2.30pm. **T·P**

🚇 Harlesden

Built in 1958 to the 'Middlesex' design, Park Royal Fire Station is a two storey fire station with appliance bays that can accommodate two fire appliances. It has a four storey drill tower in the yard and backs onto the Grand Union Canal.

Periscope House

🚶 1 Woodville Road, London, NW6 6HQ

🕐 Sat Architect-led tour, every 45 mins (10.15am–5.30pm, max 10, shoes off). **X·A·Q**

🚇 Queen's Park

🚌 206

Periscope House was designed to convert a disused infill garage site in Queens Park into a joyful home within the high-density urban fabric of our city. Groves Natcheva Architects, 2019

• Periscope House © Helenio Barbetta 2018

The Granville

🚶 140 Carlton Vale, NW6 5HE

🕐 Sat 10am–4pm (Open access to the garden, café and main community space) + Architect-led tour, hourly (max 10). Last entry 3.30pm. **T·R·D·A·O**

🚇 Queen's Park, Kilburn Park

🚌 6,316

The Granville is a mixed-use workspace and community hub operated by the South Kilburn Trust, funded by the Mayor of London and housed in a refurbished Edwardian building owned by Brent Council. RCKa, 2018

The Library at Willesden Green

🚶 95 High Road, NW10 2SF

🕐 Sat/Sun 10am–5pm (No access to the performance space before 3pm). Last 4.45pm. **D·T·O**

🚇 Willesden Green, Brondesbury Park

🚌 52,98,460,266,260

A modern four storey building incorporating the much-loved Victorian library. The galleries and feature walls display exhibitions and contemporary art and a dramatic central atrium provides natural ventilation and daylight throughout. Allford Hall Monaghan Morris, 2015

The Tin Tabernacle / Cambridge Hall

🚶 12–16 Cambridge Avenue, NW6 5BA

🕐 Sat/Sun 1.15pm–4pm + Corrugation at 2.15pm (max 100, sit down performance, approx. 45 mins). Last entry 3.30pm. **R·T·O**

❗ Pre-book only: (Dance performance) priceart@btinternet.com

🚇 Kilburn Park, Kilburn High Road

🚌 31,328,316,32,206

Built 1863 – a large corrugated iron chapel. The inside was transformed after the last war into a battleship by local sailors, for Sea Cadets, and it has decks, portholes, bridge and even a Bofors gun. Also the set from the film Becket.

Willesden Jewish Cemetery

🚶 Beaconsfield Road, NW10 2JE

🕐 Sun 10am–1pm + Tour at 10am, 11.30am (max 20). Last entry Sun 12.15pm. **D·P·T·O**

❗ Pre-book only: theus.org.uk/events

🚇 Dollis Hill, Willesden Green

🚌 6,226,302,98,52,260,460,266

London's pre-eminent Victorian Jewish cemetery, now embarking on a once in a generation conservation project with Heritage Lottery Fund support. The 'House of Life' will share stories of a community and remarkable biographies. Harry Ford, Nathan Solomon Joseph, Lewis Solomon & Son, 1873

Walks & Tours

Exploring Wembley Park: Guided Tours of the Neighbourhood

🚶 Meet: Market Square, Exhibition Way, Wembley Park, HA 0TG

🕐 Sat 11am, 2pm, 4pm (90 mins).

❗ Pre-book only: wembleypark.com/open-house

🚇 Wembley Park, Wembley Stadium, North Wembley

Join the teams at Quintain and the designers of Wembley Park on a journey taking you through the past, present and future of the 85-acre site around Wembley Stadium.

Roe Green Village

🚶 Meet: Village Green, opposite entrance to Roe End, Roe Lane, NW9 9BJ

🕐 Sun 11am, 2.30pm. **O**

🚇 Kingsbury, Kenton

🚌 204,302,324,183

Built in 1918–19 to provide housing for AirCo (the Aircraft Manufacturing Company based in Colindale), Roe Green was designed in the garden village idiom by Sir Frank Baines, HM Office of Works principal architect.

Ealing

www.ealing.gov.uk

Influenced by Ken Loach's Cathy Come Home, BBC television play (1996). Ealing residents established the Ealing Family Housing Association to improve and provide housing to locals.

31 Milton Road
🏃 31 Milton Rd, Churchfield Village, Acton, W3 6QA
🕐 Sat/Sun 2pm–5.30pm (max 35, downstairs living-dining-kitchen space and garden only). Last entry 5.15pm. **A·R**
❗ Pre-book only: judirosecookery@gmail.com
(Book for cookery demonstration only. General access does not require booking.)
🚇 Acton Central, Acton Town
🚌 266,207,70,607,E3
Split into two 2-bedroom flats in the 1970s, this 1875 semi was recently converted back to a single family home. The ground floor flat was reconfigured to create a loft-style living space with many long-hidden original Victorian features. David Buckingham, 2016

Acton Gardens
🏃 Acton Gardens Community Centre, Unit A, Munster Court, Bollo Bridge Road, Acton, W3 8UU
🕐 Sat 10am–5pm (max 20) + Hourly tour (11am–4pm, max 20). Last entry Sat 4.15pm. **T·R·D·O**
🚇 Acton Town, South Acton
🚌 440,70
Acton Gardens is a partnership between L&Q and Countryside Properties. This collaboration is delivering the award-winning regeneration of South Acton to create 3,463 new homes, community facilities and retail, play and green spaces. GRID, Allies and Morrison, Levitt Bernstein Architects, PCKO Architects, Maccreanor Lavington, Stitch, Alison Brook Architects, HTA Design LLP, 2012

Chestnut Grove
🏃 56 Chestnut Grove, side gate from Almond Avenue, W5 4JS
🕐 Sat/Sun Tour at 2pm, 3.30pm (max 15, presentation is a mixture of technical details and our story.). **A·R·T**
❗ Pre-book only: https://docs.google.com/forms/d/e/1FAIpQLSf4uyg0uShVyUKl4Tct3H0QjSo_qeYjWE8Vv_j6I9xqldPp4A/viewform
🚇 South Ealing
🚌 65,E3
A 1925 semi, refurbished to Certified PassivHaus Standard, with a side and rear extension. Robert Juhasz, 2010

Dormers Wells High School
🏃 Dormers, UB1 3HZ
🕐 Sat 10am–1pm + ½ hourly tour. Last entry 12.15pm. **P·T**
🚇 Greenford, Southall
🚌 105,95
Rebuilt as part of the BSF programme, the school aims to encourage educational aspiration through supporting social inclusion and community cohesion. Very Good status by CABE, BREEAM Excellent. Nicholas Hare Architects, 2012

Ealing Abbey Church of St Benedict
🏃 Charlbury Grove, W5 2DY
🕐 Sat 1pm–5pm + Hourly tour. Last entry 4.30pm. **D·T·P·R·B·O**
🚇 Ealing Broadway
🚌 E10,E2,E9,297
Begun in 1897 and a century later is almost completed. Architects include F and E Walters (1897, the nave), Stanley Kerr Bates (1960, transepts), and Sir William Whitfield (1997, choir and apse). Frederick A Walters, 1897

• Dormers Wells High School

• Full Metal Jacket

Full Metal Jacket
🚶 29 Hillcroft Crescent, W5 2SG
🕐 Sun 10am–5pm (max 15, downstairs only) +
Architect-led tour of extension, ½ hourly.
Last entry 4.30pm. **A**
🚇 North Ealing, Ealing Broadway
🚌 E10,226,E2,E7,E8,65,207
Striking zinc-clad contemporary extension provides
flexible family living space and improved relationship to
the garden using generous sliding doors & sliding solar
shutters. Special features include dramatic timber lined
acoustic ceiling. KSKa Architects, 2019. *kska.co.uk*

Gunnersbury Park & Museum
🚶 Popes Lane, W5 4NH
🕐 Sun 10am–4pm + Gardens Tour at 11am, 1.30pm (max
25, 90 mins, appropriate footwear) · House Tour at
11am, 1.30pm (max 25, 90 mins). Last entry 3.15pm.
D·B·A·R·P·T·O
❗ Pre-book only: visitgunnersbury.org
🚇 Acton Town, Kew Bridge
🚌 E3
Former residence of the Rothschild family, now a local
history museum in a beautifully restored 19C mansion.
Set on an elevated terrace overlooking 186 acres of
parkland with historical outbuildings dating from the
18C, ponds and a lake. Alexander : Sedgley, 1802

Hanwell Community Centre
🚶 Wescott Crescent, Hanwell, W7 1PD
🕐 Sat 10.30am–4pm/Sun 10am–3pm (max 30, access to
basement and ground floor only) + Building history
and usage tour at 11am, 2pm (max 30, duration 90
minutes to 2 hours). Last entry Sat 4.15pm | Sun
2.15pm. **T·R·P·D·O**
❗ Pre-book only: (Tours) info@h3c.org.uk
🚇 Castle Bar Park, Ealing Broadway
🚌 E3,E1,e11
Victorian Grade II-listed former Central London District
School, known as the 'Cuckoo Schools', was 'home' to
up to 1500 pauper children from inner London from
1857–1933. Tress & Chambers, 1856

Old Torpedo Factory
🚶 St Leonards Road, NW10 6ST
🕐 Sat 9am-4pm
🚇 North Acton, Willesden Junction
🚌 266
A prominent local landmark building. Believed to have
been a soap factory originally, and was linked to its
neighbouring properties. Named by the present owners
after its role as a torpedo manufacturing site in WWII.

Pitzhanger Manor & Gallery
🚶 Mattock Lane, Ealing, W5 5EQ
🕐 Sat 10am-3pm. Last entry Sat 2.00pm. **D·R·T**
🚇 South Ealing, Ealing Broadway
🚌 65,207,427,607,483
Designed by Sir John Soane as a family home and
country residence. Following a three-year conservation
project, Pitzhanger has been returned to Soane's
innovative original design and reopened to the public
earlier this year. Sir John Soane, 1800

Preedy Glass
🚶 Stanley Works, 7B Coronation Road, NW10 7PQ
🕐 Sat 8am-5pm + Managing Director-led factory tour of
the glass processing factory, hourly (8am-4pm, max
30). Last entry Sat 4.00pm. **T·R·P·D**
🚇 North Acton, Park Royal
🚌 260,487,226
An industrial building originally built for maintaining
railways with a modern rear extension now housing a
modern glass processing company.

South Ealing Cemetery Chapels
🚶 South Ealing Road, W5 4XZ
🕐 Sat 11.30am-5pm (max 25, access to the South Chapel,
viewing only of the North Chapel) + Talk on the South
Ealing Cemetery Chapel Options Appraisal at 12pm
(max 25) · Walk exploring the history and development
at 1.30pm (max 25) · Cemetery Tree and Wildlife
Walk at 2.30pm (max 25) · Talk on Victorian Gothic
Architecture at 4pm (max 25). Last entry 4.15pm. **A**
🚇 South Ealing
🚌 65,E3
Designed by local architect Charles Jones in 1861, the
chapels are constructed of ragstone with limestone
dressings in a Gothic style. There is a central porte
cochere with clock and belfry, flanked by the south and
north chapels. Charles Jones, 1861

St Mary the Virgin Perivale
🚶 Perivale Lane, Perivale, UB6 8SS
🕐 Sat/Sun 11am-5pm (max 30) + Brief tour of the
church (max 30). Last entry 4.45pm. **T·P**
🚇 Perivale, Ealing Broadway
🚌 95,E2,E9
Grade I-listed 12C church with later additions, now an
arts centre run by The Friends of St Mary's.

St Mary's Church Ealing

🚶 St Mary's Road, W5 5RH

🕐 Sat 10am–5pm (No access to tower). Last entry 4.30pm. T·D·O

🚇 South Ealing, Ealing Broadway

🚌 65

A large Victorian building transformed from a simple church by SS Teulon in the 1860s. The exterior is largely unchanged but the interior was refurbished in stages, finishing in 2003 to create the wonderful space we see today. SS Teulon, 1860

The Playhouse at Gypsy Corner

🚶 26-29 Victoria Industrial Estate, Victoria Road, W3 6UU

🕐 Sat staff-led talk and demonstration, every 90 mins (10am-2.30pm, max 16, Access to Playhouse only).

🚇 North Acton

🚌 95,260,266,460

Recreating the themes and magic of theatre, this themed working environment draws inspiration from Frank Matcham's work and our desire to create an imaginative space in which to work and collaborate with our customers and colleagues. Fred Foster, 2006.

The Questors Theatre

🚶 12 Mattock Lane, W5 5BQ

🕐 Sat 10am–5pm + Hourly tour. Last entry 4.15pm. D·T·P·R·O

🚇 South Ealing, Ealing Broadway

Originally planned in 1954, the first new theatre after the war, the Questors Playhouse opened in 1964, by which time its design had been followed by the Chichester Festival Theatre and the Crucible, Sheffield. Norman Branson, 1964

The Treatment Rooms

🚶 4 Fairlawn Grove, Chiswick, W4 5EH

🕐 Sat/Sun 10am–5pm (max 25, downstairs only). Last entry 4.15pm.

🚇 Chiswick Park, South Acton

🚌 94

Family home of the artist Carrie Reichardt. Over the last 20 years the outside of the house has been covered in mosaic and ceramic tiles. This is a rare opportunity to see the inside of this mosaic house.

The White House

🚶 46 Park View Road, Ealing, W5 2JB

🕐 Sat/Sun 10am–4pm + Ballet performance at 2pm (max 50). Last entry 3.30pm. P·R·T

🚇 North Ealing, Ealing Broadway

🚌 112,483

Louis XVI palace set in the private gardens and based on the owner's grandmother's palace in Poland. Marble arch entrance is the first in London for over 200 years. Extremely opulent interiors with marble, gold cornices and chandeliers.

Walks & Tours

A Ruskinian Walk Through Shared Heritage

🚶 Meet: Building 3, Chiswick Business Park, 566, Chiswick High Road, W4 5YA

🕐 Sat 12pm/ Sun 2pm (Meet at Building 3, Chiswick Park Business Estate, 566 Chiswick High Road, W4 5YA. The walk lasts approx. 2 hours, with a comfort stop en route.) R·T

🚇 Chiswick Park, Gunnersbury

🚌 70,237,267,391,440

Ruskinian walk from RIBA award-winning Chiswick Business Park, Gunnersbury Triangle Nature Reserve through South Acton Estate, birthplace of artist Patrick Caulfield; Woodlands Park Ice House; to home of Wm Willett, of Daylight Saving Time. Stanley Slight, Acton Borough Engineer, 1951

Brentham Garden Suburb

🚶 Meet: The Brentham Club, 38 Meadvale Road, W5 1NP

🕐 Sat/Sun 10.30am (max 30). D·P·R·T·O

🚇 Hanger Lane, Ealing Broadway

🚌 E2,E9

Britain's first co-partnership garden suburb, first houses built 1901. Parker and Unwin's plan introduced 1907, mainly Arts and Crafts style; fascinating social history. (Organised by The Brentham Society.). Parker & Unwin, G L Sutcliffe, G C Pearson & others, 1901

Ealing Common Walk

🚶 Meet: at Hanger Lane end of Inglis Road, behind Iron Duke train sculpture, Ealing, W5 3RN

🕐 Sat 2pm (max 50, ppen-air tour, weather dependent). R·T

🚇 Ealing Common, North Ealing

🚌 112,483

Walk across Ealing Common, taking in the range of architectural styles. Highlights: the home of a Wimbledon champion and the death mask of a prime minister. 1890

Hanwell Flight of Locks & Three Bridges

🚶 Meet: in pub forecourt, The Fox public house, Green Lane, W7 2PJ

🕐 Sat/Sun Tour led by members of the Middlesex Branch of the Inland Waterways Association, hourly (12pm–3pm, max 25). P·R·T·O

🚇 Boston Manor, Hanwell

🚌 E8,427,207,195,83,607

Restored flight of locks at Hanwell is a Scheduled Ancient Monument. Three Bridges is a unique stacked intersection of road, rail and canal and Brunel's last major railway project. Walks led by knowledgeable enthusiasts. Isambard Kingdom Brunel, James Barnes (Resident Engineer), William Jessop (Chief Engineer), 1794

Hammersmith & Fulham

hammersmith & fulham

Social Capital

In the early years of the borough there was substantial employment loss – from a relatively small base – but by 2015 employment was higher than in 1965.

ArtWest Open Studios, Hythe Road, and 6 other buildings

🏃 17–19 Hythe Road, NW10 6RT
🕐 Sat/Sun 1pm-6pm (Only to studios that have agreed to open, please see our latest Press Release and our website) + Anonymous Postcard Exhibition at 1pm (max 10, takes place in Acava Studios, Hythe Road and ACME Studios, Harrow Road). Last entry 5.30pm. **T**
🚇 Willesden Junction
🚌 220

17–19 Hythe Road is an Edwardian light industrial brick building, formerly used for making metal casement windows.Currently it has 16 studios on the first floor with Danny Lane's famous glass sculpture-making studio on the ground floor. 1905

Bridget Joyce Square, Community Rain Park (SuDS)

🏃 Australia Road, W12 7PH
🕐 Sat/Sun 10am-5pm + Hourly tour (11am-4pm, max 50). Last entry 4.45pm. **R·P·F·D·A·O**
🚇 Shepherd's Bush Market, White City
🚌 283,228

A public park with community needs at its heart that also manages rainwater to reduce flooding and pollution. 'Wiggly wall' between trees and grassy basins that store rain and 'rain sculptures' in the raingardens. Robert Bray Associates, 2015. *robertbrayassociates.co.uk*

● Bridget Joyce Square

Bush Theatre

🏃 7 Uxbridge Road, W12 8LJ
🕐 Sat 10am-1pm/Sun 1pm-5pm (max 15, limited access to backstage areas) + ½ hourly tour. Last entry Sat 12.15pm | Sun 4.15pm. **R·B·T·O**
🚇 Shepherds Bush, Shepherd's Bush Market
🚌 94,207,260,607

Former Victorian library designed in the English Renaissance style and commissioned by philanthropist John Passmore Edwards – the second most prolific architect of public libraries prior to WWI. Redeveloped in 2016 and reopened March 2017. Maurice Adams, 1895

Colet House

🏃 151 Talgarth Road, W14 9DA
🕐 Sat 10am-5pm. Last entry 4.15pm. **B·T·O**
🚇 Hammersmith, Kensington Olympia
🚌 220,9,27,190,295,391,23

Unique building for artists with three large studios, all with north light through expansive windows. Originally called Barons Court Studio, Colet House was built 1885 on market garden land in what was a leafy backwater called Red Cow Lane. Fairfax B Wade-Palmer, 1885

Emery Walker's House

🏃 7 Hammersmith Terrace, W6 9TS
🕐 Sun 2pm-5pm (max 10, ground floor and garden only). Last entry 4.15pm. **X·Q**
🚇 Hammersmith, Stamford Brook
🚌 190,267,391,H91

The home of Emery Walker, printer, antiquary and mentor to William Morris. A unique Arts and Crafts domestic interior. Furnishings by Philip Webb and William Morris, 1750

Fulham Palace

🏃 Bishop's Avenue, Fulham, SW6 6EA
🕐 Sun 11am-4pm (access to all public areas of the Palace including the Museum rooms, temporary exhibition, Great Hall, Chapel, Bishop Sherlock's Room, Howley's Dining Room and the Porteus Library), every 90 mins (11am–2pm, max 25) + Glory of the Garden at 11am (Suitable for ages 3+ Children must be accompanied by an adult). Last entry 3.15pm. **F·D·B·R·T·O**
🚇 Putney Bridge, Putney
🚌 22,93,14,74,220,414,430

Residence of the Bishop of London until 1973. Tudor red-brick courtyard with Georgian additions & Butterfield Chapel (1867). Walled garden. Completed an HLF-funded restoration project in spring 2019. Stiff Leadbetter, 1766

Greenside Primary School
🏃 51 Westville Road, W12 9PT
🕐 Sun ½ hourly tour (12.30pm-4pm). **R·T**
🚇 Goldhawk Road, Shepherd's Bush Market
🚌 266,94,237,283,260,207
One of only two schools designed using Ernö Goldfinger's school building system – precast reinforced concrete frame with brick infill. Fine, top-lit mural by Gordon Cullen, restored 2014. Grade II*-listed. Ernö Goldfinger, 1952

Jonathan Tuckey Design Studio
🏃 58 Milson Road, W14 0LB
🕐 Sat 10am–5pm (max 20). Last entry 4.30pm.
　　T·D·A·0
🚇 Kensington (Olympia), Shepherd's Bush
This transformation of a derelict pub into an architecture studio doubles up as a gallery and lecture theatre. The new office is an example of the practice's approach towards existing structures and intelligent architectural interventions.

Kenneth Armitage Foundation
🏃 22a Avonmore Road, W14 8RR
🕐 Sat 10am–5pm. Last entry 4.30pm. **T**
🚇 West Kensington, Kensington Olympia
🚌 9,27,28,49
Arts and Crafts pioneer James M MacLaren built this artist's house and studio in 1888. Once the residence of sculptor Kenneth Armitage, since 2005 occupancy of the house and studio has been offered as a biennial sculpture fellowship. James M MacLaren, 1888

Koestler Arts Centre – Former Governor's House of HM Prison Wormwood Scrubs
🏃 168a Du Cane Road, W12 0TX
🕐 Sat/Sun 10am–5pm (max 30). Last entry 4.30pm. **P·T**
🚇 White City, East Acton
🚌 7,70,72,272,283
The former governor's house in the gates of HMP Wormwood Scrubs houses Koestler Arts, the UK's leading prison arts charity. Paintings, drawing and sculpture, all for sale, cover walls and plinths throughout the 3-storey building. Edmund Du Cane, 1891

LAMDA (London Academy of Music & Dramatic Art)
🏃 155 Talgarth Road, W14 9DA
🕐 Sat 9.30am–4pm + Tour every 45 mins (10am–3.15pm, main foyer will be open to the public). Last entry 3.15pm. **D·R·T**
❗ Pre-book only: (Tours) lamda.ac.uk/whats-on/events
🚇 Barons Court
🚌 9,10,27,391

• Jonathan Tuckey Design Studio © James Brittain 2018

LAMDA's home since 2003. Victorian building with more recent extensions, including a new £28.2m centre for world-leading drama training which opened in June 2017. Facilities include three theatres, rehearsal studios and technical spaces. Niall McLaughlin Architects, 2017

Oaklands Grove
🏃 32 Oaklands Grove, W12 0JA
🕐 Sat 10am–5pm + Designer-led tours, ½ hourly (10.30am–4.30pm). Last entry Sat 4.15pm. **A**
🚇 Shepherd's Bush Central, Shepherd's Bush Market
🚌 283,260,228,207,607
An award-winning design of a quirky and crafted family home featuring oak framing and a playful focus on natural light, materials and texture. Studio McLeod, Beata Heuman, 2018

Polish Social and Cultural Association
🏃 238–246 King Street, Hammersmith, W6 0RF
🕐 Sat/Sun 10am–5pm + ½ hourly tour (max 20). Last entry 4.30pm. **R·T·B·0**
🚇 Ravenscourt Park
🚌 H91,391,267,190
Built 1971–74 in Brutalist style. The largest Polish centre in Western Europe, it contains a theatre, the Polish Library, the Polish University Abroad, a Joseph Conrad collection, Jazz Café, art gallery and art collection on public display. A Grzesik, 1971. *posk.org/en/home*

Roca London Gallery
🏃 Station Court, Townmead Road, SW6 2PY
🕐 Sat/Sun 10am–5pm + Exhibition. Last entry 4.45pm.
　　D·A·T·0
🚇 Fulham Broadway, Imperial Wharf
🚌 C3,391
A unique space where water acts as the architectural theme, offering an innovative and interactive experience with Roca, the global bathroom brand. Zaha Hadid Architects, 2011.
rocalondongallery.com/activities/open-house-2019

St Augustine's Church

🕴 55 Fulham Palace Road, W6 8AU

🕐 Sat 10.30am–6.30pm/Sun 9am–7.30pm + A guided tour of the church at 3pm + Audio installation by Dave Hunt 'Syrinx' (except during mass times). Last entry Sat 5.45pm | Sun 6.45pm. **D·O**

🚇 Hammersmith

🚌 9,27,72,190,211,220,295

The Order of St Augustine has carried out a national RIBA award-winning refurbishment of its church. The Church has been transformed into a place with a calm, ethereal quality, wholly fitting for a sacred space. Roz Barr Architects, 2017. *austin-forum.org @austinforum*.

St Paul's Girls' School

🕴 Brook Green, Hammersmith, W6 7BS

🕐 Sat 10am–5pm (No access to staff rooms or to staff offices) + Tour, led by the archivist and estates manager , every 45 mins (10.45am–2.30pm, max 30, accessible route). Last entry 4.15pm. **P·T**

❗ Pre-book only: (Tours) eventbrite.co.uk/e/open-house-2019-tickets-59312621648

🚇 Shepherd's Bush, Hammersmith

St Paul's Girls' School consists of an array of fine buildings, dating from 1904 to the present. The original school and its adjoining Music Wing were designed by Gerald Horsley, 1862-1917, FRIBA, a distinguished Arts and Crafts architect. Gerald Callcott Horsley, 1904

The Hurlingham Club

🕴 Ranelagh Gardens, SW6 3PR

🕐 Sat Tour at 11am, 3pm (max 90, meet 15 mins prior at main gate). **T**

🚇 Putney Bridge, Putney

🚌 14,22,39,74,85,93,220,265,270,424

Last of the grand 18C mansions which once fronted this part of the river, with magnificent interiors and extensive grounds. Dr William Cadogan, 1760

• Roca Gallery London © Hufton+Crow

The Round House

🕴 188 Blythe Road, W14 0HD

🕐 Sat 12pm–3pm (max 15) + tour of Round House by architect Alex Michaelis, ½ hourly (12pm–3pm, max 15, pre-book only). Last entry Sat 2.30pm. **A**

🚇 Kensington Olympia

🚌 295,283,220,72

The house uses traditional building materials while seeking to showcase great modern design, skilfully demonstrating that new builds can be imaginative and family homes needn't sacrifice style. Michaelis Boyd Associates, 2016

Tin House

🕴 Smugglers Yard, Devonport Road, W12 8PB

🕐 Sat 10am–1pm (max 50) + hourly tour (10am–12pm, max 15). Last entry 12.30pm. **D·T**

🚇 Shepherd's Bush Market, Goldhawk Road

🚌 207,260,283,607

Making efficient use of an irregular urban site, this house is made up of interconnecting top-lit pavilions arranged to define a tranquil private courtyard. Henning Stummel Architects, 2015

William Morris Society – Kelmscott House

🕴 26 Upper Mall, W6 9TA

🕐 Sat/Sun 11am–5pm (max 50, The Coach House and basement only). Last entry 4.30pm. **R·B·T·O**

🚇 Ravenscourt Park, Hammersmith

🚌 190,267,391,H91

Residence of Sir Francis Ronalds, George MacDonald and (1878–96) William Morris. Organised by William Morris Society. 1780

Wormwood Scrubs, The Chapel of Saint Francis

🕴 HMP & YOI Wormwood Scrubs, Du Cane Road, W12 0AE

🕐 Sat tour at 11.30am (max 20, meet in Koestler building, duration 2.5 hours). **X·D·T**

🚇 East Acton

🚌 7,70,72,272,283

❗ Pre-book only: wormwoodscrubsopenhouse2019. eventbrite.co.uk

Sits within the grounds of HMP & YOI Wormwood Scrubs. Victorian-built Category B adult male prison. Completed by prison labour in 1891, it is undoubtedly the finest prison chapel in England, and an architectural jewel which demonstrates the wealth of talent available in prisons.

Walks & Tours

West Kensington and Gibbs Green

🕴 Meet: on Mund Street Green, opposite the Blue Council office and infront of Churchward & Fairburn Houses, Mund Street, W14 9LW

🕐 Sat 2pm (max 40). **T·R·D·A**

🚇 West Kensington, West Brompton

🚌 28,391

A resident-led tour around West Kensington & Gibbs Green Estates, who have been at the centre of the political storm of the Earl's Court Regeneration, concluding with a talk on the role of architects and planners in estate-led regeneration. People's Plan (alternative to demolition) ASH & Residents, 2016

Harrow

Social Capital

Harrow churches began an
association in 1964 to provide
homes for its elderly members
after a particularly cold winter
in 1963.

BUILDING A **BETTER**
HARROW

Canons Park
🏃 Donnefield Avenue entrance, Edgware, HA8 6RH
🕐 Sun 10am–5pm + Tour by historian Graham at 2pm
(max 25, Suitable for ages 14+). Last entry 4.00pm.
D·P·R·T·0
🚇 Canons Park
🚌 186,79,340,142
Grade II-listed historic park landscape containing
several listed buildings, including an 18C 'temple'
building, bothy and compound, and walled kitchen
garden, converted in 1937 to an informally planted
garden by Harrow Council. Various architects, 1713

Church of St Lawrence, Little Stanmore
🏃 Whitchurch Lane, Edgware, HA8 6RB
🕐 Sun 1pm–4pm. Last entry 3.45pm. **P·0**
🚇 Canons Park
🚌 186,340,79
Unique Continental Baroque church rebuilt in 1715 by
James Brydges, first Duke of Chandos. Painted walls
and ceiling with trompe l'oeil effect. Wood carvings by
Grinling Gibbons and the organ on which Handel played.
John James, 1715

• Heath Robinson Museum © Jack Hobhouse 2018

Former Grosvenor Cinema, now Zoroastrian Centre For Europe
🏃 440–442 Alexandra Avenue, Middlesex, HA2 9TL
🕐 Sat 11am–5pm. Last entry 4.15pm. **D·P·R·T**
🚇 Rayners Lane
🚌 H9,398,H10,H12
Grade II*-listed Art Deco building with well-preserved
interior. Auditorium with deep coved ribs; proscenium
arch flanked by fluted columns. Restoration fully funded
by donations from Zoroastrian faith community, without
government grants. FE Bromige, 1936

Harrow School: Old Schools, Fourth Form Room
🏃 Church Hill, Harrow-on-the-Hill, HA1 3HP
🕐 Sun 2pm–5pm. Last entry 4.15pm.
🚇 Harrow On The Hill, Harrow & Wealdstone
🚌 258,H17
Best-preserved 17C schoolroom in the country. Wainscot
panelling, benches, tables and chairs. Original fireplace
replaced in 1730, oriel window inserted in 1820. Walls
carved with names of every Harrow pupil until 1847.
Sly, 1615

Harrow School: Old Speech Room Gallery
🏃 Church Hill, Harrow-on-the-Hill, HA1 3HP
🕐 Sun 2pm–5pm. Last entry 4.15pm.
🚇 Harrow & Wealdstone, Harrow On The Hill
🚌 H17,258
Purpose-built room intended for the teaching of public
speaking which figured prominently in the classical
curriculum. Converted 1976 by Alan Irvine into modern
gallery with mezzanine floor. CR Cockerell, 1819

Heath Robinson Museum
🏃 Pinner Memorial Park, West End Lane,
Pinner, HA5 1AE
🕐 Sat 11am–4pm (max 30). Last entry 3.30pm.
T·R·P·D·B·A
🚇 Pinner
🚌 183,H13,H12,H11
This NLHF supported, accredited, purpose-built museum
in Pinner Memorial Park displays a collection of Heath
Robinson's work, he having lived nearby. It includes
permanent and temporary exhibition galleries, activity
studio and shop. ZMMA, 2016

• Church of St Lawrence

Kenton Library
🏃 Kenton Lane, Kenton, HA3 8UJ
🕐 Sat 10am–5pm. Last entry 4.15pm. **D·T·P·O**
🚇 Kenton, Harrow & Wealdstone
🚌 H9,H10,H18,H19,114
Built in the Middlesex County Architects' Department's style which gave distinctive architectural form to the London suburbs. One of the best examples of inter-war library design in London. Grade II-listed with original internal fittings. Curtis and Burchett, 1939

Pinner House
🏃 Church Lane, Pinner, HA5 3AA
🕐 Sat 10am–4pm. Last entry 3.15pm. **R·T**
🚇 Pinner
🚌 183,H11,H12,H13
Grade II*-listed early Georgian house with pilastered front and magnificent oak-panelled dining room. Former rectory of the vicar of Harrow and Nell Gwynne's daughter by Charles II.

St Alban Church
🏃 The Ridgeway, North Harrow, HA2 7PF
🕐 Sat 10am–5pm/Sun 12pm–5pm + Tour to top of tower at 3pm, 11am (max 15). Last entry 4.15pm. **P·T·O**
🚇 North Harrow
🚌 H9,H10,H11

Notable 1930s Grade II-listed church with Swedish and German influences externally. Landmark tower. Stepped tunnel-vault with arches to side aisle walls giving a light lively interior. Marquetry panelling to Lady Chapel. Arthur Kenyon, 1936

St Panteleimon Greek Orthodox Church
🏃 660 Kenton Road, Harrow, HA3 9QN
🕐 Sat 10am–5pm/Sun 10am–1pm. Last entry Sat 4.15pm | Sun 12.15pm. **D·B·P·T·O**
🚇 Kingsbury
🚌 183,79,204
Built in traditional Byzantine style with dome and cross shape, the materials and form reflect a past era while meeting current building and thermal efficiency requirements. Internal superstructure, including mezzanine floor and dome. Neo Architects, 2011

Walks & Tours

Modernism in Metroland
🏃 Meet: outside Stanmore tube station, London Road, Stanmore, HA7 4PD
🕐 Sat 10am, 2pm. **O**
🚇 Stanmore
🚌 142,324,H12
A walking tour of Stanmore's Art Deco and modernist homes,t from the birth of Metroland to the post-war era. Douglas Wood/Gerald Lacoste/Owen Williams/RH Uren/ Rudolf Frankel

Hillingdon

HILLINGDON
LONDON

Social Capital

Hillingdon does not have a legacy of 1960s and '70s social housing estates with most borough housing built in brick and in the form of small terraces or as semi-detached houses.

Brunel University: Indoor Athletics Centre
🚶 Kingston Lane, Uxbridge, UB8 3PH
🕐 Sat/Sun 10am–5pm. Last entry 4.15pm. **T·P·D**
🚇 Uxbridge, West Drayton
🚌 U1,U3,U4,U7
Situated at the gateway of campus is this world-class indoor athletics facility shape defined by the requirements of the sports within. The curved roof is a catenary arch supported on wishbone steels, minimising the foundations required. David Morley Architects, 2006

Cranford Stable Block & St Dunstan's Church
🚶 Cranford Country Park, The Parkway, Cranford, TW5 9RZ
🕐 Sat/Sun 10am–5pm + Sat tour at 11am. Last entry 4.15pm. **P·R·T·O**
🚇 Hounslow West, Hayes & Harlington
🚌 H98,105,111,81,222,E6,195
Restored 18C stable block of now demolished Cranford House, former seat of the Earls of Berkeley. The front has arches with stone keystones facing a cobbled yard.

Eastcote House Gardens
🚶 High Road Eastcote, Eastcote, HA5 2FE
🕐 Sun 10am–5pm + Classic Car Rally (11am-4pm). Last entry 4.15pm. **X·R·T·O**
🚇 Eastcote
🚌 282,H13
Restored timber-framed 17C stables, 18C brick dovecote and large walled garden, all set in parkland of the former Eastcote House (dem. 1964). Family home of the Hawtrey family to 1930. Interiors largely as originally constructed.

Manor Farm Site, Manor House
🚶 Bury Street, Ruislip, HA4 7SU
🕐 Sat/Sun 10am–5pm. Last entry 4.15pm. **P·T·O**
🚇 Ruislip, West Ruislip
🚌 331,H13,U10,U1,398,114,E7
Oldest heritage site in Hillingdon, occupied since 11C. 16C Manor Farm House, with a modern interpretation centre. Grade II-listed 13C Great Barn, second largest in the country. 16C Little Barn, now a library. Listed monument Norman Motte.

• Cranford Stable Block St. Dunstan's Church © Jack Hobhouse 2018

• Eastcote House Gardens

St Martin's Church, Ruislip
🚶 High Street, Ruislip, HA4 8DG
🕐 Sat 10am-5pm. Last entry 4.15pm. **D·P·T·O**
🚇 Ruislip
🚌 114,E7,331
Church dates from 1250 with 15C additions and Victorian restorations. Grade II-listed. Fine late Medieval wall paintings and funeral hatchments.

St Mary the Virgin Church
🚶 High Street, Harmondsworth, UB7 0AQ
🕐 Sat 10am-5pm/Sun 12pm-5pm. Last entry 4.15pm. **R·T**
🚇 Heathrow Terminals 1 2 3, West Drayton
🚌 350,U3
Parts of the building date back to 11C, a fine Norman doorway and a Saxon sundial outside on the south wall. Carden & Godfrey, 1300

St Mary's Church, Harefield
🚶 Off Church Hill, Harefield, UB9 6DU
🕐 Sat 10am-5pm (max 75)/Sun 1pm-5pm (max 75). Last entry 4.15pm. **P·R·T·O**
🚇 Uxbridge
🚌 u9,331
Exceptionally fine 12C Medieval church, surrounded by large country churchyard, including Anzac Cemetery from WWI. Many notable monuments including Lady Spencer, Countess of Derby. Fine 18C three-decker pulpit. Grade I-listed. The Newdigate Family, 1180

St Peter & St Paul Harlington
🚶 St Peter's Way, High Street, Harlington, UB3 5AB
🕐 Sat 10am-4pm/Sun 1pm-5pm. Last entry Sat 3.45pm | Sun 4.45pm. **T·P·R·O**
🚇 Hatton Cross, Hayes & Harlington
🚌 H98,90,140
Grade I-listed church dating from 1086, with Norman font and Norman stone arch, carved with cats' heads. Interesting monuments including Easter sepulchre. Ancient yew tree in churchyard. Good restoration between 1830 and 1860.

Swakeleys Estate
🚶 Swakeleys Road, Ickenham (access from Milton Road), UB10 8LD
🕐 Sat 10am-4pm. Last entry Sat 3.45pm.
🚇 Hillingdon, Ickenham
🚌 U1,U2,U10
A most important house in Ickenham an outstanding example of Jacobean architecture built in the 1630s. Red brick construction laid in English bond on an H plan. Great Hall includes the 1655 Harrington Screen, 18C marble fireplace panelling.

The Great Barn, Harmondsworth
🚶 Manor Court, High Street, Harmondsworth, UB7 0AQ
🕐 Sat 10am-5pm (max 100)/Sun 10am-5pm (max 100) + Live horse-drawn vehicle display at 3pm (max 100) · Morris dancing at 2pm (max 100). Last entry 4.45pm. **D·B·P·O**
🚇 Heathrow Terminals 1 2 3, West Drayton
🚌 350,U3
The timbers of this great Medieval barn (1426-7), over 190 feet long and nearly 40 feet high, are 95% original. Displays include the conservation/repairs carried out in 2014 and its place in the agricultural history of the village.

Uxbridge Quaker Meeting House
🚶 150 York Road (corner of Belmont Road), Uxbridge, UB8 1QW
🕐 Sat 10am-4pm (max 70) ½ hourly (10am-3.45pm, max 10)/Sun 12.30pm-4.30pm (max 70) ½ hourly (12.30pm-4.15pm, max 10). Last entry Sat 3.45pm | Sun 4.15pm. **R·T·O**
🚇 Uxbridge
An early 19C meeting house, with a little-altered large meeting room, within a garden – retains much of its original character and fabric, full-height shutters and fixed seating in the elders' stand. Site of Quaker worship from late 1600s. Hubert Lidbetter, 1818

Hounslow

Social Capital

Hounslow has benefits from being on major roads and railways linking Heathrow Airport to central London and retains its mix of industrial uses and suburban housing.

London Borough of Hounslow

Adobe Village Hounslow Heath Infant and Nursery School
🏃 Martindale Road, TW4 7HE
🕐 Sat 12pm–4pm. Last entry 3.15pm. **P·R·T**
🚇 Hounslow West, Hounslow
🚌 H28,237,117,235,116
A unique striking playscape and adobe home structure that integrates outside learning with innovative earth forms. Construction is 'rammed' earth made from earth filled tubes. Adobe construction is recognised for sound reducing properties. Small Earth, 2011

Brentford & Isleworth Quaker Meeting House
🏃 Quakers Lane, London Road, Isleworth, TW7 5AZ
🕐 Sat 10am–5pm. Last entry 4.30pm. **D·P·R·T**
🚇 Syon Lane
🚌 235,H28,237,267,E8
Grade II*-listed late Georgian Quaker Meeting House (1785) set in garden with burial ground. Meeting room has wood panelling, elders' bench, upper gallery with drop shutters, and fine brickwork detailing. Contemporary brick boundary wall.

Brentford Canal Toll House and Gauging Lock
🏃 Access off High Street, Brentford, TW8 8EE
🕐 Sat/Sun 10am–5pm. Last entry 4.15pm.
🚇 Brentford
🚌 195,235,237,267,E2,E8
Single-storey canal toll house (1911) where tolls were collected for passing through the lock. Grand Junction Canal connected the Thames at Brentford to the Industrial Midlands in 1794 at the height of the industrial revolution.

Chiswick House
🏃 Burlington Lane, W4 2RP
🕐 Sat/Sun 10am–5pm + Tour at 11am, 12pm, 2.30pm (max 20). Last entry 4.30pm. **B·P·R·T**
🚇 Turnham Green, Chiswick
🚌 190,272,E3
One of the earliest and finest examples of Neo-Palladian design in the UK, Chiswick House is an 18C villa in West London. The 65 acres of Grade I-listed gardens are the birthplace of the English Landscape Movement. Lord Burlington, William Kent, 1727

Gunnersbury Park & Museum
🏃 Popes Lane, W5 4NH
🕐 Sun 10am–4pm + Gardens tour at 11am, 1.30pm (max 25, 90 mins, appropriate footwear) · House Tour at 11am, 1.30pm (max 25, 90 mins). Last entry 3.15pm. **D·B·A·R·P·T·O**
❗ Pre-book only: visitgunnersbury.org
🚇 Acton Town, Kew Bridge
🚌 E3
Former residence of the Rothschild family, now a local history museum in a beautifully restored 19C mansion. Set on an elevated terrace overlooking 186 acres of parkland with historical outbuildings dating from the 18C, ponds and a lake. Alexander : Sedgley, 1802

Osterley Park House
🏃 Jersey Road, Isleworth, TW7 4RD
🕐 Sat/Sun 12pm–4pm (Principal floor rooms, stair access only). Last entry 3.00pm. **B·P·R·T**
🚇 Osterley, Isleworth
🚌 H28,H91
Osterley Park and House is one of the last surviving country estates in London. Late 18C redesign by Robert Adam for the Child family. It was a party palace for entertaining friends and clients, fashioned for show. Robert Adam, 1761

Spring Grove House (West Thames College)
🏃 London Road, Isleworth, TW7 4HS
🕐 Sat 10am–4pm (max 100, ground floor rooms only) + Guided tour, every 45 mins (max 20). Last entry 3.15pm. **F·D·P·R·T**
🚇 Osterley, Isleworth
🚌 E8,117,H37,235,237
Example of late Victorian architecture and interior design, including stained glass windows and mosaics. Grade II-listed. Previous owners include Pears 'Soap' family and Sir Joseph Banks. Restored and refurbished 2011–12. Sir John Offley, 1754

St Mary's Convent
- 🚶 10 The Butts, Brentford, TW8 8BQ
- 🕐 Sat Tour at 10am, 12pm, 3pm (max 8, Duration 1.5 hours; includes historical talk). **P·T**
- ❗ Pre-book only: 020 8568 7305
- 🚇 Boston Manor, Brentford
- 🚌 195,235,237,267,E2,E8

Convent in 18C Grade II-listed house, c1764–92, with original features including fine decorative plasterwork. Various additions including west wing (1913–15), and harmonious care home facilities and chapel by PRP Architects (1998–2001).

Walks & Tours

A Ruskinian Walk Through Shared Heritage
- 🚶 Meet: Building 3, Chiswick Business Park, 566 Chiswick High Road, W4 5YA
- 🕐 Sat 12pm/Sun 2pm (Meet at Building 3, Chiswick Park Business Estate, 566 Chiswick High Road, W4 5YA. The walk lasts approx. 2 hours, with a comfort stop en route.) **R·T**
- 🚇 Chiswick Park, Gunnersbury
- 🚌 70,237,267,391,440

Ruskinian walk from RIBA award-winning Chiswick Business Park, Gunnersbury Triangle Nature Reserve through South Acton Estate, birthplace of artist Patrick Caulfield; Woodlands Park Ice House; to home of Wm Willett, of Daylight Saving Time. Stanley Slight, Acton Borough Engineer, 1951

Bedford Park
- 🚶 Meet: St Michael and All Angels Church, Bath Road, W4 1TT
- 🕐 Sun 2.30pm.
- 🚇 Turnham Green
- 🚌 94,272,E3

Bedford Park is known as the first garden suburb. Buildings by R Norman Shaw, EJ May, Maurice B Adams, and CFA Voysey. Some 400 houses, in Queen Anne Revival style. A landmark in suburban planning.

Hounslow Open House Guided Cycle Tour
- 🚶 Meet: Brentford Market Place, Brentford, TW8 8AH
- 🕐 Sun 12.45pm (max 20). **P·T**
- ❗ Pre-book only: rides@hounslowcycling.org (please indicate the number of riders attending the tour. Any queries call 07968 486482).
- 🚇 Brentford
- 🚌 195,235,237,267,E2,E8

Guided architectural bike tour led by local Hounslow Cycle Campaign (HCC) group around Open House buildings in West London.

The Changing Face of Brentford
- 🚶 Meet: outside Verdict Bakery in old Magistrates Court, Market Square, Brentford, TW8 4EQ
- 🕐 Sun 11am (linear walk along pavements, paths and riverside walkways).
- 🚇 Brentford
- 🚌 237,195,235,E2,267,E8

The walk starts in the Medieval market place, proceeds through 17C development and 18C housing then explores 19/20C industrial legacy and striking new 21C Thames-side regeneration schemes. Assael Architecture, 2018

Unseen Isleworth – Exploring this Thames-side village
- 🚶 Meet: Outside Isleworth Public Hall, South Street, Isleworth, TW7 7BG
- 🕐 Sat 10.30am.
- 🚇 Isleworth
- 🚌 110,267,H37

Unseen Isleworth – a guided walking tour to discover a recently opened part of the Thames Path while contrasting a variety of working class cottages with grander 18/19C properties one of which was home to the artist Vincent Van Gogh. Manning Clamp & Partners, 1976

• Spring Grove House (West Thames College) 2012

Richmond upon Thames

LONDON BOROUGH OF
RICHMOND UPON THAMES

Social Capital

Completed in 1895, Manor Grove, a street of modest Victorian terraced housing was the first council housing in London. It was built through the efforts of Richmond's 'People's Champion', William Thompson.

Bethlehem Chapel
🏃 Church terrace, London, TW10 6SE
🕐 Sat 10am–5pm (max 20) + ½ hourly tour.
 Last entry 4.15pm. **T·R·O**
🚉 Richmond

An independent Calvinistic chapel on the east side of Church Terrace in Richmond, London. Built in 1797, the small one-storey stuccoed building is Grade II*-listed. It still has its original galleried interior with pews and pulpit. A Huntington Chapel, 1797

Bushy House
🏃 National Physical Laboratory,
 Queens Road, Teddington, TW11 0EB
🕐 Sun 10am–5pm (downstairs only).
 Last entry 4.30pm. **T**
🚉 Teddington
🚌 X26,R68,33,281,285

Original house was built for Edward Proger. From 1797 the residence of William, Duke of Clarence (later William IV) and his mistress Dora Jordan. Now part of the National Physical Laboratory (NPL). William Samwell, 1663

Clifton Lodge and the Violet Needham Chapel
🏃 Clifton Lodge, St Margaret's Drive, Twickenham, TW1 1QN
🕐 Sat/Sun 1pm–5pm + Student-led tours, hourly (max 15) + Sat Dance Performance at 2.30, 4pm. Last entry 4.15pm. **R·F·D·T·P**
🕐 Pre-book only: (Special events only) rambertschool.org.uk
🚉 Richmond, St Margaret's
🚌 H37

Clifton Lodge is the last remaining original feature of St Margarets House. Originally an orangery, it is now the home of Rambert School of Ballet and Contemporary Dance. The Violet Needham Chapel houses two further dance studios. *rambertschool.org.uk*

Garrick's Temple to Shakespeare, Hampton
🏃 Garrick's Lawn, Hampton Court Road, Hampton, TW12 2EN
🕐 Sun 1pm–5pm (max 50) + Talk by volunteer guides, hourly (1pm–4pm, max 15, on the hour.). Last entry 4.45pm. **D·R·T·O**
🚉 Hampton, Hampton Court, Kingston
🚌 111,216,R68

Grade I-listed Georgian garden building. Tribute to Shakespeare built in the Ionic style by actor David Garrick. Arcadian Thames-side setting in restored 18C gardens thought to be by Capability Brown.

Grove Gardens Chapel
🏃 Richmond Cemetery, Grove Gardens, Lower Grove Road, TW10 6HP
🕐 Sun 1pm–5pm. Last entry 4.45pm. **T**
🚉 Richmond, North Sheen
🚌 371

A small, charming Gothic Revival cemetery chapel made from Kentish ragstone, with plate tracery and a mosaic alterpiece. It was deconsecrated and then restored for community use. Thomas Hardy was apprenticed to the architect. Sir Arthur Blomfield, 1873

Ham House and Garden
🏃 Ham Street, Ham, TW10 7RS
🕐 Sat 12pm–4pm (Gardens, shop and café open 10am–5pm). Last entry 3.30pm. **B·R·T·Q**
🚉 Kingston, Richmond
🚌 371,65

Built in 1610, Ham House was greatly extended in the 1670s. One of a series of grand houses and palaces built along the Thames, and one of the best examples of a 17C home in England. Fine interiors and historic gardens.

Kew House
🏃 10 Cambridge Road, Kew, TW9 3JB
🕐 Sat 10am–5pm (max 30). Last entry 4.30pm. **R·T**
🚉 Kew Gardens, Kew Bridge
🚌 391,65

A playful family home set around a courtyard and formed from two gabled Corten steel buildings. Part of Open House and evolving every year since 2014. Piercy & Company, 2014

Kilmorey Mausoleum
🏃 275 St Margaret's Road (opposite Ailsa Tavern), TW1 1NJ
🕐 Sun 1pm–5pm (max 5). Last entry 4.45pm.
🚉 Richmond, St Margaret's
🚌 H37

Egyptian-style, pink and grey mausoleum created for the second Earl of Kilmorey. The form relates to the shrines at the heart of Egyptian Temples. HE Kendall, 1854

Langdon Down Centre
🚶 2a Langdon Park, Teddington, TW11 9PS
🕐 Sun 12pm–5pm + Tour at 1.30pm, 3.30pm (max 15) +
Children's trail · Talk at 12.30pm/2.30pm.
Last entry 4.15pm. **F·D·B·P·R·T·O**
🚉 Hampton Wick
🚌 281
Grade II*-listed Normansfield Theatre and Langdon
Down Museum of Learning Disability. Gothic proscenium
arch and elaborate stage and scenery. Built as part of
the Normansfield Hospital for patients/students with
learning disabilities. Rowland Plumbe, 1877

Lépine Residence
🚶 23 Halford Rd, TW10 6AW
🕐 Sat 10am–5pm (max 20). Last entry 4.15pm. **A**
🚉 Richmond
Transformation confronting restrictions of the original
property. It is optimised for daylight penetration and
spatial flow with fully integrated structural elements
allowing uninterrupted surfaces and continuous spaces.
Chris Lépine, 2018

Orleans House Gallery
🚶 Riverside, Twickenham, TW1 3DJ
🕐 Sun 10am–5pm (max 60) + Heritage tour at 11.30am,
2.30pm (max 30). Last entry 4.30pm. **D·T·P·B·O**
❗ Pre-book only: (Tours) orleanshousegallery.org/
whats-on
🚉 St Margaret's, Twickenham
🚌 33,490,H22,R68,R70
Louis Philippe, Duc d'Orleans, lived here between
1815–17. Gibbs' baroque Octagon Room and adjoining
gallery/19C stable block are the remaining parts of
Orleans House. The Octagon Room was restored in 2018.
James Gibbs, 1720

Parish Church of St Anne
🚶 Kew Green, TW9 3AA
🕐 Sat 10am–4pm + Tour at 10.30am, 11.30am (max 30) +
A talk by Sue Mason FLS at 2pm (max 30). Last entry
3.45pm. **P·R·T·O**
🚉 Kew Gardens, Kew Bridge
🚌 65,391
Grade II*-listed, originally built as a chapel under the
patronage of Queen Anne in 1714 and subsequently
enlarged. Many notable memorials including to
scientist William Jackson Hooker and tombs of Thomas
Gainsborough and Johan Zoffany. 1714

Pope's Grotto (at Radnor House School)
🚶 Radnor House School, Pope's Villa, Cross Deep, TW1
4QG
🕐 Sat 10am–12.30pm (max 30, access to Grotto and
school café/terrace only). Last entry 12.00pm. **B·R·T**
❗ Pre-book only: ticketsource.co.uk/popesgrotto
🚉 Twickenham, Strawberry Hill
🚌 281,33,R68,R70,H22,267
Grotto with mineral decoration is last remaining part
of Alexander Pope's villa built 1720. The villa was
demolished 1808 and replaced and redeveloped many
times in following years but Pope's Grotto remains.
William Kent, Alexander Pope, 1720

Richmond and Hillcroft Adult Community College
🚶 Parkshot, Richmond, TW9 2RE
🕐 Sat 10am–4pm + Hourly tour (11am–3pm). Last entry
3.15pm. **D·R·T·O**
🚉 Richmond
A centre of excellence for adults, providing learning,
training and personal development. As a beacon for
adult learning, this project facilitates an accessible,
effective teaching environment that is substantially
more sustainable. Morris+Company, 2015

Richmond, the American International University in London
🚶 Richmond Hill Campus, Queen's Road, TW10 6JP
🕐 Sat 1pm–5pm/Sun 10am–1pm (max 20, regular
student-led tours). Last entry Sat 4.00pm | Sun
12.00pm. **T·P**
🚉 Richmond
🚌 371
An impressive neo-Gothic building set in 5 acres.
Originally home of the Wesley Theological Institution
and now Richmond University, built of Bath stone with
façade largely unchanged. Grounds contain many rare
specimens of plants and trees. Andrew Trimen, 1843

Royal Botanic Gardens, Kew: School of Horticulture
🚶 Access through the Jodrell Laboratory Gate, large
wooden gate on Kew Road just south of Mortake
Road; TW9 3AE
🕐 Sat 10am–4pm/Sun 10am–4pm (max 100).
Last entry 3.30pm.
🚉 Kew Gardens, Kew Bridge
🚌 65,391
Enjoy an exciting glimpse into the past life of the
building formerly known as the Reference Museum and
currently hosting the renewed School of Horticulture,
with Kew researchers bringing the museum back to life
through historic artefacts. Decimus Burton, 1847

Royal School of Needlework

🚶 East Front Gardens, Hampton Court Palace, KT8 9AU

🕐 Sat/Sun 10am–4.30pm + Tour at 11am, 1pm, 3pm
(max 20). Last entry 4.00pm. **X · B · T**

🚇 Hampton Court

🚌 216,411,R68,111

Baroque palace built for King William III and Mary II.
The original Tudor towers and chimneys were replaced by
grand and elegant exteriors that dominate the buildings
today. Sir Christopher Wren, 1689. *royal-needlework.org.uk*

Sir Richard Burton's Mausoleum

🚶 St Mary Magdalen's RC Church, 61 North Worple Way,
Mortlake, SW14 8PR

🕐 Sun 1pm–5pm. Last entry 4.45pm. **O**

🚇 Mortlake

🚌 209,33,337,493,485

Grade II*-listed mausoleum in the form of an Arab tent
with ripples in the stone imitating canvas. Interior is
embellished with oriental lamps, devotional paintings
and camel bells. Isabel Arundell Burton, 1890

St Leonards Court Air Raid Shelter, East Sheen

🚶 Palmers Road, East Sheen, SW14 7NG

🕐 Sun 1pm–5pm (max 15) + Volunteer-led tour, every 10
mins. Last entry 4.45pm. **Q**

🚇 Mortlake

🚌 337,493,33

The Air Raid Shelter is a hidden historic gem in
Mortlake. This World War II shelter was built in 1938
for the the residents of St Leonards Court. It has day
and night rooms, with some of the original details
remarkably well preserved.

Strawberry Hill House

🚶 268 Waldegrave Road, Twickenham, TW1 4ST

🕐 Sun 4.30pm–6.30pm (max 20) + Tour 4.30pm. Last
entry 5.30pm. **T · R · B**

❗ Pre-book only: strawberryhillhouse.digitickets.
co.uk/category/13844

🚇 Strawberry Hill, Twickenham

🚌 33,R68

Influential early Gothic Revival building restored to its
dramatic original glory, recreating Walpole's original
intention for his own home. Horace Walpole, 1749

• Strawberry Hill House © Justin Coe Photography 2018

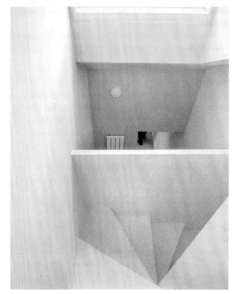

• Lépine Residence

The Boat and the Pavilion
🚶 11 Orchard Road, St Margarets, TW1 1LX
🕐 Sat 10am–5pm (Ground floor, extension and garden only). Last entry 4.15pm. **A**
🚇 Richmond, St.Margaret's (Greater London)
🚌 H37
Ground floor rear extension for a family of sailors. The open-plan layout is defined by curved, floating walls (the boat) and a sculpted ceiling (the pavilion), playfully combining compressed and expanded spaces. Unagru, 2016

The Boathouse Design Studio
🚶 27 Ferry Road, Teddington, TW11 9NN
🕐 Sat/Sun 10am–1pm (max 18). Last entry 12.45pm. **D·R·T**
🚇 Teddington
🚌 R68,281,285
Originally built to house the Royal Barge in 1862 and then used for boat building for three generations, the Boathouse is now office space for the creative industries.

The National Archives
🚶 Ruskin Avenue, Kew, Surrey, TW9 4DU
🕐 Sat 10am–5pm + Behind the scenes at 1pm, 11am, 2pm, 3pm (max 15). Last entry 4.15pm. **B·P·R·T·O**
❗ Pre-book only: (Tours) eventbrite.co.uk/e/open-house-london-tickets-62582588206
🚇 Kew Gardens, Kew Bridge
🚌 65,391,R68
South West London's hidden Brutalist masterpiece. McMaster/Clavering/Miller/O'Reilly, 1977

The Old Town Hall, Richmond
🚶 Whittaker Avenue, TW9 1TP
🕐 Sat 9.30am–5pm + tours led by the Local Studies team, hourly (10am–2pm, tours start from the War Memorial on Whittaker Avenue). Last entry 4.45pm. **T·O**
🚇 Richmond
Red brick and Bath stone grand 'Elizabethan Renaissance' style building altered by war, political changes and reflecting Richmond's history. Overlooking the war memorial and the Thames. WJ Ancell, 1893

Turner's House in Twickenham
🚶 Sandycombe Lodge, 40 Sandycoombe Road, TW1 2LR
🕐 Sat/Sun 10am–1pm (max 12). Last entry 12.30pm. **T**
❗ Pre-book only: turnershouse.org/booking
🚇 St.Margaret's
🚌 490,33,H37,R70,R68,H22
Sandycombe Lodge was built in 1813 to the designs of England's great landscape painter, JMW Turner; working here as his own architect to create a quiet retreat for himself, away from the pressures of the London art world. JMW Turner, 1813

York House
🚶 Richmond Road, TW1 3AA
🕐 Sun 1pm–4pm. Last entry 3.15pm. **T**
🚇 Twickenham
490,33,H22,R68,R70
Mid-17C house, a Scheduled Ancient Monument, with fine staircase and 18C additions.

Walks & Tours

Hampton Court Palace: Apartment 6
🚶 Meet: East Front, Hampton Court Palace, East Molesey, KT8 9AU
🕐 Sat/Sun Tour of Apartment 6, every 10 mins (10.30am–4.30pm). **D·B**
🚇 Hampton Court
🚌 111,216,411,R68
An opportunity to visit Apartment 6 at Hampton Court Palace, a former Grace & Favour apartment, then exhibition area and now an event space called the Albemarle Suite. Henry Wise and others, Daniel Marot, 1690

Camden

Social Capital

In 1977, the Ham & High newspaper, writing about Camden Council's recently completed Branch Hill Estate reported: "These are the most expensive council houses in England, to their defenders an act of political faith, to critics socialism gone mad."

2 Willow Road
🚶 Hampstead, NW3 1TH
🕐 Sat/Sun 11am–5pm (max 15, entry via timed tickets available on day. Every 20 mins). Last entry 4.15pm. **X**
🚇 Hampstead, Hampstead Heath
🚌 24,46,168,268,C11
Goldfinger's unique Modernist home, largely in original condition. Designed for flexibility, efficient use of space and good day-lighting. Complete with fittings and furniture designed by Goldfinger and an impressive modern art collection. Ernö Goldfinger, 1939

20 Triton Street, Regent's Place Estate
🚶 Regent's Place, NW1 3BF
🕐 Sat/Sun 10am–5pm (Lobby and reception areas only). Last entry 4.15pm. **T·D**
🚇 Great Portland Street, Warren Street
🚌 453,30,88,18,27,205
Ten-storey office complex housing a community theatre and event space. The accessible part of the building is the atrium, where artwork by Gary Webb is displayed. Terry Farrell and Partners, 2009

39-47 Gordon Square (Birkbeck School of Arts)
🚶 43 Gordon Square, WC1H 0PD
🕐 Sat/Sun ½ hourly tour (10am–5pm, max 20). **T**
🚇 Euston Square, Euston
🚌 168,59,68,91
Georgian terrace, centre of the Bloomsbury Group activities. Grade II-listed. Includes radical interior intervention at basement and ground floor levels. RIBA Award Winner 2008. Thomas Cubitt, 1830

• SPPARC Architecture Studio

8 Stoneleigh Terrace
🚶 N19 5TY
🕐 Sat/Sun Hourly tour (2pm–4pm, max 25). **T**
🚇 Archway
🚌 4,C11
Built during the golden era of Camden public housing by an architect who studied with Ernö Goldfinger and worked with Denys Lasdun. Peter Tábori, Camden Architect's Department, 1972

8a Belsize Court Garages
🚶 NW3 5AJ
🕐 Sat/Sun 10am–1pm (max 10) + How this came to be (max 10). Last entry 12.30pm. **T·A**
🚇 Belsize Park, Hampstead Heath
🚌 168,268,46
Originally a late 19C coachman's living quarters and stable, this mews house combines an award-winning architect's studio and spacious light-filled maisonette after a two-phase carbon-reducing retrofit. Sanya Polescuk Architects, 2012

Acland Burghley School
🚶 93 Burghley Road, NW5 1UJ
🕐 Sat 10am–5pm. Last entry 4.15pm. **T**
🚇 Tufnell Park, Kentish Town West
🚌 4,134,390
An important example of 1960s comprehensive school design in the Brutalist style. Acland Burghley has recently celebrated its 50th anniversary and a Grade II listing. Howell, Killick, Partridge & Amis Architects, 1966

Aga Khan Centre
🚶 10 Handyside Street, N1C 4DN
🕐 Sat Guided Tour of Building & Gardens, hourly (11am–4pm, max 60). Garden access weather permitting) + Exhibition by Bahia Shaheb (max 15). **T·R·B·O·Q**
🚇 King's Cross St. Pancras
🚌 476,259,214,205,91,73,63,46,30,17,390
Designed by Pritzker prize-winning architect Fumihiko Maki, houses the UK institutions of the Aga Khan Development Network. A unique feature are its six gardens inspired by different regions of the Muslim world. Fumihiko Maki of Maki and Associates, 2018

Alexandra Road Estate
🚶 Rowley Way, NW8 0SN
🕐 Sat 10am–5pm (Self-guided visits) + Guided Tours, ½ hourly / Sun 10am–1pm (Self-guided visits). Last entry Sat 4.15pm | Sun 12.15pm. R·T
🚇 Kilburn Park, South Hampstead
🚌 31,189,139
The estate is among the most ambitious social housing schemes of its time and was listed Grade II* in 1993. Open House visits to the estate will focus on recent community initiatives to restore and reuse various areas for local benefit. Neave Brown, 1978

BT Tower
🚶 45 Maple Street, W1T 4BG
🕐 Sat/Sun 9.30am–6.30pm. Public ballot only (max 100, access to floor 34 revolving floor). Last entry 5.45pm. D·R·T
❗ Pre-book only: openhouselondon.open-city.org.uk/ ballots/9/entries/new/ballots/9/entries/new
🚇 Warren Street, Great Portland Street
🚌 453,88,29,73,18,24
An enduring, distinctive feature of the London skyline for the last 54 years, visit the famous revolving floor, 158m above the capital. GR Yeats, Eric Bedford, Min of Public Buildings & Works, 1965

Burgh House
🚶 New End Square, Hampstead, NW3 1LT
🕐 Sun 10am–5pm. Last entry 4.15pm. B·R·T·O
🚇 Hampstead, Hampstead Heath
🚌 46,268
Grade I-listed Queen Anne house retaining original panelling and staircase with a café, modern gallery and museum, set in a small Gertrude Jekyll terrace garden.

Camden Mews (aka Max Fordham House)
🚶 6 Camden Mews, NW1 9DA
🕐 Sat 10am–5pm. Last entry 4.15pm. D·A
🚇 Camden Town, Camden Road
🚌 46,274,253,29
Conceived for renowned physicist and engineer Max Fordham, this all-electric house is designed to be tested without any heating due to the Passive House approach, novel insulated shutters and heat pump technology. Winner of two RIBA Awards. Bere Architects, 2018

Cecil Sharp House
🚶 2 Regent's Park Road, NW1 7AY
🕐 Sat/Sun 1pm–5pm. Last entry 4.00pm. D·R·T·O
🚇 Camden Town
🚌 274,29,253,168
Purpose-built to house the English Folk Dance and Song Society, this Grade II-listed building was designed by members of the Art Workers Guild of the time. Bomb-damaged in 1940, rebuilt and reopened in 1950. Iconic Ivon Hitchins mural. Stillman and Eastwick-Field, 1930

Coal Drops Yard
🚶 King's Cross, N1C 4DQ
🕐 Sat 10am–5pm + Architect-led tour , hourly (12pm–4pm, max 30). Last entry 4.15pm. T·D·A
🚇 King's Cross St. Pancras
🚌 214,46,390
Gain insight into the complex design behind King's Cross' reimagined Victorian industrial buildings, and learn how Victorian craftsmanship together with complex engineering led to a sculptural 'kissing point' between the buildings. Heatherwick Studio, 2018

Congress House
🚶 Great Russell Street, WC1B 3LS
🕐 Sun Hourly tour (11am–4pm, max 20, ground and lower ground floor public space. A small exhibition). T·D
❗ Pre-book only: hbilton@tuc.org.uk
🚇 Tottenham Court Road
🚌 24,8,38,73,390,14
Congress House epitomises lightness and perfectionism. The free-flowing space on the ground and lower ground floors can be seen through the large windows showcasing Jacob Epstein's Pieta. David du Rieu Aberdeen, 1948

Conway Hall
🚶 25 Red Lion Square, WC1R 4RL
🕐 Sat/Sun 10am–5pm + hourly tour. Last entry 4.15pm.
🚇 Holborn
🚌 98,19,38,8,55
The home of the Conway Hall Ethical Society, a long-standing organisation renowned as a hub for free speech and progressive thought. Grade II-listed building with both Arts and Crafts and Art Deco features adding to its distinctive style. Frederick Herbert Mansford, 1929

Dartmouth Park House
🚶 25 Dartmouth Park Hill, NW5 1HP
🕐 Sun 12pm–5pm (max 25, Ground floor only). Last entry 4.45pm. A
🚇 Tufnell Park
🚌 4
This 17m-wide house extension creates a new dining room with oak framed sliding doors. A separate glazed evening room allows uninterrupted garden views. An outdoor kitchen is provided between these two spaces, with new landscaping. Architecture for London, 2019

École Jeannine Manuel
🚶 43–45 Bedford Square, WC1B 3DN
🕐 Sat 10.30am–4.30pm. Last entry 4.00pm. T
🚇 Tottenham Court Road
🚌 390,73,29,24,14
Once home to Bloomsbury hostess Lady Ottoline Morrell, and Prime Minister HH Asquith. Now a bilingual school, the houses are a blend of Georgian elegance and contemporary functionality. Robert Palmer, 1770

Eleventh Church of Christ, Scientist, London
🚶 11 St Chad's Street, WC1H 8BG
🕐 Sat 10am–5pm/Sun 1pm–5pm (max 100) + Volunteer-led tours (10.30am–4.30pm) + Sat Lecture by architect at 1pm. Last entry 4.15pm. **D·A·B·T·O**
🚇 King's Cross St. Pancras
🚌 18,205,30,390,17,63
New home for Eleventh Church of Christ, Scientist, London with 60-seat auditorium, reading room, bookshop, Sunday school, offices and supporting spaces by converting and expanding an existing dilapidated building in a conservation area. Benedetti Architects, 2015. *eleventhlondon.com*

Fenton House
🚶 Hampstead Grove, NW3 6SP
🕐 Sat/Sun 11am–5pm. Last entry 4.30pm. **T**
🚇 Hampstead, Hampstead Heath
🚌 46,210,268
Beautiful town house retaining many original features and housing important decorative arts collections. Surrounded by a walled garden. William Eades, 1686

Freemasons' Hall
🚶 60 Great Queen Street, WC2B 5AZ
🕐 Sat/Sun 10am–5pm + Art Deco Tour, every 90 mins (11am–4pm) + Make and take Lego for children. Last entry 4.30pm. **R·F·T·B·O**
🚇 Covent Garden, Holborn
🚌 1,59,68,91,168,188
Monumental Art Deco exterior belying elaborate and varied interior decoration: extensive use of mosaic, stained glass, decorated ceilings and lighting. Ashley and Newman, 1927. *ugle.org.uk/freemasons-hall/*

Garden Court Chambers
🚶 57–60 Lincoln's Inn Fields, WC2A 3LJ
🕐 Sat 10am–5pm/Sun 10am–1pm (max 25, entry exhibition only, full access via guided tours) + Barrister-led tours, hourly + Exhibition. Last entry Sat 4pm | Sun 12.45pm. **D·T·Q**
🚇 Holborn
🚌 1,59,68,91,168,188,243
Inigo Jones' design at No. 59–60 copied by No. 57–58, with portico and elliptical staircase added by Soane. Refurbished by current occupiers, a barristers' chambers. Retains original features, staircases, fireplaces, and mouldings. Inigo Jones, 1640

Hampstead Friends Meeting House
🚶 120 Heath Street, Hampstead, NW3 1DR
🕐 Sun 1pm–5pm (max 50, no access downstairs). Last entry 4.30pm. **R·T·O**
🚇 Hampstead
🚌 210,268,46
Listed Arts and Crafts freestyle building with plain interior and many charming original features, sympathetically modernised in 1991. Entrance via listed gateway. Frederick Rowntree, 1907

• Freemasons Hall

Hampstead Synagogue
🚶 Dennington Park Road, West Hampstead, NW6 1AX
🕐 Sun Talk and Tour, hourly (2pm–4pm, max 50). **T·D**
❗ Pre-book only: 020 7435 1518
🚇 West Hampstead Thameslink, West Hampstead
🚌 C11,139,328
Opened in 1892 with an eclectic French Gothic/Romanesque style. Enlarged in 1901. Features stained glass windows by Solomon, Sochachewsky and Hillman. Extensively restored in 2008. Delissa Joseph, 1892

Haverstock School
🚶 24 Haverstock Hill, Chalk Farm, NW3 2BQ
🕐 Sat Tour, hourly (11am–3pm, max 20). **T·R**
🚇 Chalk Farm, Kentish Town West
🚌 393,168
Located in the heart of Camden on a site that has been occupied by schools for more than 145 years. This seven-form entry school for 1,275 students opened in 2006 funded through a PFI contract. Feilden Clegg Bradley 2006

Highgate Literary & Scientific Institution
🚶 11 South Grove, N6 6BS
🕐 Sun 1pm–5pm (max 15, ground floor and first floor only) + Tour ½ hourly. Last entry 4.15pm. **D·T**
🚇 Highgate, Archway
🚌 214,210,271,143
Fine stuccoed building overlooking Pond Square, and home to Institution since 1840. Formed from 1790 coach house, stables and yard, with final additions c1880. R Parkinson remodelled, 1840

Isokon Building (Lawn Road Flats)
🚶 Lawn Road, NW3 2XD
🕐 Sat/Sun 11am–4pm (max 10, Selected flats only, plus Isokon Gallery). Last entry 3.30pm. **B·T·O·Q**
🚇 Belsize Park, Hampstead Heath
🚌 46,C11,168,24
Grade I-listed residential block of flats in Hampstead, designed by the Canadian Modernist architect Wells Coates for clients Jack and Molly Pritchard. English Heritage blue plaque for the Bauhaus masters Gropius, Breuer and Moholy-Nagy. Wells Coates, 1934

Keats House

🏃 Keats Grove, NW3 2RR

🕐 Sat/Sun 11am–5pm (max 100) + Volunteer-led tour every 90 mins (max 25) + Family workshop (max 25, drop-in). Last entry 4.30pm. **F·B·T**

🚇 Hampstead, Hampstead Heath

🚌 24,46,168,268,C11

This early 19C, Grade I-listed Regency villa was the home of Romantic poet John Keats from December 1818 to September 1820. Join us during the Keats200 bicentenary to discover how this special place inspired his greatest works. William Woods, 1814

Kenwood

🏃 Hampstead Lane, NW3 7JR

🕐 Sat/Sun 10am–5pm + 350th Anniversary of the death of Rembrandt van Rijn. Last entry 4.15pm. **D·B·P·R·T·O**

🚇 Golders Green, Hampstead Heath

🚌 210

A striking Neoclassical villa in tranquil gardens, boasting breath-taking interiors and a world-class art collection, with paintings by Rembrandt, Vermeer, Van Dyck, Gainsborough, Reynolds and Turner. George Saunders, Robert and James Adam, 1764

Lauderdale House

🏃 Highgate Hill, Waterlow Park, N6 5HG

🕐 Sun 11am–5pm (max 100) + Tours at 11.30am, 2.30pm (max 15) + Family activities: Dressing-up, Colouring in (max 25, Drop-in). Last entry 4.30pm. **F·D·R·T·O**

❗ Pre-book only: (Tours) lauderdalehouse.org.uk

🚇 Archway

🚌 143,210,214,271,W5

Grade II*-listed building in Waterlow Park dating to 1582 and recently refurbished. Original Tudor wooden framework adapted by successive owners over the centuries. Today the house runs primarily as an arts, heritage and education centre. Haines Phillips Architects, 2016

Leaning Yucca House

🏃 27a Cantelowes Rd, NW1 9XR

🕐 Sat 10am–5pm (max 5, downstairs only). Last entry 4.00pm. **A**

🚇 Caledonian Road, Camden Road

🚌 390,274

An elegant extension and re-invention of a Victorian semi-detached home in North West London, establishing a stronger connection with the garden through its cedar-clad extension and openings. DF_DC architects, 2018

London School of Hygiene & Tropical Medicine

🏃 Keppel Street, WC1E 7HT

🕐 Sat/Sun 10am–4pm (max 20) + Hourly tour 40 mins. Last entry 3.15pm. **D·T·O**

🚇 Russell Square, Euston

🚌 14,24,29,73,390

Beautiful Grade II-listed Art Deco building with highly decorated façade, period library, north courtyard extension and new south courtyard building. P Morley Horder & Verner O Rees, 1929

Lumen United Reformed Church and Café

🏃 88 Tavistock Place, WC1H 9RS

🕐 Sat 10am–5pm (max 20, Limited access to 1820s crypt with accompanied tours of that part of the building only. ½ hourly tour. Last entry 4.45pm. **D·T·O**

🚇 King's Cross St. Pancras, Russell Square

🚌 17,46,205,30,73,390

A remodelled shell of a 1960s church building, which itself includes the crypt of an 1820s church hit by a V2 missile in 1945. Includes a café, two dramatic 8m high windows and a distinctive conical reflective space. RIBA Award Winner 2009. Theis + Khan, 2007

Mount Pleasant

🏃 52-54 Mount Pleasant, WC1X 0AL

🕐 Sat/Sun Tours led by Council staff and Peter Barber Architects, hourly (10.30am-3.30pm, max 8). **A·T**

🚇 Chancery Lane, King's Cross St. Pancras

🚌 46,17,243,55,19,38

A former Victorian workhouse that has been transformed through LB Camden's Community Investment Programme into a state of the art facility for 50 homeless people laid out around a beautiful suntrap courtyard. Peter Barber Architects, 2014

Old Hampstead Town Hall

🏃 Wac Arts, 213 Haverstock Hill, NW3 4QP

🕐 Sat/Sun 10am–4pm (max 120) + Town Hall tour, every 120 mins (11am-3pm, max 20, No step free access to air raid shelters.) + Change makers; (max 100). Last entry 3.15pm. **T·D**

❗ Pre-book only: (Tours) wacarts.co.uk

🚇 Belsize Park, Hampstead Heath

🚌 46,168,C11

The Old Hampstead Town Hall is a restored Grade II-listed building of three architectural styles: Victorian Italianate (1877), Edwardian (1910) and a striking 20C extension. The grounds contain air raid shelters used during WWII. HE Kendall and Frederick Mew, 1877

Paul McAneary Architects

🏃 6 Flitcroft Street, WC2H 8DJ

🕐 Sat/Sun 11am–6.30pm (max 100). Last entry Sat 6.15pm. **T**

🚇 Tottenham Court Road, Leicester Square

🚌 19,24,29,176,38

Two-storey studio with expressive use of space, houses a drawing atelier & laboratory with design details that underscore the practice's 'warm minimalist' approach. A curated exhibition space also showcases the practice's latest projects. Paul McAneary Architects, 2015

Phoenix Gardens Community Building

🏃 21 Stacey Street, WC2H 8DG

🕐 Sat/Sun 10am–5pm (max 200) + Architect + Gardener-led tour at 3pm, 12pm. Last entry 4.15pm. **D·A·T**

🚇 Tottenham Court Road, Leicester Square

🚌 29,24,14,19,38

The first purpose-built new-build community centre to be built in the heart of Soho for generations, located within the renowned Phoenix Gardens. Office Sian Architecture + Design, 2016

Pushkin House

🏃 5a Bloomsbury Square, WC1A 2TA

🕐 Sat/Sun 10am–5pm (max 20). Last entry 4.15pm. **T·B·O**

🚇 Holborn

🚌 1,8,19,38

A centre of Russian culture in London, this Grade II*-listed house has a fine staircase which has been meticulously restored. Henry Flitcroft, 1744

Regent High School

🏃 Chalton Street, entrance opposite Cranleigh Street, NW1 1RX

🕐 Sat 10am–3pm + Architect-led tour at 11am (max 20) · Staff-led tour of building, every 45 mins (max 20) + I-spy trail for children. Last entry 2.15pm. **F·D·A·T**

🚇 Mornington Crescent, Euston

🚌 46,214,168,253

Five-time award-winning new build and refurbishment. Featuring a triple-storey 'arcade' that links to the existing Victorian building, simplifies movement around the school and provides passive supervision. Walters & Cohen Architects, 2014

Royal College of General Practitioners

🏃 30 Euston Square, NW1 2FB

🕐 Sat/Sun Architect-led tour at 11am (max 16) · Tour, hourly (11am-4pm, max 16). **R·T·O**

❗ Pre-book only: openhouse@rcgp.org.uk

🚇 Euston, King's Cross

🚌 18,30,73,205

Grade II*-listed building. Recently restored to showcase magnificent Edwardian faience tile work, mosaic floor and other historic features in transformed modern surroundings that now provide the new headquarters of the RCGP. Arthur Beresford Pite, 1908

Royal College of Physicians

🏃 11 St Andrew's Place, Regents Park, NW1 4LE

🕐 Sat 10am–5pm + Hourly tour (max 20) + Jayne Wilton artist workshop (max 20, Check website for start time) · Architecture talk at 3pm (max 100). Last entry 4.45pm. **F·D·R·B·T·O**

❗ Pre-book only:

🚇 Warren Street, Great Portland Street

🚌 18,27,30,88,205,453

One of London's most important post-war Grade I-listed buildings. Dramatic interior spaces and white mosaic exterior elevated on piloti and distinct Modernist lines. Sir Denys Lasdun, 1964

SPPARC

🏃 10 Bayley Street, Bedford Square, WC1B 3HB

🕐 Sat/Sun 10am–5pm (max 50) + Lecture at 3pm (max 30). Last entry 4.30pm. **A·R·T**

🚇 Goodge Street, Tottenham Court Road

🚌 14,24,29,390,73,8,55,98,19,38

This award-winning practice has an exciting UK & International portfolio & invites you to take part in live debates, explore its workshops, listen to talks & become part of the design process. SPPARC ARCHITECTURE, 2014

spparcstudio.com

Sir John Soane's Museum, No.14

🏃 14 Lincoln's Inn Fields, WC2A 3BP

🕐 Sat/Sun 10am–4pm (max 40, Separate access to main museum). Last entry Sat/Sun 3.15pm. **X·T·Q**

🚇 Holborn

🚌 8,243,188,168,91,68,59,1

Special access to no. 14 Lincoln's Inn Fields, let out in his lifetime as a private house. A rare and beautiful example of the architect's late work with a number of fine interiors. Sir John Soane, 1824

St George's Bloomsbury

🏃 Bloomsbury Way, WC1A 2SA

🕐 Sat 10am–5pm / Sun 1pm–5pm. Last entry 4.15pm. **D·T·O**

🚇 Tottenham Court Road, Holborn

🚌 8,19,38,55

One of the twelve new churches designed and paid for under the 1711 Act of Parliament for building fifty new churches, and the sixth and final London Church designed by Hawksmoor. Nicholas Hawksmoor, 1720

St Pancras Chambers and Clock Tower

🏃 The Forecourt, St Pancras Station, Euston Road, NW1 2AR

🕐 Sat/Sun Tours of hotel and apartments, every 20 mins (10am-4pm). **T**

❗ Pre-book only: openhousewaxchandlers2019.eventbrite.co.uk

🚇 King's Cross St. Pancras

Former Midland Grand Hotel, now St Pancras Renaissance Hotel and Chambers apartments. Includes hotel lobby and clock tower. George Gilbert Scott, 1868

St Pancras Church & Crypt

🚶 Euston Road/Upper Woburn Place NW1, NW1 2BA
🕐 Sat 10am–5pm/Sun 1pm–5pm (max 100) + Tours, hourly (max 20). Last entry 4.30pm. **T·R·O**
🚇 Euston
🚌 390,253,205,18,30,73,91,59,68,168

Unique Greek-style parish church. Grade-I listed inspired by the ionic temple of the Erectheum on the Acropolis. A notable feature are the Caryatids guarding the entrances to the crypt. William Inwood & son, 1822

Swiss Cottage Library

🚶 88 Avenue Road, NW3 3HA
🕐 Sat 10am–5pm. Last entry 4.15pm. **B·R·T·O**
🚇 Swiss Cottage, South Hampstead
🚌 31,13,268,187,46

Grade II-listed building by renowned Modernist which has been refurbished and remodelled while protecting the building's landmark status. Basil Spence, 1963

The Art Workers' Guild

🚶 6 Queen Square, WC1N 3AT
🕐 Sun 11am–5pm (max 50, Ground floor and basement only) + Table Top Museum. Last entry 4.15pm. **D·T·R**
🚇 Russell Square, Holborn
🚌 59,68,91,168,188

1713 terraced house with 1914 hall at rear. Notable renovated Arts and Crafts interior. Newly refurbished glass vaulted courtyard. Portraits of Guild Masters since 1884.

The Brunswick Centre

🚶 The Brunswick, WC1N 1BS
🕐 Sat/Sun 10am–5pm. Last entry 4.15pm. **T·R·P·D·O**
🚇 Russell Square
🚌 168,91,68,59

The Brunswick Centre is a Grade II-listed residential and shopping centre in Bloomsbury, located between Brunswick Square and Russell Square. Patrick Hodgkinson, 1972

The Building Centre and NLA

🚶 26 Store Street, WC1E 7BT
🕐 Sat 10am–5pm + Family Workshop at 11am (New London Model Talk at 12pm (max 30, 30 min talk) / Sun 10am–5pm. Last entry 4.15pm. **R·F·D·B·T·O**
🚇 Goodge Street
🚌 14,24,29,73,390,19,38,55

The Building Centre is a not-for-profit organisation which educates the construction industry and those it serves. NLA is an independent forum for discussion, debate and information about architecture, planning and development in London. Messrs. Tapperell & Haase, 1914

The Coal Office

🚶 1 Bagley Walk, King's Cross, N1C 4PQ
🕐 Sat/Sun 10am–5pm (max 20) + Architect-led tour at 11am, 1pm, 3pm (max 8). Last entry 4.15pm. **T·R·D·B·A·O·Q**
🚇 King's Cross St. Pancras

Built in 1851, David Morley Architects' carefully focused interventions have enhanced and retained the buildings' strong historical character. The scheme incorporates retail showrooms, restaurant and Headquarters for Tom Dixon. David Morley Architects, 2016

The Layered Gallery

🚶 29 Percy St, London, W1T 2DA
🕐 Sat 11am–5pm (max 15). Last entry 4.15pm. **A**
🚇 Goodge Street, Tottenham Court Road
🚌 390,73,29,24,14

The private gallery for an art collector provides a space to view and sort parts of the collection prior to hanging in the rest of the house. Conceived as part of the garden landscape, the extension is built of Cor Ten steel and glass. Gianni Botsford Architects, 2016

The Penn Club

🚶 21 Bedford Place, WC1B 5JJ
🕐 Sat Hourly tour (11am-4pm, max 10). **T·R**
❗ Pre-book only: eventbrite.co.uk/e/open-house-tours-2019-tickets-60759922564
🚇 Russel Square
🚌 168,68,59,188,91,14

Club occupies three interlinking houses in a Georgian terrace built in the 1800s retaining some of its original features. James Burton, 1805

The Perimeter

🚶 20 Brownlow Mews, London, WC1N 2LE
🕐 Sun Architect-led tour, hourly (11am-4pm, max 8, Break for Lunch (1pm-2pm)).
❗ Pre-book only: open-house-the-perimeter-2019.eventbrite.co.uk
🚇 Russell Square, Chancery Lane
🚌 243,55,19,38,17,46

An interlocking set of gallery spaces and archive across 5 floors of an old 3-storey 19C warehouse in a mews street in Bloomsbury. Its dark brick concealing a newly luminous interior carved out inside. 6a Architects, 2017

The Poetry Society

🚶 22 Betterton Street, WC2H 9BX
🕐 Sat 11am–5pm (max 30, access to The Poetry Café, downstairs performance and exhibition space only). Last entry 4.15pm. **D·T·R·O**
🚇 Holborn, Covent Garden
🚌 8,1

A 19C tenement building with a history relating to both Victorian Covent Garden market trading and 1960s counterculture. Now the home of The Poetry Society. Mills Power, 2017

The Swedenborg Society

🕴 20-21 Bloomsbury Way, WC1A 2TH

🕒 Sat 10am–5pm (Bookshop, Swedenborg Hall, Gardiner Room, David Wynter Room and Light Well). Last entry Sat 4.45pm. **T·D·B·O**

🚇 Tottenham Court Road, St.Pancras

🚌 8,19,38,55

Grade II-listed Georgian domestic building c1760, formerly part of Bedford Estate. Interior refurbished 1924-5 to form lecture hall (restored 2014), library, bookshop and offices. Oak woodwork and green Doulton tiles line the staircase.

The Wiener Library

🕴 29 Russell Square, WC1B 5DP

🕒 Sun 1pm–5pm (max 40) + Tour , ½ hourly (max 15). Last entry 4.15pm. **D·B·T·O**

🚇 Russell Square

🚌 59,68,168,188

Sensitive yet bold refurbishment of historic Grade II-listed townhouse for The Wiener Library including dramatic first floor reading room, mezzanine and ground floor exhibition spaces. Barbara Weiss Architects, 2011

Torriano Primary School STEM Lab

🕴 Torriano Avenue, NW5 2SJ

🕒 Sat 1pm–5pm (max 15, STEM Lab space only). Last entry 4.45pm. **A**

🚇 Kentish Town, Camden Road

🚌 29,253,390,393

Remodelling of a two-storey turret atop an existing Victorian school building to provide a science lab for dynamic hands-on experiments, including a CNC-cut internal timber structure, a shiny shingled rooftop extension and a living façade. Hayhurst and Co., 2018

UCL Pathology Museum

🕴 2nd Floor, Medical School, Royal Free Campus, Rowland Hill Street, NW3 2PF

🕒 Sat/Sun 10am–5pm (max 60) + Curator's Tour at 2pm (max 20). Last entry 4.15pm. **D·T·O**

❗ Pre-book only: ucl.ac.uk/event-ticketing/booking?ev=18016

🚇 Belsize Park, Hampstead Heath

🚌 C11,268,168,46,24

Set inside the Royal Free Hospital in Hampstead, UCL Pathology Museum is London's newest medical museum. The displays consist of some 2,000 human medical specimens relating to the study of disease and the history of medicine. lucienneroberts+, 2018

Victorian Waterpoint

🕴 St Pancras Cruising Club, Camley Street, N1C 4PN

🕒 Sat/Sun 10am–5pm. Last entry 4.45pm. **R·T·O**

🚇 King's Cross St. Pancras

🚌 390,46,214

At around 9m x 6m and 3-storeys high, the top floor originally contained a vast 70 cubic metre capacity cast iron water tank. This tank now forms an impressive viewing gallery; the exterior has ornate brickwork and elaborate detailing. Sir George Gilbert Scott, 1872

Willing House (Heatherwick Studio)

🕴 356–364 Gray's Inn Road, King's Cross, WC1X 8BH

🕒 Sat 10am–5pm (max 70). Last entry 4.30pm. **T·D·A**

🚇 St.Pancras, King's Cross St. Pancras

🚌 476,390,259,205,91,73,63,46,30,17

Opening to the public for the first time, Willing House is home to internationally renowned designers Heatherwick Studio, and houses 25 years of the studio's unique models, collections and artefacts. Heatherwick Studio, 2009

Zayed Centre for Research into Rare Disease in Children

🕴 20 Guilford Street, WC1N 1DZ

🕒 Sat 9.30am–11.45am (max 30) + Tour every 45 mins (max 10). Last entry 11.00am. **T·D·A**

❗ Pre-book only: eventbrite.co.uk/e/open-house-zayed-centre-for-research-into-rare-disease-in-children-tickets-61779895330?ref=estw

🚇 Russell Square

🚌 59,91,68

The Zayed Centre for Research into Rare Disease in Children will be a world-leading centre of excellence that will tackle some of the most challenging scientific questions in rare disease research. Stanton Williams, 2019

Walks & Tours

Camden Highline

🕴 Meet:, Camden Gardens, Camden Street, NW1 9PT

🕒 Sat/Sun Tour every 90 mins (9.30am-3.30pm, max 25).

❗ Pre-book only: openhousecamdenhighline.eventbrite.com

🚇 Camden Town, Camden Road

Join Head of Project, Adam Richards for a tour of the proposed Camden Highline park connecting Camden Town to King's Cross. Edwin Henry Horne, 1870
camdenhighline.com

Kings Cross Masterplan

🕴 Meet: King's Cross Visitor Centre, 11 Stable Street, N1C 4AB

🕒 Sat 1.30pm/Sun 11.30am (max 30). **D·O**

❗ Pre-booking only: press@alliesandmorrison.com

🚇 King's Cross St. Pancras

🚌 30,17,46,214,390

The King's Cross Masterplan established a framework for the incremental redevelopment of this industrial heritage site through a mix of uses and a network of public spaces structuring new urban blocks and knitting the site into its context. Porphyrios Associates, Allies and Morrison, 2007

City of London

CITY of LONDON

Social Capital

Only around 500 residents remained in the City in 1950, a mere 50 of whom lived in Cripplegate – the eventual site of the Barbican Estate.

1 Finsbury Circus
🏃 EC2M 7EB
🕐 Sat/Sun 10am–1pm (max 20). Last entry 12.30pm.
   X·D·T·Q
🚇 Liverpool Street, Moorgate
🚌 43,76,100,141
Grade II-listed building that has been comprehensively redeveloped to provide a high-quality contemporary interior, with a fully glazed spectacular atrium roof to maximise daylight and aspect. Sir Edwin Lutyens, 1925

10 Exchange Square
🏃 EC2A 2BR
🕐 Sat/Sun 10am–5pm. Last entry 4.15pm.
🚇 Moorgate
🚌 47,42,35,26,11,8
A relatively new addition to the Broadgate family, 10 Exchange Square, designed by Skidmore, Owings and Merrill, was completed in 2004. Owings & Merrill, Skidmore, 2004

100 Victoria Embankment - Unilever House
🏃 100 Victoria Embankment, EC4Y 0DY
🕐 Sat 11am–5pm (max 200, Atrium only, no access to floors or roof terrace). Last entry 4.15pm. **T**
🚇 Blackfriars
🚌 4,40,63
Landmark curved Grade II-listed building which has been transformed to give it a new lease of life. RIBA Award Winner 2009. James Lomax Simpson, 1930

199 Bishopsgate
🏃 EC2M 3TY
🕐 Sat/Sun 10am–5pm (Reception only). Last entry 4.15pm.
🚇 Shoreditch High Street, Liverpool Street
🚌 47,42,35,26,11,8
This 12-storey office building was completely refurbished in 2012. Skidmore Owings & Merrill, 1989

8-10 Moorgate
🏃 EC2R 6DA
🕐 Sat 10am–5pm (max 75, access to 7th Floor and roof terraces) + ING UK Art Collection Tour at 11am, 2pm (max 25). Last entry 4.15pm. **T**
🚇 Bank, Moorgate
🚌 21,43,141

Dutch bank ING moved its UK office to this special building in 2016. The building blends a historic exterior (including its original Portland stone façade) with a modern 135,220 sq ft of office space. City Heritage Award winner 2015. Allies and Morrison, 2016

Aldgate Square
🏃 Aldgate High Street, EC3N 1AF
🕐 Sat/Sun 7am–11pm + Exhibition at 12pm. Last entry 10.45pm. **R·D·O**
🚇 Aldgate, Fenchurch Street
At this new square's centre is a pavilion with an asymmetrical steel structure and sliding glass walls set between three triangular support points. Over time, the roof will oxidise and eventually turn orange and brown. Gillespies, Make Architects, 2018

Apothecaries' Hall
🏃 Black Friars Lane, EC4V 6EJ
🕐 Sun 10am–3pm. Last entry 2.15pm. **D·T·Q**
🚇 Blackfriars, St. Paul's
🚌 4,11,15,26,63,76,40
A courtyard building with some of the best-preserved 17C livery hall interiors. Built on the site of the Blackfriars Priory and replacing the original hall burned down in 1666. Courtyard refurbished in 2017. Thomas Locke, 1672

Barbican Centre
🏃 Silk Street, EC2Y 8DS
🕐 Sun 10am–11pm (Public areas only) + Hourly tour (11.30am-4.30pm, max 20). Contact Box Office for full details.) + British Sign Language Tour at 11am (max 20). Last entry 10.15pm. **P·B·R·T·Q**
❗ Pre-book only: barbican.org.uk/whats-on/tours-public-spaces (Special events and tours only)
🚇 Barbican, Moorgate
🚌 100,4,56,153
A Grade II-listed building, the Barbican is Europe's largest multi-arts and conference venue and one of London's best examples of Brutalist architecture. Chamberlin Powell & Bon, 1963

Bells and Belfries at St Botolph Aldgate

🧍 St Botolph's Church, Aldgate High Street, EC3N 1AB
🕐 Sun 12pm–5pm + talk about bellringing followed by demonstration, ½ hourly (1pm-4pm, max 20, no tour at 14.30). Last entry 4.30pm. **R·T·O**
🚇 Aldgate, Fenchurch Street
🚌 15,25,42,78,100,135,205,242,343
Opportunity to hear a description and watch a demonstration of bell ringing (on Sunday only). Church built by architect of Mansion House and contains London's oldest organ. George Dance the Elder, 1744

Bevis Marks Synagogue

🧍 Bevis Marks, EC3A 7LH
🕐 Sun 10am–2pm (max 100) + ½ hourly tour + lecture and Q&A by the synagogue general manager at 10.15am (max 100). Last entry 1.45pm. **D·B·T**
🚇 Liverpool Street, Aldgate
🚌 42,78,100,135,205
One of the best-preserved houses of worship of its period still in use and oldest synagogue in Britain. Contains one of the finest collections of Cromwellian and Queen Anne furniture in the country. Joseph Avis, 1701

Billingsgate Roman House and Baths

🧍 101 Lower Thames Street, EC3R 6DL
🕐 Sat/Sun 11am–4pm. Last entry 3.30pm. **T·Q**
🚇 Monument, Cannon Street
🚌 15,35,43,47,48,133,141,344
Some of London's best Roman remains and the only accessible Roman house, comprising late 2C house with a 3C bath house built within its courtyard. First discovered in 1848.

Bishopsgate Institute

🧍 230 Bishopsgate, EC2M 4QH
🕐 Sat 10am–5pm + ½ hourly tour (10am-4pm, No access to the Boardroom suite). Last entry 4.15pm. **R·T·O**
🚇 Liverpool Street
This beautifully restored historic Grade II*-listed building combines elements of Arts and Crafts/Art Nouveau/Victorian architecture. Charles Harrison Townsend, 1894

Bloomberg European Headquarters

🧍 3 Queen Victoria Street, EC4N 4TQ
🕐 Sat Tour 10–5pm/Sun Tour 10am–1pm, every 15 mins (max 25, by public ballot ONLY). **D·A·T·R**
❗ Pre-book only: openhouselondon.open-city.org.uk/ballots/10/entries/new
🚇 Mansion House, Cannon Street
🚌 25,15,26,17
Bloomberg's European headquarters is the world's most sustainable office building. Home to the financial technology and information company's 4,000 London-based employees, its unique design promotes collaboration and innovation. Foster + Partners, 2017

Butchers' Hall

🧍 87 Bartholomew Close, EC1A 7EB
🕐 Sat 10am–4pm. Last entry 3.15pm. **T·R·D**
🚇 St. Paul's, Barbican
🚌 4,8,25,56
The sixth Butchers Hall and second on this site (1883 to present) following considerable damage from Zepplins in 1915 and bomb damage twice during WWII. First opportunity to view the newly refurbished Hall, which reopens in September 2019. DMFK, 2019

Carpenters' Hall

🧍 1 Throgmorton Avenue, EC2N 2JJ
🕐 Sat 10am–4pm (Function Rooms). Last entry 3.30pm. **D·T**
🚇 Moorgate, Liverpool Street
🚌 43,11,76,100,8,21,26,133,388
Livery Hall first built in 1429, much altered then demolished and rebuilt in 1880, destroyed in 1941 except for external walls (WW Pocock). Designed as a showpiece for the craft of carpentry, the third Hall on the site. Herbert Austen Hall, Clifford Wearden, William Wilmer Pocock, 1956

City Information Centre

🧍 St Paul's Churchyard, EC4M 8BX
🕐 Sat 9.30am–5.30pm + Architect-led tours, ½ hourly (10am–12pm, max 20) / Sun 10am–4pm. Last entry Sat 5.15pm | Sun 3.45pm. **D·B·O**
🚇 Mansion House, Blackfriars, St. Paul's
🚌 11,15,26,17,76
London's main tourist information centre is clad in a specially manufactured system of 220 pre-finished stainless steel panels. This subtly reflective surface provides a striking counterpoint to St Paul's. RIBA Award Winner 2009. Make Architects, 2007

City of London Police Museum

🧍 5 Aldermanbury, EC2V 7HH
🕐 Sat 10am–4pm + short talks will be running throughout the day. Last entry 3.30pm. **T·O**
🚇 Bank, Moorgate
🚌 8,100,133,21,76
Includes the 1911 architectural model of the buildings where the Houndsditch Murders took place. Made out of wood, designed and produced by a City of London Police Officer for the Old Bailey trial of the suspected murderers. Sir Giles Scott, Son + Partners, 1974

Clothworkers' Hall

🧍 Dunster Court, Mincing Lane, EC3R 7AH
🕐 Sat 10am–5pm (Principal ceremonial rooms only). Last entry 4.15pm. **D·T·Q**
🚇 Tower Hill, Fenchurch Street
🚌 15,25
Built in 1958 and refurbished in 1985–86 in styles evoking the history of English classical architecture from Wren to the present. Sumptuous interiors include a stunning new Chris Ofili designed tapestry, made by Dovecot Studios. Herbert Austen Hall, 1958. *clothworkers.co.uk*

• Exchange House

Custom House
🚶 20 Lower Thames Street, EC3R 6EE
🕐 Sat/Sun 9.30am–4pm + Displays, Historical Talk, Childrens Quiz. Last entry 3.30pm. **T**
🚇 Tower Hill, Fenchurch Street
🚌 15
Iconic elegant late-Georgian building partly rebuilt by Smirke after subsidence. The 58m Neoclassical Long Room was the central reporting point for all London Customs business in the 19C. Sir Robert Smirke, 1813

Cutlers' Hall
🚶 4 Warwick Lane, EC4M 7BR
🕐 Sat 11am–5pm (max 120). Last entry Sat 4.15pm. **T·D·B·Q**
🚇 City Thameslink, St. Paul's
🚌 8,25,56
On the former site of the Royal College of Physicians, now home to The Worshipful Company of Cutlers. The façade is decorated with a terracotta frieze depicting the processes of knife-making by the sculptor Benjamin Creswick. T Tayler-Smith, 1888

Dr Johnson's House
🚶 17 Gough Square, EC4A 3DE
🕐 Sat/Sun 10am–5pm. Last entry 4.15pm. **B·T·Q**
🚇 City Thameslink, Chancery Lane
🚌 15,26,76,341,63
Fine example of an early four-floor Queen Anne town house with original panelling, open staircase and famous 'swinging panels' on the open-plan first floor. Johnson compiled his famous 'Dictionary of the English Language' (1755) here. Richard Gough, 1698

Exchange House
🚶 EC2A 2BQ
🕐 Sat/Sun 10am–5pm. Last entry Sat/Sun 4.15pm.
🚇 Shoreditch High Street, Liverpool Street
🚌 47,42,35,26,11,8
Exchange House is a 10-storey building sitting above 18 busy railway lines. Owings & Merrill, Skidmore, 1990

Fishmongers' Hall
🚶 London Bridge, EC4R 9EL
🕐 Sat Tour every 90 mins (9am–2pm, max 30). **T**
🕐 Pre-book only: fishmongers-company.eventbrite.com
🚇 Monument, London Bridge
🚌 17,43,21,149
Fishmongers' Hall is a rare example of a Greek Revival building. Designed by the architect Henry Roberts, a student of Sir Robert Smirke, the Hall's classical simplicity is contrasted by the magnificence of its interior rooms. Henry Roberts, 1834

Golden Lane Estate
🚶 Fann Street, EC1Y 0RD
🕐 Sat/Sun 10am–5pm (Access to Community Centre and guided tours around the Estate. NB There will be access to the roof garden on Sunday) + Hourly tour (11am–4pm, pre-book only) + ½ hourly tour (10am–4pm, tours of the Estate plus half hourly tours of the Roof Garden at Great Arthur House. Pre-book only). Last entry 4.15pm. **T·R**
❗ Pre-book only: (Tours) goldenlaneestate.org
🚇 Barbican, Old Street
🚌 153,56,4,243,55
Golden Lane is one of Britain's most important post war housing developments – Grade II and II* listed. The Estate includes a tower block with a roof garden, community centre and allotments. Chamberlin Powell & Bon, 1957

Gresham College – Barnard's Inn Hall
🚶 Barnard's Inn Hall, Holborn, EC1N 2HH
🕐 Sat 10am–5pm. Last entry 4.15pm. **T·O**
🚇 Chancery Lane, Farringdon
🚌 8,17,46
Barnard's Inn dates back to the mid 13C. The hall contains three wooden bays dating from 15C with later linenfold wood panelling added in 1525. It was the Mercers' School and today is home to Gresham College (free lectures for all).

Guildhall Galleries
🚇 St. Paul's, Moorgate, Bank
🚌 8,25,43,76,100

Guildhall
🚶 Gresham Street, EC2V 7HH
🕐 Sat/Sun 10am–5pm + ½ hourly tour. Last entry 4.30pm. **D·T·O**
The City's seat of municipal government since 12C. Grade I-listed, rare example of Medieval civic architecture with post-war extensions and rebuilding. John Croxton, 1440

Guildhall Art Gallery
🚶 Guildhall Yard, EC2V 5AE
🕐 Sat/Sun 10am–5pm + Gallery Tours, ½ hourly. Last entry 4.45pm. **D·B·T·O**

• Golden Lane Estate © Steve Lavers

Houses the City of London's art collection, built over remains of London's 2C Roman amphitheatre. Façade uses Portland stone and Collyweston stone slates. Interior uses finishes of marble, American elm, damask and painted wall coverings. Richard Gilbert Scott, 1999

Guildhall Library
🏃 Aldermanbury, EC2V 7HH
🕐 Sat Library Tour at 11am, 1pm, 3pm. **D·B·T·O**
Purpose-built over five floors to house printed books and manuscripts. Features include former pneumatic tube ticket delivery system and 56 listed translucent pyramid roof lights. Sir Giles Scott, Son + Partners, 1974

Guildhall Yard
🏃 EC2V 7HH
🕐 Sat/Sun 10am–5pm. Last entry 4.15pm. **D·T·O**
Grade I-listed Medieval civic architecture, located above 2C Roman amphitheatre. The amphitheatre is accessible through Guildhall Art Gallery and the outline of the arena is outlined by a black oval on the Yard floor. George Dance the Younger, 1789

King's College London, The Maughan Library
🏃 Chancery Lane, WC2A 1LR
🕐 Sat/Sun 1.30pm–5pm. Last entry 4.30pm. **T**
🚇 Chancery Lane, Temple
🚌 11,15,26,341,76
London's first fireproof building, built to house records of the Court of Chancery. Now renovated to house a fine university library. J Pennethorne and Sir John Taylor, 1851

Leadenhall Market
🏃 Gracechurch Street, EC3V 1LT
🕐 Sat/Sun 10am–5pm. Tour every 120 mins (10.30am–4.30pm). Last entry 4.15pm. **T·R·F·D·O**
🚇 Monument, Liverpool Street
🚌 149,25,35,48,344
Iconic Victorian covered market. Today, more than 40 renowned retail brands and outstanding food and drink venues are set within the stunning market place. Sir Horace Jones, 1881

Leathersellers' Hall
🏃 7 St Helen's Place, Bishopsgate, EC3A 6AB
🕐 Sat Archivist tours, hourly (10am–4pm, max 25, no tour at 1pm.). **T**
❗ Pre-book only: enquiries@leathersellers.co.uk (Tours on Saturday)
🚇 Bank, Liverpool Street
🚌 35,47,48,149,344
New Livery Hall behind a retained early 20C façade. This is the 7th Hall in the Leathersellers' Company's history since its foundation in the Middle Ages. Eric Parry Architects, 2016

Lloyd's Register Group
🏃 71 Fenchurch Street, EC3M 4BS
🕐 Sat 10am–5pm (Access to Rogers building entrance and reception only; Collcutt building reception hall, Chairman's office, library and General Committee room) + From Coffee to Seaweed: Engineering a safer world since 1760 (max 50) · Costumed interpretation (max 30) · Children's Trail. Last entry 4.30pm. **F·T·O**
🚇 Aldgate, Fenchurch Street
🚌 25,15,35,47
Sumptuous building with many original decorative and architectural features. Sympathetically extended by Richard Rogers Partnership whose glass and steel structure soars above as a fine example of high-tech architecture. RIBA Award Winner. Thomas Collcutt, 1901
hec.lrfoundation.org.uk

Maggie's Barts
🏃 St Bartholomew's Hospital, EC1A 7BE
🕐 Sun 10am–5pm (max 100) + Architect-led tour, hourly (10.30am–4.30pm, max 15, pre-book only). Last entry 4.45pm. **D·A·T·R·O**
❗ Pre-book only: bartsfundraising@maggiescentres.org
🚇 St. Paul's, Farringdon
🚌 46,56
Maggie's Barts opened in December 2017. Maggie's Centres are unique, welcoming and uplifting places with qualified staff on hand to provide free practical, emotional and social support for people with cancer, their families and friends. Steven Holl, 2016

Mansion House
🏃 Walbrook, EC4N 8BH
🕐 Sat Hourly tour (9am–4pm). **T**
❗ Pre-book only: cityoflondon.gov.uk/openhouse (tours) Bank, Cannon Street
🚌 8,11,21,25,26,149,15
The official residence of the Lord Mayor of the City of London, retaining its 18C character, with superb plaster-work and wood carving. George Dance the Elder, 1739

Masonic Temple, Andaz Liverpool Street (former Great Eastern Hotel)

🚶 Entrance on Bishopsgate, EC2M 7QN

🕐 Sat/Sun 10am–5pm. Last entry 4.15pm. **T·Q**

🚇 Liverpool Street

🚌 8,11,26,35,42,47,48,78,100,133,149

Grade II-listed grand Victorian railway hotel refurbished with stylish contemporary interiors. Greek Masonic Temple with magnificent Grade I-listed interior of marble and mahogany, built 1912 at immense cost. Charles Barry, 1912

Museum of London

🚶 150 London Wall, EC2Y 5HN

🕐 Sat/Sun 10am–5.45pm + History and Architecture, ½ hourly (11am–4.30pm, max 30, 12:30 & 14:00 family tours) · Sun The Rotunda and Bone Store, every 120 mins (11am–3pm, max 20, Please note that this tour deals with skeletal human remains. Photography is prohibited.) Last entry 5.30pm. **F·B·R·T·O**

🚇 Barbican

🚌 4,8,25,56,76,100

Part of an ambitious redevelopment of the area following WWll bombing, this building forms part of the Barbican complex. The architects were inspired by post-war Modernism to include green design elements and raised walkways. Powell and Moya, 1976

New Museum of London, West Smithfield

🚶 Central Markets Charterhouse St London EC1A 9LY

🕐 Sat 1pm-5pm/Sun 10am-5pm. Last entry 4.45pm + half hourly tours. **D·A**

🚇 St. Paul's, Farringdon, Barbican

🚌 25,17

The Museum of London is creating a new museum in the derelict General Market and adjacent post-war Poultry Market. For the first time in 20 years we are inviting the public to explore these spaces in historic and creative Smithfield.

Painters' Hall

🚶 9 Little Trinity Lane, EC4V 2AD

🕐 Sat 10am-3pm (No access above 1st floor). Last entry 2.30pm. **D·T**

🚇 Cannon Street, Mansion House

🚌 17,8,4,11,15,25,26,76

Acquired in 1532 and rebuilt in 1670 after the Great Fire, the Hall was partially rebuilt in 1941 by enemy action and rebuilt in a Neo-Georgian style in 1960. The original charter, portraiture and stained glass are of particular interest. Harrington, 1961

Salters' Hall

🚶 4 London Wall Place, EC2Y 5DE

🕐 Sat Family Tour at 11.15am (max 30) · Tour every 15 mins (10.30am–4.30pm, max 20) + Conservator led talks in the Archive. **D·T·Q**

🚇 St. Paul's, Moorgate

🚌 100,21,43,141,76

A rare example of a Brutalist Livery Hall which underwent extensive refurbishment in 2016. New Pavilion, exhibition and archive space and garden. Sir Basil Spence, 1976

Smithfield Market

🚶 EC1A 9PQ

🕐 Sat 10am–4pm/Sun 10am–3pm (Access permitted to the buyers walks areas of all three market buildings, balcony Grand Avenue and the balcony in the Poultry Market). Last entry Sat 3.30pm | Sun 2.30pm. **T·P·D·O**

🚇 Farringdon, City Thameslink, St. Paul's

🚌 4,17,40,46,56,63,153

Smithfield Market comprises three buildings; two Victorian and one 1960s. All three buildings are Grade II*-listed. Smithfield is the only remaining wholesale market in the City of London and the site is operational Monday to Friday. TP Bennett Partnership, Ove Arup & Partners, Sir Horace Jones, 1868

St Botolph Building

🚶 138 Houndsditch, EC3A 7DH

🕐 Sat 10am–5pm (max 40, main receptions, lower ground lift lobbies, Level 13) + Hourly tour (max 40). Last entry 4.15pm. **D·A·R·T**

🚇 Aldgate, Liverpool Street

🚌 25,205,15,115,254

Grimshaw's design creates a highly adaptable commercial building for landlord DEKA Immoblien and agents CBRE. The St Botolph Building is a landmark building with a striking façade, stunning interior and large floor plates. Grimshaw Architects, 2010

St Giles' Church Cripplegate

🚶 Fore Street, Barbican, London, EC2Y 8DA

🕐 Sat/Sun 10am–5pm. Last entry 4.45pm. **D·O**

🚇 Moorgate, St. Paul's

Medieval church built on Norman and Saxon foundations by the Roman Wall.

St Vedast alias Foster

🚶 4 Foster Lane, EC2V 6HH

🕐 Sat/Sun 10am–5pm. Last entry 4.15pm. **R·T·O**

🚇 St. Paul's

🚌 100,76,56,25,11,8,4

12C church. During the Great Fire of 1666 the church building escaped total destruction, and was restored. Christopher Wren was eventually called in to rebuild St Vedast, completing the work in October 1673. Sir Christopher Wren, 1170

Stationers' Hall

🚶 Ave Maria Lane, EC4M 7DD

🕐 Sun 10am–5pm (max 400, Limited wheelchair access - please ask in advance) + tours, ½ hourly + Exhibition of Craft Bookbinding (max 60). Last entry 4.15pm. **B·R·T·O**

🚇 St. Paul's, Blackfriars

🚌 17,4,15,76,26,11

17C livery hall with courtroom and garden. Oak panelling and stained glass windows. Undamaged in WWII. Selected items from the archives on display. Access to the church of St Martin-within-Ludgate from 2pm onwards. Robert Mylne, 1673

The Broadgate Tower
- 🕴 4th Floor, 20 Primrose Street, EC2A 2EW
- 🕐 Sat/Sun 10am–5pm (max 30). Last entry 4.15pm. **D·A·T**
- ❗ Pre-book only: marina.miceli@som.com
- 🚇 Liverpool Street, Shoreditch High Street
- 🚌 8,26,48,149,388

An opportunity to gain insight into the workings of this globally renowned architecture, engineering and urban planning firm within a building they designed. SOM, 2008

The City Centre
- 🕴 City Centre, within Guildhall Complex (entrance at 80 Basinghall Street, leading from Gresham Street), EC2V 5AR
- 🕐 Sat/Sun 10am–5pm + Model talk with Q&A at 11am · Drop-in screen-printing workshop (1pm–3pm). Last entry 4.30pm. **D·T·O**
- 🚇 Bank, Moorgate
- 🚌 43,8,21,76,133,100

An overview of the latest developments and architecture in the City of London via the interactive 1:500 scale Pipers model that shows the future skyline with all of the proposed new towers. 2016

The City Churches

There are 42 churches within the City of London, the range of styles include Norman, pre-fire Medieval, Wren's masterpieces and modern reworkings. Three churches are listed here, full list available on Open House website.

St Helen's Bishopsgate
- 🕴 EC3A 6AT
- 🕐 Sat 10am–5pm/Sun 12.30pm–3.30pm + Historical building tour, every 45 mins (10.15am–4.15pm) + Church service at 10.30am · Church service at 4pm. Last entry Sat 4.30pm | Sun 3pm. **F·B·R·T·O**
- 🚇 Aldgate, Liverpool Street

One of the few City buildings to survive the Great Fire. Contains the best pre-Great Fire collection of monuments in any London parish church. Damaged by terrorist bombs in 1992, then extensively and controversially reordered in 1993.

St Michael Cornhill
- 🕴 St Michael's Cornhill, St Michael's Alley, EC3V 9DS
- 🕐 Sat 10am–2pm (max 20) / Sun 2pm–4pm (max 20). Last entry Sat 1.30pm | Sun 3.30pm. **T·O**
- 🚇 Bank, Liverpool Street
- 🚌 43,25,11,8

• The Priory Church of St Bartholemew the Great

A Christian church has occupied this sight for at least a thousand years. Destroyed in the Great Fire of 1666, but rebuilt in the 1670s. Known as a Wren church, the architect was Nicholas Young. Sir Christopher Wren's Office, 1670

The Priory Church of St Bartholomew the Great
- 🕴 Cloth Fair, EC1A 7JQ
- 🕐 Sat 10am–5pm (max 50, The Cloister will be closed for a function). Last entry Sat 4.15pm.
- 🚇 St. Paul's, Barbican
- 🚌 8,25,46,153,56,4

The oldest surviving church in the City of London founded in 1123. Originally part of an Augustinian Priory the church survived the Great Fire and the Blitz. 1123t

The Old Bailey (Central Criminal Court)
- 🕴 EC4M 7EH
- 🕐 Sat Hourly tour (9am–4pm, max 25, No tour at 1pm). **T·X·D**
- ❗ Pre-book only: cityoflondon.gov.uk/openhouse
- 🚇 St. Paul's, City Thameslink
- 🚌 8,25,56

The Edwardian baroque of Mountford's building has a base of Cornish granite with Portland stone facing above. Inside, the lower grand hall and Grand Hall are lined with rich marble and the arches are of white Ancaster stone. Edward Mountford, 1907

The Salvation Army International Headquarters
- 🕴 101 Queen Victoria Street, EC4V 4EH
- 🕐 Sat 10am–4.30pm. Last entry 4.15pm. **D·T·O**
- 🚇 St. Paul's, Blackfriars
- 🚌 76,4,11,15,17,26

A transparent and welcoming working environment with full-height glazing and feature steel columns. Brief was to create a space 'modern in design, frugal in operation and evangelical in purpose'. Sheppard Robson, 2004

Tower 42
🚶 25 Old Broad Street, EC2N 1HQ
🕐 Sun 10am–4pm (max 50, entry will be to the viewing platform on Level 42 only). Last entry 3pm. **D**
❗ Pre-book only: eventbrite.co.uk/e/open-house-2019-tower-42-tickets-60759688865
🚇 Liverpool Street, Bank

The City's original tallest skyscraper, consisting of 3 hexagonal chevrons, at 690ft Tower 42 was the first to break previous restrictions on tall buildings in London. Glass entrance added during a comprehensive refurbishment in 1995. Richard Seifert & Partners, 1981

Trinity House
🚶 Trinity Square, Tower Hill, EC3N 4DH
🕐 Sat 10am–1pm (max 150). Last entry 12.15pm. **D·T**
🚇 Tower Hill, Fenchurch Street
🚌 100,78,42,15,40,343

Fine late Georgian exterior with interior painstakingly reconstructed after destruction by incendiary bomb in 1940. Good fittings, statues and works of art from original building. Samuel Wyatt, 1796

Watermen's Hall
🚶 18 St Mary-at-Hill, EC3R 8EF
🕐 Sat 9am–2pm (max 35). Last entry 1.15pm. **X**
❗ Pre-book only: apply in writing to Assistant Clerk, Watermen's Hall, St Mary-at-Hill, London EC3R 8EF
🚇 London Bridge, Monument
🚌 15,35,47,48,344

Only remaining Georgian hall in the City of London, and perfect example of domestic architecture of the period. William Blackburn, 1780

Wax Chandlers' Hall
🚶 6 Gresham Street, EC2V 7AD
🕐 Sat Tour of principal rooms, ½ hourly (10am–4pm, max 24). **T**
❗ Pre-book only: openhousewaxchandlers2019.eventbrite.co.uk
🚇 St. Paul's
🚌 8,56,76,100,25

The sixth livery hall to be built on a site owned by the Company since 1501. The 1958 building stands on part of 1854 hall largely destroyed in WWII. East wall recently refaced. Completely refurbished and remodelled internally 2006–07. Charles Fowler, 1854

City of London Walks
🚶 Meet: in ambulatory of Guildhall West Wing, Guildhall Yard, EC2V 5AE
🕐 Tickets are allocated on a first-come first-serve basis from 9:30am in Guildhall Yard.
🚇 St. Paul's, Moorgate
🚌 4,8,15,21,25,43,133,141

All Change at Aldgate: The East of the City
🕐 Sat/Sun Hourly tour (10am–2pm, max 30).

Travel through the East of the City of London where your guide will introduce you to stories and tales of people and places. You'll see gems including Fredericks Place and travel through some hidden places towards your destination. 2018

Murder, Mystery & Medicine: Alleyways North
🕐 Sat/Sun Hourly tour (10.30am–2.30pm, max 30).

Walk with a City guide towards the North of the City of London. You'll journey towards Smithfield to hear stories of murder, mystery and medicine and see places including West Smithfield and St. Bartholomew the Great Church.

Up In The World! Highways and Byways of the City
🕐 Sat/Sun Hourly tour (10.45am–2.45pm, max 30).

Take a chance to look up in the City and walk through the Highwalks and byways of the Square Mile. See the Cripplegate area and walk towards Barbican Hall. We'll show you the Roman Wall and a church with a link to Shakespeare. 2018

Westward Ho! Courtyards & Passages in the City
🕐 Sat/Sun Hourly tour (10.15am–2.15pm, max 30).

Walk towards St. Bride's church with your guide around the West of the City. You'll go through some of the Courtyards and Passages that take you Westwards. See Stationer's Hall and learn why Christopher Wren was able to inspire a baker.

• The Old Bailey Central Criminal Court
© Corporation of London

Islington

Social Capital

Islington is home to Berthold Lubetkin's Priory Green Estate, considered seminal in its application of British Modernist ideas to public housing.

⚜ ISLINGTON

---

13 Alwyne Place
🚶 N1 2NL
🕐 Sat Architect-led tour , ½ hourly (10am–4.30pm, max 10, No tour at 1:30pm.). **A·T·Q**
❗ Pre-book only: eventbrite.co.uk/e/13-alwyne-place-open-house-2019-tickets-61226486068
🚇 Essex Road, Highbury & Islington
🚌 476,341,73,56,271,38
A new-build off-site manufactured courtyard home set within a unique site in Canonbury. The contemporary brick design creates an open-plan, day-lit house with stunning connections to the large garden. RIBA London Award 2019 winner. Marlo, Mitzman Architects, 2017
mitzmanarchitects.com

73 St Pauls Road
🚶 N1 2LT
🕐 Sat 10am–1pm (max 20). Last entry 12.15pm. **A**
🚇 Canonbury, Highbury & Islington
🚌 30
Refurbishment and extension of a 1970s Neo-Georgian terrace house. Stripped back to the outer walls and roof a dramatic new interior with a curved stair and triple hight space has been inserted. There is a terrazzo-clad rear extension. Gundry + Ducker , 2019

Alphabeta
🚶 14-18 Finsbury Square, EC2A 1BR
🕐 Sat/Sun 10am–5pm. Last entry 4.15pm. **X·D**
🚇 Moorgate, Liverpool Street
🚌 271,76,21,141,153,43,214
The refurbishment and extension of an historic office building to create a contemporary space geared towards progressive changes in workplace culture. Studio RHE Ltd., 2015

Ashmount Primary School
🚶 Crouch Hill Park, 83 Crouch Hill, N8 9EG
🕐 Sat/Sun Architect-led tour, hourly (10am–12pm, max 40, Includes rooftop view). **D·A·T**
🚇 Crouch Hill; or Finsbury Park then bus
🚌 W7
Carbon neutral building. BREEAM Award for Highest Scoring Project in the Education Sector. RIBA National Architecture Award 2015. Penoyre & Prasad, 2012

Bunhill Heat and Power Energy Centre
🚶 Central Street, EC1V 8AB
🕐 Sat Tour every 20 mins (10am–4.45pm, max 20).
🚇 Old Street, Barbican
🚌 243,56,55,4
A ground-breaking district heating scheme located in the south of the borough, and part of Islington Council's wider strategy to reduce fuel poverty and produce financial and environmental benefits for the community. Tim Ronalds Architects, 2012

Caledonian Park: Clock Tower Tours
🚶 Cally Clock Tower Centre, Market Road, N7 9PL
🕐 Sat/Sun Tour at 12.15pm, 2.30pm (max 12). **T·A·O**
❗ Pre-book only: eventbrite.co.uk/e/open-house-clock-tower-tours-tickets-62928230030
🚇 Caledonian Road, Caledonian Road & Barnsbury
🚌 274,390,17,91,259
Opened in 1855 as centrepiece of the Metropolitan Cattle Market. The clock tower offers magnificent views over London. The clock mechanism was made by John Moore of Clerkenwell. Renovated with help from the Heritage Fund. JB Bunning, 1850

City, University of London
🚶 St John Street, EC1V 4PB
🕐 Sat 10am–4pm + Hourly tours. Last entry 3.15pm. **D·R·T**
🚇 Angel
🚌 4,56,153
Grade II-listed building in the Arts and Crafts style. College building has been prominent in Islington life throughout its history, surviving bomb damage in WWII and major fire in 2002. 2019 marks the 125th anniversary of City. EW Mountford, 1896. *125-anniversary.city.ac.uk*

Cullinan Studio Office
🚶 5 Baldwin Terrace, N1 7RU
🕐 Sun 11am–3pm (Open access at canal level. Access to the rest of the building by regular guided tour only) + presentation (max 40 every half hour by the architect.) · Natural Design. Last entry 2.30pm. **D·A·T·R**
🚇 Old Street, Angel
🚌 271,205,73,141,341,19,4
Converted Victorian warehouse into BREEAM 'Excellent' office in 2012. An inserted steel frame works with the existing structure to provide a double-height mezzanine space with views onto the canal. Cullinan Studio, 2012

Estorick Collection of Modern Italian Art
🚶 39a Canonbury Square, N1 2AN
🕐 Sat 11am–6pm/Sun 12pm–5pm (max 100) + Tour at 12pm, 3pm (max 25). Last entry Sat 5.30pm | Sun 4.30pm. **D·T·B**
🚇 Essex Road, Highbury & Islington
🚌 341,73,56,38,43,30,19,4,271
The Estorick Collection is housed in a beautiful Georgian building previously known as Northampton Lodge. Today, the museum comprises six galleries over three floors, as well as a library, offices, a café and bookshop. Henry Leroux of Stoke Newington, 1807

Hafren Barge
🚶 The Moorings Fife Terrace, N1 9RA
🕐 Sat/Sun 11am–5pm (max 8). Last entry 4.45pm. **F**
🚇 King's Cross St. Pancras
🚌 17,91,259
Hafren barge is a residential houseboat on Regent's Canal. While the boat is modern, the interiors are antique or reclaimed. Rachel Allen, 2013

Hugo Road
🚶 1 Hugo Road, N19 5EU
🕐 Sat/Sun 10am–5pm (max 20, access to lower ground, ground floor and garden only). Last entry 4.30pm. **A**
🚇 Tufnell Park
🚌 390,134,4
A locally listed end-of-terrace family home that was fundamentally reworked through side, rear and loft extensions. Robert Rhodes Architecture + Interiors, 2017

Impact Hub King's Cross
🚶 34b York Way, N1 9AB
🕐 Sat 10am–5pm (max 20) + Social Enterprise Exhibition. Last entry 4.45pm. **D·T·R**
🚇 King's Cross St. Pancras
Collaborative workspace for social entrepreneurs housed within a Grade II-listed building. Featuring an original hipped roof structure and skylight, hanging glass meeting rooms and recycled wooden fittings. Architecture 00, 2008

• Hugo Road © Matt Clayton 2019

Ironmonger Row Baths
🚶 1 Norman Street, EC1V 3AA
🕐 Sat/Sun 10am–5pm (max 40). Last entry 4.15pm. **P·R·T·O**
🚇 Old Street
🚌 394,55,43,205,214,243
Grade II-listed building, refurbished from May 2010 to November 2012. Original features, Turkish baths, laundry, swimming pool. Historical details of 1931 bath, maps and photos in a purpose-built history room. AWS & KMB Cross, 1930

Islington Square
🚶 Esther Anne Place, N1
🕐 Sat/Sun 10am–4pm. Last entry 3.30pm. **A**
🚇 Angel
🚌 4,19,30,43
A new 170,000 sq ft landmark development housed in North London's former Postal Sorting Office. Tucked away behind a historic façade on Upper Street, in the heart of Islington. CZWG Architects, 2019

Islington Town Hall
🚶 Upper Street, N1 2UD
🕐 Sun tour at 10.30am (max 30).
❗ Pre-book: eventbrite.co.uk/e/islington-town-hall-art-deco-on-upper-street-tickets-63471045606
🚇 Highbury & Islington, Angel, Essex Road
🚌 4, 19, 30, 43
Grade II-listed. Original Art Deco style interiors, staircases and the impressive council chamber. Original clocks, paintings and decorative panels have survived for nearly a century in this lovely municipal building. ECP Monson, 1922

London Metropolitan Archives
🚶 40 Northampton Road, EC1R 0HB
🕐 Sat 10am–5.30pm (Access to first floor visitor lounge, public areas and cloakrooms) + Conservation studio, box making facility and strong room tour, hourly (max 20) · Sound studio tour, hourly (11am–4pm, max 20) + Underground London (Curator-led tours, 12 and 2pm). Last entry Sat 4.30pm. **T·O**
❗ Pre-book only: (Tours) open-house-2019-lma.eventbrite.co.uk
🚇 Angel, Farringdon
🚌 19,38,341,63,55,243,153
LMA's older building was built in the late 1930s for the Temple Press and has many original features. Purpose built extension in early 1990s for archival storage. Public rooms remodelled by Bisset Adams in 2000s. FW Troup, HR Steele, 1939

Marx Memorial Library
🚶 37a Clerkenwell Green, EC1R 0DU
🕐 Sat 10am–3pm. Last entry 2.15pm.
🚇 Farringdon
🚌 55,63,243
Grade II-listed, built as a Welsh Charity School in 1738. A library with a focus on Marxism and Socialism since 1933. Lenin worked here 1902–03 and his office is preserved. Fresco by Jack Hastings in 1st floor. Late 15C tunnels. Sir James Steere, 1738

Oak Room, New River Head
🚶 New River Head,, 173 Rosebery Avenue, EC1R 4UL
🕐 Sat/Sun Hourly tour (10am–4pm, max 15).
❗ Pre-book only: oakrooms2019.eventbrite.co.uk
🚇 Angel
🚌 19,38,153,341
Formerly boardroom of the 17C water house, the Oak Room is a fine late Renaissance room demonstrating the New River Company's wealth. 1697 carved oak interior, attributed to Grinling Gibbons, including overmantel and panels over the doors. 1696

Paxton Locher House
🚶 8-9 Clerkenwell Green, EC1R 0DE
🕐 Sat/Sun 10am–5pm (max 60). Last entry 4.45pm. T
🚇 Farringdon
🚌 63,153,55,243
A unique modern courtyard house making brilliant use of a restricted site. A retractable glass roof gives wonderful natural light and opens the house to the sky in dry weather. Paxton Locher Architects, 1995

Pollard Thomas Edwards (Diespeker Wharf)
🚶 38 Graham Street, N1 8JX
🕐 Sat 10am–5pm. Last entry Sat 4.15pm. T
🚇 Angel
🚌 394,205,43,214
Conversion of a canal-side Victorian warehouse, formerly a timberyard, into spacious offices, garden and glazed extension with one of the best waterside views in London.

The Bower
🚶 207–211 Old St, EC1V 9NR
🕐 Sat 10am–4pm (max 10) + Architect-led tours, ½ hourly. Last entry 3.15pm. T·D·A
🚇 Old Street
🚌 21,43,55,205,141
Extending AHMM's involvement in the regeneration of the Old Street area, The Bower reinvents a collection of underperforming buildings into a coherent mix of workspace, ground floor retail/restaurants and a new public realm. Allford Hall Monaghan Morris, 2016

The Charterhouse
🚶 Charterhouse Square, EC1M 6AN
🕐 Sat/Sun 11am–5pm (Access to the museum, Jacobean chapel and Tudor Great Chamber restored following the Blitz) + Family Tour hourly (11.30am–2.30pm, Suitable for age 5+ accompanied by an adult) + Drop-in architecture crafts for families at 11am · Tudor Great Chamber at 12pm). Last entry Sat/Sun 4.30pm. D·F·B·T·O
🚇 Barbican, Farringdon
🚌 4,56,153
Founded as a Black Death burial ground, the site has served as a Carthusian monastery, Tudor mansion, school and an almshouse, which it remains to this day. The Charterhouse opened to the public in 2017 with a new museum. Henry Yevele, 1371

Union Chapel
🚶 Compton Terrace, N1 2UN
🕐 Sun 1pm–5pm + tours, ½ hourly (1.30pm–4.30pm) + Organ Music at 1.30pm. Last entry Sun 4.30pm. B·T
🚇 Highbury & Islington
🚌 4,19,30,43,271
An architectural Grade I treasure that's home to an inclusive church, an award winning venue, a unique organ and The Margins Project for those homeless and in crisis in London. James Cubitt, 1877. *unionchapel.org.uk*

White Collar Factory
🚶 1 Old Street Yard, EC1Y 8AF
🕐 Sat 10am–5pm/Sun 1pm–5pm (max 150, access to ground floor lobby and roof terrace only) + Tour at 11am. Last entry 4.15pm. A·R·T·O·Q
🚇 Old Street
🚌 271,243,55,43,135,205,214
New office space that combines the wisdom of well-built industrial spaces with innovative design, sustainable principles, future-proof flexibility and panoramic views. It has achieved BREEAM Outstanding. Allford Hall Monaghan Morris, 2016

Walks & Tours

Caledonian Park: Park Walking Tour
🚶 Meet: Caledonian Park, Market Road, N7 9PL
🕐 Sat/Sun 11am, 4pm (max 20, the walk takes place outside, please dress suitably.). T·D·A
❗ Pre-book only: eventbrite.co.uk/e/open-house-park-tours-tickets-62927797737
🚇 Caledonian Road, Caledonian Road & Barnsbury
🚌 390,17,91,259
Tour of the park and local area, discover how Copenhagen Fields became Caledonian Park and how diplomacy gave way to debauchery and agitation and then butchery and commerce. J.B. Bunning, 1850

Kensington & Chelsea

THE ROYAL BOROUGH OF
KENSINGTON
AND CHELSEA

Social Capital

Trellick tower, designed by Ernö Goldfinger and built five years after Balfron Tower in Tower Hamlets is, at 98 metres, five metres taller than its older East end counterpart.

11 Bina Gardens

🏃 Flat E, 11 Bina Gardens, SW5 0LD
🕐 Sat/Sun 10am–5pm (max 10, access only to Flat E). Last entry 4.30pm. **D·A**
🚇 Gloucester Road
🚌 C1,430,49

A minimalist Scandinavian style flat in South Kensington, fully refurbished in a contemporary style with original period features retained. A beautiful calm space hidden among the trees of Bina Gardens. YAM Studios, 2019. *yamstudios.com*

18 Stafford Terrace: The Sambourne Family Home

🏃 W8 7BH
🕐 Sat/Sun 10am–5pm (max 15). Last entry Sat/Sun 4.30pm. **B·T**
❗ Pre-book only: bit.ly/2YyRjQn
🚇 High Street Kensington, Kensington Olympia
🚌 9,27,28,49,328,23

From 1875, the home of the Punch cartoonist Edward Linley Sambourne, his wife Marion, their two children and their live-in servants. The house is recognised as the best surviving example of a late Victorian middle-class home in the UK. Joseph Gordon Davis, 1871

264 Westbourne Park Road

🏃 W11 1EJ
🕐 Sat/Sun 10am–5pm (max 8, closed 12pm–3pm shoes off). Last entry 4.15pm. **X·A·Q**
🚇 Ladbroke Grove
🚌 7,70,452,52,23

New building as an urban accent – two independent houses atop each other. Contemporary in design, it draws from the tectonic composition of adjacent Victorian houses. Features include rain water harvesting, roof garden, solar water heating. Studio Bednarski, 2011

Dana Research Centre & Library, Science Museum

🏃 Wellcome Wolfson, 165 Queen's Gate, SW7 5HD
🕐 Sat 10am–5pm. Last entry 4.30pm. **D·T·O**
🚇 South Kensington, Gloucester Road
🚌 74,70,345,360

A world-class environment for academic research into the Museum's collections. A double layer of steel-perforated panels lines the double-height glazing that dominates the reading room, dappling sunlight to create an inspirational space. Coffey Architects, 2016

Earls Court Tube Station

🏃 Earls Ct Rd, Kensington, SW5 9QA
🕐 Sun tour, hourly (10.30am–3.30pm, max 20). **T·O**
❗ Pre-book only: See Open House website
🚇 Earl's Court
🚌 C3,C1,328,74

Earls Court is a mix of architectural styles. The tour will discuss the architecture of the station from the Victorian-era train shed to the 1930s extension to Warwick Road as well as more recent modernisations. John Wolfe Barry, 1878

Embassy of Slovakia

🏃 25 Kensington Palace Gardens, W8 4QY
🕐 Sat/Sun 10am–5pm + Sat Tour at 11am + Velvet Generation Exhibition. Last entry 4.15pm. **T**
🚇 Notting Hill Gate
🚌 148,27,28,52,70,94

Modern Brutalist-style building awarded by RIBA in 1971. The building of former Czechoslovak Embassy is made of reinforced concrete panels with wooden partitions separating the interior spaces. Jan Bocan, Jan Sramek and Karel Stepansky, 1970

Embassy of the Republic of Estonia

🏃 44 Queen's Gate Terrace, SW7 5PJ
🕐 Sat 10am–3pm (max 50) + Hourly tour + Estonian-language themed activities & pop-up shop (max 50). Last entry 2.30pm. **R·D·T**
❗ Pre-book only: bit.ly/2S1yUJE
🚇 High Street Kensington, Gloucester Road
🚌 9,,49,52,452,70,23

Representing Neo-Classicist style characteristic of the mid-19C, many of the details of the house have been restored to their original splendour. The interior design is inspired by Estonian nature: swamps, lakes and forests. William Harris, James Matthews, 1859

Happy Kids Dental Clinic Chelsea

🏃 18 Cadogan Gardens London, SW3 2RP
🕐 Sat/Sun 9am–7pm (max 20) + tours, every 15 mins + Sun lecture at 11am (max 20). Last entry 6.45pm. **T·R·P·F·O**
❗ Pre-book only: marketing@happykidsdental.co.uk
🚇 Sloane Square
🚌 319,11,19,22,137,360

A multi-award-winning children's dental clinic. It has a unique design, with a giant whale greeting you at the reception, a pirate ship in the waiting room, four floors of 100% instagrammable fun.

Holy Trinity Church
🕇 146 Sloane Street (just off Sloane Square), SW1X 9BZ
🕐 Sat Tour every 120 mins (12pm–4pm, max 40) / Sun Tour every 90 mins (1pm–5pm, max 40) + Arts and Crafts Festival 2019 · 11am (Talk by stained glass expert) · Stained glass workshop at 3pm (max 12). **F·D·B·R·T·O**
🚇 Sloane Square
🚌 19,22,137,C1,360
A sumptuous feast of Victorian stained glass and bold sacred sculpture at what Sir John Betjeman called the "cathedral of the Arts and Crafts movement". Work by William Morris, Edward Burne-Jones, William Blake and Christopher Whall. JD Sedding, Henry Wilson, 1888

Institut français du Royaume-Uni
🕇 17 Queensberry Place, SW7 2DT
🕐 Sat/Sun 11.45am–6pm (max 30) + Hourly tour. Last entry 5.15pm. **D·T·O**
🚇 South Kensington, Gloucester Road
🚌 14,49,70,74,345,C1
1939 Art Deco Grade II-listed building refurbished in 1950, then restructured and modernised in 2014. Contains an authentically classic cinema, private salons and multi-media library. Patrice Bonnet, 1939

Kensal House Estate Community Rooms
🕇 Ladbroke Grove, W10 5BQ
🕐 Sat 1pm–5pm/Sun 10am–1pm. Last entry Sat 4.15pm | Sun 12.15pm. **T**
🚇 Kensal Green, Kensal Rise
🚌 316,295,228,70,23,452,52

• Bina Gardens © Ana Saprygina

Grade II*-listed community rooms 10 mins from Grenfell Tower and home to SPID. Designed in 1937 by architect Maxwell Fry and social reformer Elizabeth Denby, it is part of an urban village vision for estate life.

Leighton House Museum
🕇 12 Holland Park Road, W14 8LZ
🕐 Sat/Sun 10am–5.30pm. Last entry Sat 5pm. **X·T·B·Q**
🚇 Kensington Olympia, High Street Kensington
🚌 C1,9,27,28,49,23
Originally the studio home of Lord Leighton, President of the Royal Academy, the house is one of the most remarkable buildings of 19C. The museum houses an outstanding collection of High Victorian art, including works by Leighton himself. George Aitchison, 1865

Marlborough Primary School
🕇 Draycott Avenue, SW3 3AP
🕐 Sat 10am–1pm (max 12). Last entry 12.15pm. **D·T**
🚇 South Kensington
🚌 452,22,19,11,137,49,C1,74,414,14,360
This RIBA award-winning school features a series of cascading roof terraces arranged across an urban site with a dynamic day-lit interior. The school caters for children aged 3–11 and includes a nursery and specialist provision for autism. Dixon Jones, 2012

Moravian Close
🕇 381 Kings Road, SW10 0LP
🕐 Sat/Sun 1pm–5pm. Last entry 4.15pm. **R·T·O**
🚇 Earl's Court, Sloane Square
🚌 328,22,19,319,11,49,345
A former stable yard of Sir Thomas More's Chelsea estate, now an 18C Chapel, other buildings, and burial ground. Parts of the enclosing walls are Tudor in origin. E and M Gillick enhanced the grounds in the 20C.

National Army Museum
🕇 Royal Hospital Road, Chelsea, SW3 4HT
🕐 Sun 10am–5pm: The family-friendly workshop at 11am. Last entry 4.15pm. **F·B·R·T·O**
🚇 Sloane Square, Victoria
🚌 170
Site previously formed part of the infirmary of the Royal Hospital Chelsea. Brutalist, completed in 1971. A leading authority on the British Army and its impact on society. Five galleries with thousands of objects from their collections. William Holford & Partners, 1960

Peter Jones
🕇 Sloane Square, SW1W 8EL
🕐 Sat Hourly tour (10am–4.15pm, max 15)/Sun Hourly tour (12pm–4.15pm, max 15). **T·O**
🚇 Sloane Square
🚌 11,19,22,319,C1,137
Grade II*-listed building, involving complex mix of new build and restoration. Britain's first ever curtain walling and listed features such as spiral staircase. Sloane Room has one of best views over Chelsea. RIBA Award Winner 2005. Crabtree, Slater & Moberley, 1936

Royal Hospital Chelsea

🏃 Royal Hospital Road, Chelsea, SW3 4SR
🕐 Sat 10am–5pm (max 50, Closed 12pm-2pm. Access restricted to Great Hall, Chapel, State Apartments and Museum). Last entry 4.15pm. **D·R·T·O**
🚇 Sloane Square, Victoria
🚌 360,11,137,452,170

The hospital buildings are one of England's architectural glories, built in brick in the decades after the Great Fire of London and sitting in 66 acres of beautiful gardens. John Soane, Sir John Vanbrugh, Nicholas Hawksmoor, Sir Christopher Wren, 1682

Serpentine Pavilion 2019, by Junya Ishigami

🏃 Serpentine Gallery, Kensington Gardens, W2 3XA
🕐 Sat/Sun 10am–5pm. Last entry 4.15pm. **D·B·R·T·P·O**
🚇 Knightsbridge, South Kensington
🚌 9,52,94,148,23

The Japanese architect Junya Ishigami, celebrated for his experimental structures that interpret traditional architectural conventions and reflect natural phenomena, has been selected to design the Serpentine Pavilion 2019. Junya Ishigami, 2019

Silchester Estate

🏃 Freston Road, W10 6TT
🕐 Sat 10am–1pm (max 20) + Hourly tour. Last entry 12pm. **A**
🚇 Latimer Road
🚌 295,316,7

New development of 112 mixed tenure homes, community and retail facilities delivered by Peabody and RBKC. Designed around a communal garden and integrating an existing 20-storey tower within a new urban block. Haworth Tompkins, 2016

South Kensington Tube Station

🏃 SW7 2ND
🕐 Sat tour of the station, hourly (10am–3pm, max 20). **O**
❗ Pre-book only: see Open House website
🚇 South Kensington
🚌 C1,430,414,360,74,49,345,14

In honour of the 150th anniversary of the District line, this tour will discuss the history of the station, the architectural features dating from the Victorian, Edwardian, and modern eras, and the operational functions of the station. Sir John Fowler, 1868

The Coronet Theatre, Notting Hill

🏃 103 Notting Hill Gate, W11 3LB
🕐 Sat 10am–1pm (max 60. Please contact the box office for further information) + Building Tours, ½ hourly (max 10) / Sun 10am–5pm + Building Tours, hourly (11am–4pm, max 10). Last entry Sat 12.30pm | Sun 4.15pm. **T·R·B**
❗ Pre-book only: thecoronettheatre.com
🚇 Notting Hill Gate
🚌 452,328,148,94,52,31,28,27

Designed by WGR Sprague opening in 1898, The Coronet Theatre presented major artists before becoming a much loved cinema in 1923. The original auditorium featuring plaster work is the Louis XVI manner and two balconies is remarkably intact. WGR Sprague, 1898

The Ismaili Centre

🏃 1–7 Cromwell Gardens, SW7 2SL
🕐 Sun 10am–4pm (max 100) Tours, every 15 mins. Last entry 3pm. **X·T**
🚇 South Kensington
🚌 14,70,74,345,414,C1

Part of an international family of Ismaili Centres, a religious, cultural and social space for the Shia Ismaili Muslim community. The serenity of the entrance fountain to the roof garden reflects Muslim traditions in architecture and design. Casson Conder Partnership.

Trellick Tower

🏃 5 Goldborne Road, W10 5UT
🕐 Sat 1/2 hourly tours (10am–4pm, max 12)
❗ Pre-book: TBC
🚇 Westbourne Park
🚌 452,7,23,28,31,52,70,328

Goldfinger's 31-storey tower built as social housing and now one of London's most desirable addresses. Monumental in style, with its free-standing service tower and surreal boiler house, it retains beautiful detailing and a rich use of materials. Ernö Goldfinger, 1972

Walmer Yard

🏃 235–239 Walmer Road, W11 4EY
🕐 Sat Tours, every 120 mins (10am–4pm, max 20). **B·T**
❗ Pre-book only: bit.ly/2XpSUe0
🚇 Latimer Road, Shepherds Bush
🚌 452,52,23,228,316,295

Forming a discreet and private set of four interlocking houses set around an open courtyard, Walmer Yard is Peter Salter's only UK project. The houses now form the home of the Baylight Foundation. Peter Salter, Fenella Collingridge, 2018

Walks & Tours

World's End Estate Walk

🏃 Meet: at the Residents Association Clubroom. 16 Blantyre Street, World's End Estate, SW10 0DS
🕐 Sat 2.30pm, 4.30pm (max 50, access to communal areas and gardens). **R·T·O**
🚇 Sloane Square, Earl's Court
🚌 11,22,19,49,328

The World's End Estate is a deliberate attempt to overcome many of the issues of previous high-rise developments and eliminate monotonous bland façades through alternative designs and materials. Eric Lyons, 1969

Lambeth

Lambeth

Social Capital

Edward Hollamby OBE (8 January 1921 – 29 December 1999), known for restoring William Morris's and Philip Webb's Red House, was Lambeth's chief architect between 1969-81.

15b Herne Hill Road

🚶 SE24 0AU
🕐 Sat/Sun 10am–6pm. Last entry 5.45pm. **A**
🚇 Loughborough Junction, Brixton
🚌 35,45,345,P4,P5

Major renovation of flat in Victorian terrace, creating new living area within restructured roof space using unusual and reclaimed materials and retrofit of substantial insulation. Space-saving design elements optimise the available volume. Colin MacInnes, 2011

163 Herne Hill Road

🚶 SE24 0AD
🕐 Sat 10am–5pm/Sun 12pm–5pm (Access to extension/ living space only). Last entry 4.45pm. **A**
🚇 Herne Hill
🚌 468,42,68,P4

Extension to an Edwardian house, conceived as a kind of garden pavilion which can be used as an informal gallery space; the junction with the main house articulated with roof glazing that brings daylight into the original living room. Colin MacInnes, 2018

1a Woodland Road

🚶 Crystal Palace, SE19 1NS
🕐 Sat 10am–5pm (max 6). Last entry 4.15pm. **A·R**
🚇 Gipsy Hill, Crystal Palace
🚌 3,450,157,202,227,322,358,363,432,417

Borrowed light streams into a compact 26m² flat from unusually high roof windows. The interior is inspired by found or free materials, yet there has been no compromise on design or the need for functionality within the restricted space. Melinda Styles and Jon Storey – Designers, 2016

1901 Arts Club

🚶 7 Exton Street, SE1 8UE
🕐 Sat 10am–5pm (max 35) + Tour and mini-recital, hourly (10.30am–4.30pm, max 35).
🚇 Waterloo, Waterloo East
🚌 43,168,188,1,59,139,176

Late Victorian schoolmaster's house elegantly converted into a European salon-inspired arts club providing space for performance, rehearsals, meetings and private events with a licensed bar. Waugh Thistleton, 1901

54 Cambria Road

🚶 SE5 9AS
🕐 Sun 10am–5pm. Last entry 4.15pm. **T·D·A**
🚇 Denmark Hill, Loughborough Junction
🚌 68,P4,35,45,176,345

Self build conversion of 19C terrace: reorganised living spaces, reclaimed materials, natural insulation, solar thermal and PV, biofuel heating, vegetable growing, bees, hens, back yard managed for diversity of habitat and sounds.

B-House

🚶 62 Ferndene Road, SE24 0AB
🕐 Sat 1pm–5pm (max 20). Last entry 4.30pm. **T·P·R**
🚇 Herne Hill, Brixton
🚌 42,P4,468,68

A passionate combination of aesthetic design with the most up-to-date practices in eco-design; retrofitted to reduce energy bills.Natural materials used to enhance indoor air quality, absorb CO_2 and start to engage with the circular economy. Enbee Architecture and Design, 2018

Brixton Windmill

🚶 Windmill Gardens, west end of Blenheim Gardens, SW2 5EU
🕐 Sat/Sun Short guided tours to meal floor, every 20 mins(1pm–4.30pm, max 6, No children under 1.2m.) · Full guided tours to top floor, ½ hourly (1pm–4.30pm, max 3) + Windmill Exhibition at 1pm. **B·R·T·O**
❗ Pre-book only: brixtonwindmill.org/visit
🚇 Brixton
🚌 137,45,59,109,118,133,159,250,333

One of very few windmills in London. Built 1816 when Brixton Hill was open fields and a working mill until 1934. Restored to working order 2011.

Central Hill Estate

🚶 Corner of Central Hill and Vicars Oak Road, SE19 1DT
🕐 Sun 10am–5pm + Resident-led tour, every 120 mins (11am–4pm) · Talk by Residents at 2pm. Last entry 4.15pm. **O**
🚇 Gipsy Hill
🚌 3,322,417,450,202

Tree-lined housing estate on the ridge of Central Hill, Crystal Palace incorporating open spaces, views over London, gardens and sense of community. Rosemary Stjernstedt, Ted Hollamby, Adrian Sansom, 1963

Cheviot Gardens
🚶 36 Cheviot Rd, West Norwood, London, SE27 0SU
🕐 Sat 1pm–5pm. Last entry 4.30pm. **D·T·R**
🚇 West Norwood
🚌 432,68,468,315,2,196
This Notting Hill Genesis development, provides modern retirement living. 84 apartments, designed for later life, which are complemented by stunning communal space, a 24hr on-site care team, restaurant and café. PRP Architects, 2014

Christ Church Clapham
🚶 39 Union Grove, SW8 2QJ
🕐 Sat 10am–5pm / Sun 1pm–5pm. Last entry 4.15pm. **F·D·R·T·O**
🚇 Clapham North, Wandsworth Road
🚌 P5,452,196,87,77
Gothic Revival church at the centre of a diverse community and is a place of sanctuary and refuge for people on their journeys, both physical and spiritual. Benjamin Ferrey, 1862

Christ Church, Streatham
🚶 3 Christchurch Road, SW2 3ET
🕐 Sat 10am–5pm / Sun 1pm–5pm (All areas except the bell tower). Last entry 4.30pm. **D·R·T·O**
🚇 Streatham Hill, Brixton
🚌 201,59,109,250,133
Grade I-listed pioneering brick polychromy. Designed with early Christian, Italian, Ottoman, Alhambran, Mamluk, Sevillean and Ancient Egyptian influences with fine mosaics and stained glass by Walter Crane, JF Bentley and John Hayward. James Wild and Owen Jones, 1841

Clapham Library
🚶 Mary Seacole Centre, 91 Clapham High Street, SW4 7DB
🕐 Sun 1pm–5pm. Last entry 4.15pm. **X·D·T·O**
🚇 Clapham Common, Clapham High Street
🚌 345,50,88,155
The building is based around a spiral theme that allows a building of multiple uses to feel like one space to reinforce a sense of community spirit. Studio Egret West, 2012

Claverdale Road
🚶 25 Claverdale Road, SW2 2DJ
🕐 Sat/Sun 10am–5pm (max 20, downstairs and rear garden only). Last entry 4.00pm. **A**
🚇 Tulse Hill, Brixton
🚌 201,2,415,432
A rear and side extension to a house in Tulse Hill, Lambeth creates a generous dining room and a bespoke kitchen with a window planter for peeking through into the garden. Architecture for London, 2019

Cressingham Gardens
🚶 Cressingham Gardens Rotunda, Tulse Hill, SW2 2QG
🕐 Sat/Sun 10am–5pm + Stain Glass Installations. Last entry Sat/Sun 4.30pm. **R·T**
🚇 Brixton, Tulse Hill
🚌 415,432,2,201
Low-rise high-density leafy estate located next to beautiful Brockwell Park noted for its innovative design, incorporating pioneering architectural elements and echoing the natural topography. Under threat of demolition by Lambeth Council. Ted Hollamby, 1967

Ebenezer Cottage
🚶 27/28 Belmont Close, SW4 6AY
🕐 Sat/Sun 10am–5pm (max 20). Last entry 4.15pm. **R·D**
🚇 Clapham Common, Clapham High Street
🚌 50,88,155,345
It was built 1852 as a Chapel, Ebenezer Chapel and the adjoining cottage was the manse. the corner stone was laid on 6/8/1852. The trustees of the Pride of Clapham, Oddfellows purchased the chapel in 1908 and are still the current owners. Ebenezer, 1852

Geek Hive
🚶 30 Goldsboro Road, SW8 4RR
🕐 Sat 10am–5.30pm (max 10). Last entry 5.15pm. **A**
🚇 Stockwell, Wandsworth Road
🚌 452,196,77,87
Renovation to a flat cleverly maximising space and storage. Futureproofing, a centralised kitchen, a Japanese bath, hexagon tiles and how to display models and curiosities including Star Wars Lego around the flat became key design elements. Hell's Architects, 2016

International Maritime Organization
🚶 4 Albert Embankment, SE1 7SR
🕐 Sat 10.30am–4pm (max 100) + Tour at 10.30am (max 100, Photo ID required and may be photographed for security purposes.)/Sun 11am–4pm hourly tour (11am–3.30pm, max 100, Photo ID required.). Last entry 3.30pm. **D·T**
🚇 Lambeth North, Vauxhall
🚌 C10,507,77,360,344
A specialised agency of the UN, responsible for the safety and security of shipping and the prevention of marine pollution by ships. It is the only UN organisation with headquarters in London. Douglass Marriott, Worby, Robinson, 1983

Lambeth Palace
🚶 Lambeth Palace Road, SE1 7JU
🕐 Sat 10am–5pm (max 20, no access to private areas). Last entry 4.00pm. **T**
❗ Pre-book only: lambethopenhouse.eventbrite.com
🚇 Lambeth North, Waterloo
🚌 3,77,344,507,C10

For nearly 800 years Lambeth Palace has been the London residence of the Archbishop of Canterbury. Oldest remaining parts date back to the 13C with buildings added and altered over time to suit changes in fashion and purpose. 1200

Lambeth Town Hall
🕈 Brixton Hill, SW2 1RW
🕒 Sat/Sun 10am–5pm + Tour of the principal internal spaces, hourly (max 20). Last entry 4.15pm. **D·T·O**
🚇 Brixton
Landmark Edwardian Baroque style town hall in red brick and Portland stone. Striking new atrium, reception and courtyard space along with grand marble lined staircase and ornate council chamber. Grade II-listed. Septimus Warwick & H Austin Hall, 1906

Morley College
🕈 61 Westminster Bridge Road, SE1 7HT
🕒 Sun 10am–5pm + Architect-led tour hourly (max 12) · Tours, ½ hourly (max 20) + 'Radio Radio' – try out our new studio (max 4) · historical exhibition (max 20). Last entry 4.15pm. **D·T·R·A·O**
🚇 Lambeth North, Waterloo
🚌 12,3,453,159,C10
Extensively damaged in WWII, its 1937 extension by Maufe survives. Rebuilt in 1958 by Cowles Voysey and Brandon-Jones, further extensions have been subsequently added. Murals by Edward Bawden, John Piper, Bridget Riley and others feature. Sir Edward Maufe, 1937

National Theatre
🕈 Upper Ground, South Bank, SE1 9PX
🕒 Sat 10am–5pm/Sun 12.15pm–5pm (Dorfman and main foyers, public areas) + Short tours of workshops and production building , ½ hourly (max 12). Last entry 4.15pm. **D·B·P·R·T·O**
❗ Pre-book only: Please see National Theatre website
🚇 Waterloo
🚌 1,26,59,68,176,172,188

• Christchurch Clapham

Housing one of the world's most important producing theatres the NT building is a key work in British Modernism (Grade II*-listed) with three theatres, designed with workshops and theatre-making all on-site. RIBA Award Winner. Denys Lasdun and Partners, 1976

Pullman Court
🕈 Streatham Hill, SW2 4SZ
🕒 Sun 10am–5pm (No access to roof terrace). Last entry 4.15pm.
🚇 Brixton, Streatham Hill
🚌 45,57,159,137,133,109,250,201,417,319,118
Grade II*-listed buildings, modern movement style with balcony walkways and period internal features. Frederick Gibberd, 1936

Rambert
🕈 99 Upper Ground, SE1 9PP
🕒 Sat Hourly tour (11am–3pm, max 15). **D·T**
🚇 Waterloo
🚌 381
RIBA National Award winner 2014, the building provides Rambert's with state of the art facilities for the creation of new choreography and music for dance. It also enables the company to unlock the riches of the Rambert archive. Allies and Morrison, 2013

Streatham Space Project
🕈 Sternhold Ave, SW2 4PA
🕒 Sat/Sun 10am–5pm (No access during performance times). Last entry 4.15pm. **T·R·F·D·O**
🚇 Streatham Hill
🚌 319,118,333,133,250
Streatham Space Project is a Theatre, Music, Comedy and events venue, aiming to bring the best live performance to South London. David Hughes Architects, 2018

The Beaufoy (Diamond Way Buddhist Centre)
🕈 39 Black Prince Road, SE11 6JJ
🕒 Sat/Sun 11am–5pm (View on great hall, entry to small hall and social areas) + Tours, every 120 mins (12pm-4pm) + Talks to Buddhism and Meditations at 1pm · Talks and Meditations at 3pm. Last entry 4.45pm. **B·T·R·O**
🚇 Kennington, Vauxhall
🚌 59,159,3,360
Edwardian Building, which was built in 1907 as a school for underprivileged children and funded by the Beaufoy family. More recently (since 2014), the building has been functioning as a Diamond Way Buddhist Centre. FA Powell, 1907. *buddhism-london.org*

The Clockworks
🕈 6 Nettlefold Place, SE27 0JW
🕒 Sat 10am–6pm + Hourly tour + Workshop demonstrations. Last entry Sat 5.30pm. **D·T·O**
🚇 West Norwood
🚌 322,2,432,196,68,468

Internationally pre-eminent museum and integral workshops devoted to electrical timekeeping and the distribution of accurate time (1840–1970). Practical education and conservation in action. Michael Crowley Architect, 2012

The Department Store
🏃 248 Ferndale Road, SW9 8FR
🕐 Sat Tour every 15 mins (10am-12.15pm, max 10).
   T·D·A
❗ Pre-book only: events@thedepartmentstore.com
🚇 Brixton
The Department Store is an award-winning refurbishment of a dilapidated Edwardian building in Brixton, completed by Squire and Partners in 2017. The design was informed by the layers of history and existing fabric of the heritage building. Squire & Partners, 1906

The Jewellery Box House
🏃 277 Railton Road, Herne Hill, SE24 0LY
🕐 Sat 10am–5pm (max 15, access to the ground floor, first floor only) + Architect-led tour, hourly (11am-4pm). Last entry 4.15pm. **T·R·D·A**
🚇 Brixton, Herne Hill
🚌 3,68,196,37
A contemporary remodelling and extension of a Victorian terrace in the heart of Herne Hill. The design fuses modern and traditional techniques, featuring a finely crafted kitchen within a light and tall extension clad in oxidised brass. Michael Collins Architect, 2019

The Kia Oval
🏃 Kennington Oval, SE11 5SS
🕐 Sat 10am–5pm (Micky Stewart Members' Pavilion access only, with certain areas restricted) + Presentation. Last entry Sat 4.00pm. **D·T**
🚇 Vauxhall, Oval
🚌 436,36,185
In 1897, architects Muirhead & Baldwin of Manchester inspired a red brick construction which, flanked by two complementary stands and the Surrey Tavern, was completed in a remarkable six months, in time for the 1898 cricket season. Muirhead & Baldwin, 1897

The South London Botanical Institute
🏃 323 Norwood Road, SE24 9AQ
🕐 Sun 1pm–5pm (max 50) + History, collections and garden, ½ hourly + Victorian House Hunt leaflet for children and microscope demonstration at 1pm (max 20). Last entry 4.30pm. **R·T·O**
🚇 Brixton, Tulse Hill
🚌 68,196,322,468
Brick-built Victorian villa with sweeping drive. Few interior changes since 1910 when AO Hume founded the SLBI. Lecture Room with bespoke wallpaper designed around plants and herbarium specimens with a nod to Hume's Indian connections. 1863

Van Gogh House London
🏃 87 Hackford Road, Stockwell, SW9 0RE
🕐 Sat/Sun 11am–5pm (max 10). Last entry 4pm.
   T·R·B·A
❗ Pre-book only: eventbrite.co.uk/e/open-house-london-van-gogh-house-timed-entry-visits-tickets-63435114134
🚇 Stockwell, Oval
🚌 3,59,133,159,333,415
The carefully renovated Van Gogh House seeks to share its story and inspire a new generation of artists through Van Gogh's London story. The house curates a dynamic programme of events anchored in the artist's practice and local heritage.

Waterloo City Farm
🏃 8 Royal Street, SE1 7LL
🕐 Sat/Sun 10am–5pm (max 30). Last entry 4.15pm. **T**
🚇 Lambeth North, Waterloo
🚌 77,341,76,381,507,59,68,168,176,12
Feilden Fowles is situated within a walled garden on a discreet corner of Waterloo City Farm. Feilden Fowles designed the farm and its office and educational spaces, which is run by two charities: Jamie's Farm and the Oasis Community Hub. Feilden Fowles, 2016

West Norwood Cemetery
🏃 Norwood Road, (corner of Robson Road), SE27 9JU
🕐 Sat 1pm–5pm + Tour at 2pm, 3pm (max 40, Meet inside cemetery main gate, duration 90 mins). Last entry 4.45pm. **B·P·T·O**
🚇 West Norwood
🚌 2,68,196,322,432,468
Opened 1837, with monuments to famous Victorians (Doulton, Tate, Reuter, Mrs Beeton). 69 Grade II/II*-listed structures, including Greek Chapel c1872, architect uncertain, mausolea by EM Barry and GE Street and entrance arch by W Tite. Sir William Tite, 1837

Wheatsheaf Community Hall
🏃 Wheatsheaf Lane, SW8 2UP
🕐 Sat/Sun 10am–5pm. Last entry 4.15pm. **R·T**
🚇 Stockwell, Vauxhall
🚌 2,88,87,77,196,452
Built as a Mission Hall, now a multi-purpose community Centre run by local volunteers. Grade II-listed. Williams, Messers Higgs and Hill, 1880

Walks & Tours

Clapham Old Town and Venn Street
🏃 Meet: by the Clock Tower next to Clapham Common tube, SW4 0BD
🕐 Sun 2pm (max 25, duration 1.5-2 hours). **T·D·A·O**
🚇 Clapham Common
This guided walk around Clapham's Old Town looks at a radically redesigned public realm which re-balanced the street environment in towards people walking and cycling. Urban Movement + LB Lambeth, 2011

Southwark

Social Capital

Southwark had the greatest proportion of social housing in England, 43.7%, at the time of the 2011 census.

Southwark Council

---

15 and a half Consort Road

🏃 SE15 2PH

🕐 Sat 10am–5pm (max 24). Last entry 4.15pm. **D·A·Q**

🚉 Peckham Rye, Queen's Road Peckham

As per 'Grand Designs', the opening roof, the retracting loo and sliding bed-bath typify this extraordinary response to constraints of a tight budget on a brownfield site. Shortlisted RIBA Awards 2006. One of nation's favourite TV houses. Richard Paxton Architects, 2002

99 John Ruskin Street

🏃 99 John Ruskin Street, SE5 0PQ

🕐 Sat 10am–5pm (max 25). Last entry 4.15pm. **A**

🚉 Kennington, Oval

🚌 P5,148,42,40,35,45,468,68,171,12,176

The project involves the refurbishment of a ground floor Victorian terrace flat that incorporates a side and rear extension to create a large open-plan family room. A granny annex/office space has been constructed in the garden. David Stanley and Romy Grabosch, 2016

AMP Studios Pavilion

🏃 897 Old Kent Road, SE15 1NL

🕐 Sun 1pm–5pm. Last entry 4.45pm. **T**

🚉 New Cross Gate, Queen's Road Peckham

🚌 453,172,53,21

Responding to the form of the brick railway viaduct, this timber, steel and polycarbonate canopy extends from two arches to form a versatile and adaptable event space, built using modular structural components. Gruff Limited, 2018

Allies and Morrison

🏃 85 Southwark Street, SE1 0HX

🕐 Sat 10am–5pm. Last entry Sat 4.15pm. **T**

🚉 Southwark, Blackfriars

🚌 381

Allies and Morrison Studios complex includes the original RIBA award-winning studio, a converted Grade II-listed warehouse and a new timber building. Allies and Morrison, 2003

Anise Gallery / AVR London

🏃 13a Shad Thames, SE1 2PU

🕐 Sat 10am–5pm + Artist tour of exhibition at 3pm + Photography Exhibition/Sun 10am–1pm + Artist tour of exhibition at 12pm + Photography Exhibition. Last entry Sat 4.15pm | Sun 12.15pm. **T·O**

🚉 Tower Hill, London Bridge

🚌 47,188,381

A Victorian spice warehouse, re-invented to house an architectural artwork gallery, an architectural illustrator's studio and a virtual reality company. The design focuses on flexibility and workspace collaboration. Tate Harmer, 2013

Blackfriars Circus

🏃 142 Blackfriars Road, SE1 8EQ

🕐 Sat 10am–2pm. Last entry 1.15pm.

❗ Pre-book only: alice.norman@barrattlondon.com

🚉 Southwark, Elephant & Castle

🚌 40,63

Barratt London's Blackfriars Circus is a new mixed-use development, comprising 336 new homes and two public squares, designed by Stirling Prize-winning architects. Maccreanor Lavington, 2018

Borealis Restaurant

🏃 180 Borough High Street, SE1 1LH

🕐 Sat 10am–5pm (max 30) / Sun 10am–1pm (max 30). Last entry Sat 4.00pm | Sun 12.45pm. **T·R·D·O**

🚉 London Bridge, Borough

🚌 21,35,133,343,C10

Borealis is connected to Fora, a pioneering co-working company, who worked together with design studio JLK to curate an atmosphere that combines effortless Scandinavian cool with a suave London member's club aesthetic. JLKDS, 2018

Brunel Museum

🏃 Railway Avenue, Rotherhithe, SE16 4LF

🕐 Sat/Sun 10am–5pm (max 150) + Train tours through Thames Tunnel, hourly (11am–4pm, max 50). Last entry Sat 9.15pm | Sun 4.15pm. **D·B·R·T**

🚉 Canada Water, Rotherhithe

🚌 47,C10,1,188,381

London's story of an engineering family that changed the world. Dramatic new staircase below sculpture garden leads to underground chamber. Travel by train through first underwater shopping arcade & fairground to view Thames Tunnel portico. Sir Marc Brunel, 1842

• Borealis Restaurant © Ming Tang Evans 2019

Canada Water Library
🚶 21 Surrey Quays Road, SE16 7AR
🕐 Sat 9am–5pm + tours hourly (10am–3pm, max 20, No tours at 12pm or 1 pm)/Sun 12pm–4pm. Last entry Sat 4.15pm | Sun 3.30pm. **T·O**
🚇 Canada Water
🚌 1,47,188,199,225,381,P12
A civic centrepiece for the regeneration of the area around Canada Water. Its inverted pyramid form is an innovative response to providing an efficient single large library floor on a smaller footprint site. CZWG Architects, 2011

City Hall
🚶 The Queen's Walk, SE1 2AA
🕐 Sun 10.30am–4.30pm. Last entry 4.00pm. **D·R·T·O·Q**
🚇 Tower Hill, London Bridge
🚌 47,42,78,381
Home of the Mayor of London and London Assembly, an environmentally aware building with innovative spiral ramp and fine views across London. Foster + Partners, 2002

Cork House
🚶 67 Algernon Road, SE13 7AS
🕐 Sat 10am–5pm (max 10, Downstairs only. Please remove shoes) + Architect-led tour hourly (11am–4pm, max 10). Last entry 4.30pm. **A**
🚇 Ladywell, Lewisham
🚌 284,122,P4,484
Shortlisted for the AJ's Small Project Awards 2019, this extension evolved through a process of co-creation with the clients. Clad externally and internally with cork, pink window frames provide a flash of colour against the dark cork. Nimtim Architects, 2018

Corner House
🚶 14 Talfourd Place, SE15 5NW
🕐 Sat 10am–5pm (max 15). Last entry 4.15pm. **A**
🚇 Peckham Rye
🚌 171,36,345,12
This new-build house repairs the end of an existing terrace – establishing a more formal turning point to the building line – while creating a characterful new building that nonetheless relates sensitively to the local context. 31/44 Architects, 2018

Dulwich College
🚶 Dulwich Common, SE21 7LD
🕐 Sun 10am–5pm (Access to the Barry Buildings and the Laboratory) + Archivist-led tour, every 90 mins (10am-1pm, max 40, Pre-Book Only). Last entry 4.15pm. **T·P·O**
🕐 Pre-book only: (Tours) events@dulwich.org.uk
🚇 West Dulwich, Tulse Hill
🚌 201,P4,P13,3
Barry Buildings: 1869. Grade II*-listed. Palladian symmetrical plan, in terracotta and stone. Extensively refurbished 2017–18. New Science Building 2016. Grimshaw Architects. RIBA National Award. Home to 'James Caird' boat. Charles Barry Junior, 1869

Dulwich Picture Gallery
🚶 Gallery Road, SE21 7AD
🕐 Sat/Sun 10am–5pm + The Colour Palace (This summer, the Dulwich Pavilion). Last entry 4.15pm. **D·T·P·R·B**
🚇 North Dulwich, West Dulwich
🚌 37,P4
Britain's oldest purpose-built public art gallery. At the centre of this seminal building Soane designed a mysterious mausoleum for the gallery's founders. Recent glass, bronze and brick extension. RIBA Award Winner. Sir John Soane, 1811

Employment Academy
🚶 29 Peckham Road, SE5 8UA
🕐 Sun ½ hourly tour (2pm–4.30pm, max 15). **T·O**
🚇 Peckham Rye, Denmark Hill
🚌 171,436,36,12,345
Grade II-listed, late Victorian 'Baroque' building that has now become a local asset to the Southwark community. Peter Barber Architects, 2013

Grove Chapel
🚶 Camberwell Grove, SE5 8RF
🕐 Sat 9.30am–4.30pm/Sun 12.30pm–5.30pm. Last entry Sat 4pm | Sun 5pm
🚇 Oval, Denmark Hill, East Dulwich
🚌 40, 42, 68, 176, 185, 468
Grade II-listed building. An elegant chapel with classical elevations and good survival of original features including three main entrances, three-sided gallery supported by decorated iron colonetters. David R. Roper 1819

Hopewell Yard
🚶 Unit 44, Hopewell Yard, Hopewell Street, SE5 7QS
🕐 Sat/Sun 10am–5pm (max 15). Last entry 4.30pm. **A**
🚇 Oval, Denmark Hill
🚌 36,436,136,343
A charismatic and detail rich warehouse conversion located within an old yard building. The main space contains a dramatic frameless glass box that penetrates the roof and is hung into the void utilising the existing wooden structure. Space Group Architects, 2018

Kaymet Factory
🚶 52 Ossory Road, SE1 5AN
🕐 Sat/Sun 10am–5pm (max 12). Last entry 4.30pm. **T**
🚇 South Bermondsey
🚌 63,363,78,21,381,172,53,453
The operational factory of Kaymet, a maker of trays and trolleys since 1947. A hidden 1950s building with a small yard, originally a printing works. It is brick built, with clear-storey glazing and tubular truss north-light main shed roof.

King's College London: Museum of Life Sciences
🚶 Hodgkin Building, Guy' Campus, King's College London, SE1 1UL
🕐 Sun 11.30am–4pm (max 25). Last entry 3.30pm. **D**
🚇 London Bridge
🚌 343,133,35,21
Constructed in 1902 as the Will's Library, part of Guy's Hospital Medical School. Building of red brick with additional stonework and partially covered in creeper. Internally are carved oak cabinets and columns.

Kingswood House
🚶 Seeley Drive, West Dulwich, SE21 8QR
🕐 Sun 12.30pm–4.30pm + ½ hourly tour + Beckenham Concert Band at 1.30pm (max 100). Last entry Sun 4.00pm. **B·P·R·T**
🚇 Sydenham Hill
🚌 450,3,322
Substantial villa built in form of stone-faced baronial castle for the founder of Bovril. Now library and community centre. HV Lanchester, 1892

Kirkaldy Testing Works
🚶 99 Southwark Street, SE1 0JF
🕐 Sat 11am–3.30pm (max 15) + Facts not Opinions – opening a unique door onto Victorian engineering (max 15). Last entry Sat 3pm. **Q**
🚇 Waterloo, Blackfriars
🚌 40,63,381
Proudly carved over the door are the words 'Facts not Opinions'. Inside, the sight – and smell – of Kirkaldy's Testing and Experimenting Works is a unique and direct link with an ingenious age of engineering. T Roger Smith, 1873

Kirkwood House
🚶 8 Kirkwood Road, SE15 3XX
🕐 Sun 10am–5pm (max 5). Last entry 4.30pm.
🚇 Nunhead, Peckham Rye
🚌 78,P12
Kirkwood renovation saw the layout of a 1960s mid-terrace house transformed in 2017 by a ground floor extension, creating a full-width kitchen and dining room, with broad folding doors that lead straight out to the garden. Jailmake, Jamie Elliott, 2017

KnoxBhavan Studio
🚶 69 Choumert Road, Peckham, SE15 4AR
🕐 Sat Architect-led tour, every 15 mins (11am–4pm, max 8). **T·B**
🚇 Peckham Rye
🚌 P13
Every square inch of this former stationery shop has been maximised in its transformation into an innovative new studio for Knox Bhavan Architects. The studio is dedicated to the idea that workplace environment directly affects wellbeing. Knox Bhavan Architects LLP, 2016

London College of Communication
🚶 Elephant and Castle, SE1 6SB
🕐 Sat Tour, ½ hourly (11am–4pm, max 30) + Design locations · Demonstration of print studios (max 15, under 16s cannot enter the print studios. Please wear closed-toe shoes if you wish to attend this demonstration). **T·D**
🚇 Elephant & Castle
🚌 176,171,12,68,45,345,40,35,415,333,155,133
A classic example of Modernism from the radical Architects Department of London County Council. An aluminium-clad tower with low-rise workshop, design and media blocks, first opened in 1964. London County Council, 1964

Metro Central Heights (formerly Alexander Fleming House)
🚶 119 Newington Causeway, SE1 6BX
🕐 Sat/Sun Tour led by Richard Walker at 11am (max 17) + Sun Talk 'Was Alexander Fleming House Goldfinger's most important building?' Talk by Elain Harwood at 2.30pm (max 40).
❗ Pre-book only: See Open House website for more information (NB: One tour per day only)
🚇 Elephant & Castle
Built in 1959–67 as offices for the Ministry of Health by architect Ernö Goldfinger. Constructed in two phases, phase one 1959–62, phase two 1964–67. Converted into a residential development, renamed Metro Central Heights in 1997. Ernö Goldfinger, 1959

• Mountview © Tim Crocker 2019

Mountview
🚶 120 Peckham Hill Street,
   (Entrance on Library Square), SE15 5JT
🕐 Sat Building tours, hourly (10am–3pm, max 18). **T·R·D**
❗ Pre-book only: mountview.org.uk/whats-on
🚇 Queen's Road Peckham, Peckham Rye
🚌 436,36,171,12
Cultural building for training and developing the performing arts. The building includes two theatres, TV, radio, acting and dance studios and production arts facilities, cafés, bars and professional rehearsal space. Carl Turner Architects, 2018

Nunhead Cemetery
🚶 Linden Grove, Nunhead, SE15 3LP
🕐 Sat/Sun 1pm–5pm (max 40) + General cemetery tour at 2pm, 3pm (max 40) · Chapel and crypt visits, every 45 mins (max 30). Last entry 4.15pm. **R·B·P·T**
🚇 New Cross, Nunhead
🚌 484,P12,78
Magnificent Victorian cemetery with Gothic chapel and restored & ruined lodge. One of London's wildest cemeteries. Part-restored with the help of a lottery grant. 52 acres of woodland, with bats, owls, foxes and squirrels. Grade II* landscape. Thomas Little & JB Bunning, 1840

ORTUS
🚶 82–96 Grove Lane, Denmark Hill, SE5 8SN
🕐 Sat 9am–3pm + 'Our Future Likes'- Exhibition. Last entry 2.15pm. **D·R·T·O**
🚇 Denmark Hill
🚌 40,42,68,176,185,468,484

A public pavilion for the Maudsley Charity promoting awareness of mental health, with spaces for learning, meeting, exhibition and events connected by a grand staircase. Morris+Company, 2014

Old Operating Theatre Museum & Herb Garret
🚶 9a St Thomas Street, SE1 9RY
🕐 Sun 10.30am–5pm (max 55, access via narrow 52 step spiral staircase). Last entry 4.30pm. **B**
🚇 London Bridge
🚌 21,35,43,47,48,133,149
St Thomas' Church attic (1703) once part of old St Thomas' Hospital, houses the hospital's Herb Garret and the oldest surviving 19C operating theatre in Europe. Thomas Cartwright, 1703

Old Waiting Room at Peckham Rye station
🚶 Station Arcade, Rye Lane, SE15 5DQ
🕐 Sat 10am–5pm + Architect-led tour of restoration work at 1pm + Photography exhibition. Last entry 4.15pm.
🚇 Peckham Rye
Originally the waiting lounge for passengers at Peckham Rye Station, designed in High Victorian style. Benedict O'Looney Architects, 2017

Quay House; Ground Floor and Top Flat
🚶 2c Kings Grove (Queens Road end), Peckham, SE15 2NB
🕐 Sat 12pm–5pm (max 150, Wheelchair access to Ground floor only) + Exhibition in Gallery Pavilion. Last entry 4.30pm. **A·B·P·R·T**
🚇 Queen's Road Peckham
🚌 436,171,12,63,P12,453,177,P13,36
As seen on BBC4 & C5 TV, conversion of 1930s milk depot. Access to ground floor 'beach huts' & residence. Top flat with wavy roof also open. Exhibition in m² gallery and 4 x m² gallery pavilion on the driveway curated by artist Iain Hales. Quay 2c, 2001

Queen's Court
🚶 2 Old Jamaica Rd, Bermondsey, SE16 4ER, SE16 4ER
🕐 Sat/Sun 1pm–5pm (max 10). Last entry 4.15pm. **A**
❗ Pre-book only: alexandra.hellyer@cgluk.com
🚇 London Bridge, Bermondsey
🚌 47,188,381,C10
Designed by CGL, Queen's Court is an affordable housing project for Notting Hill Genesis (NHG). It comprises 51 new homes arranged over five storeys enclosing a landscaped courtyard, with a beautifully restored war memorial. Child Graddon Lewis, 2016

RDA Architects Studio
🚶 16 Forest Hill Road, East Dulwich, SE22 0RR
🕐 Sat 10am–5pm (max 10). Last entry 4.30pm. **A·P·T**
🚇 Honor Oak Park, Peckham Rye
🚌 63,363
A 19C building forming part of a small parade of shops, refurbished to an extremely high standard. The front of the building has been restored to replicate the original Victorian façade. RDA Architects, 2016

Sands Films Studios & Rotherhithe Picture Research Library

🚶 82 St Marychurch Street, Rotherhithe, SE16 4HZ
🕐 Sat/Sun 10am–5pm (ground floor only) + RPRL & Sands Films studios tour, hourly (max 25) + RPRL exhibition (max 40). Last entry 4.15pm. **D·B·P·R·T·O·Q**
🚇 Canada Water, Rotherhithe
🚌 47,188,381,C10,P12

Grade II-listed riparian granary built with reclaimed timbers felled in 1700's. 1974 restoration to picture library, film studio, prop and costume workshops, cinema and theatre. International costume house for film, TV, theatre, opera, ballet. 1784

Science Gallery London

🚶 King's College London, Great Maze Pond, SE1 9GU
🕐 Sat/Sun 10am–6pm + tour, every 120 mins (11am–5pm, max 20). Last entry 5.30pm. **D·A·T·R·B·O**
🚇 London Bridge
🚌 35,21,17,141,43,149

Science Gallery London, part of King's College London, is a vibrant, interactive free to visit place where art and science collide through exhibitions developed by artists, scientists and young adults. LTS Architects, 2018

Shad Thames Water Tower

🚶 Flat 16, Butler & Colonial Wharf, 10 Shad Thames, SE1 2PX
🕐 Sun Architect-led tour of water tower, every 45 mins (10am–4.15pm, max 12). **A**
❗ Pre-book only: 020 7407 3336
🚇 London Bridge, Bermondsey
🚌 188,47,381

An unusual project which colonised the redundant volume of a disused water tower above a 19C warehouse apartment, creating usable floor area and a visual & physical link to a roof terrace in the former water tank above. FORMstudio, 2018

Small Beer Brewery

🚶 70–72 Verney Road, SE16 3DH
🕐 Sat 1pm–5pm. Last entry 4.30pm. **D·T·P·R·O**
🚇 South Bermondsey
🚌 P12,381

• Southwark Integrated Waste Management Facility

The Small Beer Brewery was founded in 2017 by James Grundy and Felix James. It is the first of its kind, specialising in brewing world-class beer at a sociable strength. Garbers & James Architects, 2018

South London Gallery

🚶 65–67 Peckham Road, SE5 8UH
🕐 Sat 11am–6pm/Sun 11am–6pm + Architect-led tour of the fire station at 2pm. Last entry 5.45pm. **B·R·T·O**
🚇 Denmark Hill, Peckham Rye
🚌 436,345,12,36,171

Public contemporary art gallery housed in 3 listed Victorian buildings restored by 6a architects. Comprising galleries, café, shop, gardens, kitchen and converted Victorian fire station. 6a Architects, 2018

Southwark Integrated Waste Management Facility

🚶 43 Devon Street, (off Old Kent Road), SE15 1AL
🕐 Sat 10am–4pm + Tour every 20 mins (max 20. For full details of tour restrictions please visit veolia.co.uk/southwark/WonderDay) + HGV and digger display · Bicycle repair workshop · Upcycling craft workshops · Birds of prey display · Ask the experts. Last entry 3.30pm. **F·R·T·Q**
🚇 Elephant & Castle, Queen's Road Peckham
🚌 P12,453,53,21,172

One of Europe's most advanced recycling facilities, comprising many sustainable features including grey water, solar panels and a green roof. Designed for the purpose of turning waste into a resource. Thorpe Wheatley, 2012. *veolia.co.uk/southwark/wonderday*

Springbank

🚶 81a Grove Park, SE5 8LE
🕐 Sun 1pm–5pm. Last entry 4.45pm. **A·T**
🚇 Denmark Hill, Peckham Rye
🚌 P13,176,185,40,63,12

One of a pair of modern houses on a sensitive site in a conservation area. A triple-height staircase atrium brings light into the heart of the house, and ground floor areas open onto courtyard gardens on three sides. Niki Borowiecki, 2013

St Paul's, Newington

🚶 Walworth Road, SE17 3QU
🕐 Sat 10am–1pm + ½ hourly tour (11am–1pm)/Sun 11.30am–1.30pm + ½ hourly tour. Last entry Sat 12.45pm | Sun 1.15pm. **D·T**
🚇 Kennington, Elephant & Castle
🚌 35,12,133,P5

Modern architecture church with large copper and lead roof and concrete, brick and stained glass external structure. Marble, wood and plaster interior and artwork by Sculptor Freda Pinto and Gerald Holtom. Woodroffe Buchanan & Coulter, 1955

Stanley Terrace

🚶 222 Lower Road, SE8 5DJ

🕐 Sat 10am–5pm (max 10) + Talk at 10.15am (max 10) · Smart Home Talk at 3pm (max 10). Last entry 4.15pm. **R**

❗ Pre-book only: info@aylaaexclusive.com

🚇 Canada Water, Surrey Quays

🚌 C10,225,199,P12,381,188,47,1

Building is over 100 years old and has been refurbished keeping the original façade. Inside, it has a modern finish with smart home technology to create a unique set of 3 smart flats. This is a well-designed but practical space. Aylaa Exclusive , 2018

Stradella Road (The Link Building)

🚶 2 Stradella Road, SE24 9HA

🕐 Sat/Sun 10am–4pm (max 10) + ½ hourly tour (11am–3.30pm). Last entry 3.30pm. **A**

🚇 Herne Hill

🚌 3,37,68,322

The Link Building was created in a gap between a house and a garage. By incorporating 12 sqm external area into the main body of the house, we increased internal floor space by over 40 sqm and unlocked the hidden potential of the site. Powell-Tuck Associates, 2016

The Belham Primary School

🚶 165 Bellenden Rd, SE15 4DG

🕐 Sat 10am–5pm (max 20) + Tour every 45 mins. Last entry 4.15pm. **T**

🚇 East Dulwich, Peckham Rye

🚌 P13,484,185,176,40

A new free school which centres around the restoration of the Grade II-listed Old Bellenden school. It balances the needs of conservation, sustainability, consultation and outstanding architecture for the benefit of its community. Haverstock, 2018

The Dixon, Tower Bridge

🚶 211 Tooley Street, SE1 2JX

🕐 Sat/Sun 2.30pm–4.30pm + Shakedown Coffee Cupping Session at 3pm (max 6). Last entry 4.00pm. **T·D·O**

🚇 Tower Hill, London Bridge

🚌 42,47,78,188,343,381

The Dixon occupies an awe-inspiring building that dates from 1905, when it served as the Tower Bridge Magistrates Court. Named after the Grade II-listed building's original Edwardian architect, The Dixon now serves as a 4* hotel. John Dixon Butler, 1905

The Hoxton, Southwark

🚶 40 Blackfriars Road, SE1 8PB

🕐 Sat/Sun Tour at 9am, 10am, 3pm (max 10). **T·R·D**

🚇 Blackfriars, Southwark

🚌 40,63

The third Hoxton in our hometown of London, The Hoxton, Southwark is a new-build property designed by Architects Lifschutz Davidson Sandilands in collaboration with Ennismore Design Studio. Lifschutz Davidson Sandilands, 2019

The Modern House

🚶 St Alphege Hall, King's Bench Street, SE1 0QX

🕐 Sun 10am–1pm (max 100). Last entry 12.30pm. **T**

🚇 Borough, Southwark

🚌 40,63,344

London headquarters of The Modern House, the design sector's preferred estate agency, renowned for selling Britain's best design-led living spaces. TDO Architecture, 2018

The Music Box

🚶 235–241 Union Street, SE1 0LR

🕐 Sat 10am–5pm (max 50). Last entry 4.15pm. **T·D·A**

🚇 Waterloo, London Bridge

🚌 40,63

A place for living; a space for learning. The Music Box designed by SPPARC is a mixed use campus for the LCCM - the erosion of its cubic form creates a longitudinal distinction between the music college and the residential apartments above. SPPARC ARCHITECTURE, 2017

The Old Mortuary

🚶 St Marychurch Street, SE16 4JE

🕐 Sat/Sun 10am–5pm (max 30) + Tour every 10 mins + Exhibition of local history. Last entry Sat/Sun 4.30pm. **D·R·T**

🚇 Bermondsey, Rotherhithe

🚌 47,188,381,C10,P12

Retains many original features including original doors, vaulted ceiling in Russell Hall, lantern skylight and iron girder in Varney Room (former post-mortem room), wooden panelling in chapel. Now community centre. Norman Scorgie, 1895

The Rye Apartments

🚶 114 Peckham Rye, SE15 4HA

🕐 Sat/Sun 10am–5pm (max 30, access to Flat 4 at Kinsale Block (4a Kinsale Road, SE15 4HL)). Last entry 4.15pm. **A**

🚇 Peckham Rye

🚌 P12,484,343,197,363,63,12,37

Sustainable residential development containing 10 apartments built as a cross laminated timber structure. Internally it features exposed CLT and a palette of natural materials. Tikari Works acted as architect, developer and contractor. Tikari Works, 2019

The School of Historical Dress
🏃 52 Lambeth Road, SE1 7PP
🕐 Sat/Sun 10am–5pm (max 75, ground floor only).
Last entry Sat/Sun 4.15pm. **D·B·T**
🚇 Waterloo, Lambeth North
🚌 C10,59,12,53,148,344,453
Now home to the School of Historical Dress, the building was originally built in 1841 as the 'Royal South London Dispensary' for the working poor. Sydney Smirke, 1841

The View from The Shard
🏃 Joiner Street, SE1 9EX
🕐 Sat/Sun 10am–5pm, by ballot only
❗ Pre-book only: openhouselondon.open-city.org.uk/
ballots/8/entries/new
🚇 London Bridge
The highest accessible point of the building at Level 72, an open-air viewing gallery 800ft/244m above ground, exposed to the elements, where guests are surrounded by the shards of glass forming the pinnacle of the building.

• Queen's Court © Richard Chivers 2016

Unicorn Theatre
🏃 147 Tooley Street, SE1 2HZ
🕐 Sun 11am–5pm (max 15) + Tours, hourly (12pm–3pm).
Last entry 4.15pm. **D·B·R·T·O**
❗ Pre-book only: unicorntheatre.com
🚇 London Bridge
🚌 343,47,381,188
The first professional, purpose-built theatre for young audiences in UK. Described as an asymmetric pavilion, the building has transparent elevations revealing its core, and was designed in consultation with young people. RIBA Winner 2006. Keith Williams Architects, 2005

Weston Street
🏃 83 & 85 Weston Street, SE1 3RS
🕐 Sun Developer-led tour, ½ hourly
(2pm–4.30pm, max 12).
❗ Pre-book only: petra@solidspace.co.uk
🚇 London Bridge
🚌 381,47,C10
Eight tessellating apartments built from in-situ concrete. Arranged over half levels, they incorporate the Solidspace DNA, generating a double-height void linking the eating, living and working spaces of the home. Allford Hall Monaghan Morris, 2018

White Cube Bermondsey
🏃 144–152 Bermondsey Street, SE1 3TQ
🕐 Sat/Sun 10am–6pm + Sat building and exhibition tour at 11am, 12pm + Exhibition: Mona Hatoum. Last entry 5.15pm. **T·D·B·O**
❗ Pre-book only: talks@whitecube.com
🚇 Borough, London Bridge
🚌 188,78,42,C10
White Cube Bermondsey opened in 2011 in a former 1970s warehouse, renovated by architects Casper Mueller Kneer. Incorporating 58,000 sq ft of interior space, the gallery has hosted many important exhibitions since its inception. Casper Mueller Kneer Architects, 2011

Walks & Tours

The Low Line
🏃 Meet: cycle hire docking station behind Southwark Tube station off Blackfriars Road, Cycle docking station behind Southwark Tube station, Blackfriars Road, SE1 8JZ
🕐 Sat 12pm (max 30). **O**
❗ Pre-book only: info@lowline.london
🚇 Blackfriars, Southwark
🚌 40,63,381
Guided walking tour of the Low Line in Bankside. The Low Line is an emerging world-class walking destination along the base of the mighty Victorian rail viaducts in South London, linking Bankside, London Bridge and Bermondsey. Various architects, 2013

Westminster

Social Capital

The central London local authority is planning to develop 1,850 new council and affordable homes by 2023.

City of Westminster

---

10 Downing Street

- 🚶 SW1A 2AA
- 🕐 Sat Tour at 11am, 2pm (max 24, by public ballot only). **X·D·T**
- ❗ Pre-book only: openhouselondon.open-city.org.uk/ballots/7/entries/new
- 🚇 Westminster, Charing Cross
- 🚌 12,24,88,11,453,3,87,159

10 Downing Street has been the residence of British Prime Ministers since 1735. Behind its famous black door the most important decisions affecting Britain for the last 284 years have been taken. William Kent, 1735

11 Savile Row

- 🚶 W1S 3PS
- 🕐 Sat 10am–1pm (max 10, Visitors will have access to the Huntsman Clubroom where a talk/insight will be given) + TBC at 12pm (max 10).
- 🕐 Last entry Sat 12.30pm.
- 🚇 Piccadilly Circus, Oxford Circus
- 🚌 6,12,14,19,38,88,94

Terraced house constructed around 1733, Grade II-listed traditional Georgian construction with retail/tailoring space on ground and basement, and offices on the upperfloors. This year is the centenary of Huntsman moving to Savile Row. Henry Flitcroft, 1733

12 Savile Row

- 🚶 W1S 3PS
- 🕐 Sat 10am–1pm (max 6, Basement – Chittleborough and Morgan). Last entry 12.30pm.
- 🚇 Piccadilly Circus, Oxford Circus
- 🚌 6,12,14,19,38,88,94

Constructed in 1740, Grade II-listed. The property has a tablet commemorating the residence of George Grote the historian. Basement of no.12 Chittleborough and Morgan who are celebrating 50 years since they introduced women's tailoring. Henry Flitcroft, 1740

16 Savile Row

- 🚶 W1S 3PL
- 🕐 Sat 10am–1pm (max 6). Last entry 12.30pm.
- 🚇 Piccadilly Circus, Oxford Circus
- 🚌 6,12,14,19,38,88,94

The property dates back to the 1730s and is Grade II-listed, of traditional construction with retail/tailoring space on the ground floor and basement. Henry Flitcroft, 1730

4 Kingdom Street

- 🚶 W2 6BD
- 🕐 Sat 10am–5pm. Last entry 4.15pm. **T**
- 🚇 Paddington, Warwick Avenue
- 🚌 205,332,27,23,7,36,46

A modern office building at Paddington Central designed with the wellbeing of its occupants in mind, providing amenities including glass pod meeting rooms, a large roof terrace and London's highest basketball court. Allies and Morrison, 2017

42 Portland Place

- 🚶 W1B 1NB
- 🕐 Sat 11am–4pm. Last entry 3.30pm. **T**
- 🚇 Regent's Park, Great Portland Street
- 🚌 453,88

Grade II* five-storey listed Georgian town house, originally designed in the late 18C as a gentleman's residence by Robert and James Adam. The building is currently occupied by Christie's Education. Robert and James Adam, 1776. *christies.edu/news/2019/june/christies-education-portland-place-open-house-london*

55 Broadway (London Underground Head Office)

- 🚶 SW1H 0BD
- 🕐 Sat/Sun Hourly tour (10am-4pm, max 25). **T**
- 🚇 St. James's Park, Victoria
- 🚌 11,24,148

HQ of London Underground described it on opening as "the cathedral of modernity". Exterior features sculptures by eminent artists of the day, including Henry Moore, Jacob Epstein and Eric Gill. Charles Holden, 1927

Argentine Ambassador's Residence

- 🚶 49 Belgrave Square, SW1X 8QZ
- 🕐 Sat 12pm–5pm. Last entry 4.15pm.
- 🚇 Hyde Park Corner, Victoria

Known as the 'Independent North Mansion' and christened by Sydney Herbert as 'Belgrave Villa' and then simply 'The Villa' by his successor the 6th Duke of Richmond. Owned by Argentina since 1936 and with sumptuous interiors still intact. Thomas Cubitt, 1851

Australia House

🚶 The Strand, WC2B 4LA

🕐 Sat/Sun 10am–5pm. Last entry 4.00pm. **T**

❗ Pre-book only: eventbrite.com/e/open-house-visit-australia-house-saturday-21-sunday-22-september-2019-registration-63766054987

🚇 Holborn, Temple

Grade II-listed building designed by Alexander Marshal Mackenzie & Son, following a competition and opened by King George V in August 1918. Much of the interior marble, stone and timber you still see today was imported from Australia during WWl. 1918

Benjamin Franklin House

🚶 36 Craven Street, WC2N 5NF

🕐 Sat/Sun 10.30am–4pm (max 15) + Tour every 45 mins. Last entry 3.15pm. **T·Q**

🚇 Embankment, Charing Cross

Grade I-listed Georgian house, the only surviving home of Benjamin Franklin, retaining many original features including central staircase, lathing, 18C panelling, stoves, windows, fittings and beams. Patrick Dillon, 1732

Berry Bros. & Rudd

🚶 3 St James's street, SW1A 1EG

🕐 Sat Tour, every 90 mins (10am–4pm, max 10)/ Sun Tour, every 90 mins (11.30am–2.30pm). **T**

❗ Pre-book only: openhouse@bbr.com

🚇 St. James's Park, Piccadilly Circus

🚌 38,19,14,6,9

First opened by the Widow Bourne in 1698, No.3 St James's Street remains Berry Bros. & Rudd's home today. Little has changed in the last three centuries, and traces of company history, including documents and artefacts, are on view.

Burlington House

🚶 Piccadilly, W1J 0BG

🚇 Green Park, Piccadilly Circus

🚌 6,14,19,38,9

Linnean Society of London

🕐 Sat 10am–5pm (Meeting Room, Library and Discovery Room) + Interactive activity in the Discovery Room (max 20). Last entry 4.45pm. **F·D·O**

The world's oldest active biological society. Founded in 1788, the Society takes its name from the Swedish naturalist Carl Linnaeus whose botanical, zoological and library collections have been in its keeping since 1829. Banks & Barry, 1873

Royal Academy of Arts

🕐 Sat/Sun 10am–6pm + Burlington Gardens Tour at 10.30am and 12.30pm (meet in Burlington Gardens Front Hall). Burlington House Tour 11.30am (meet in Burlington House Front Hall). RA architectural history tour 3pm (Meet in Burlington Gardens Front Hall). Last entry 5.30pm. **F·D·B·R·T·O**

• Berry Bros & Rudd © Alistair Jones

Discover the new Royal Academy of Arts, the product of a transformational redevelopment designed by Sir David Chipperfield RA. A new route between Piccadilly and Mayfair unites the two-acre campus and opened for its 250th anniversary.

Royal Astronomical Society

🕐 Sat 10am–5pm (max 25) + ½ hourly tour (No tours 1pm–2pm) + Astronaut training and visits from astronomers past at 10.15am/2.15pm/3.15pm. Last entry 4.30pm. **F·D·T·Q**

❗ Pre-book only: (Special events) events@ras.ac.uk

The home of the Royal Astronomical Society since 1874 with recent refurbishment. Part of the extension to Burlington House to provide accommodation for learned societies. Banks & Barry, 1874

Royal Society of Chemistry

🕐 Sat 10am–5pm. Last entry 4.15pm. **F·D·B·T**

Experience the history, architecture and science of the East Wing of Burlington House, home to the Royal Society of Chemistry. Part of the quadrangle extension to Burlington House, it was purpose-built for the learned society. Banks & Barry, 1873

Society of Antiquaries of London

🕐 Sat Guided tour (11am–4pm, max 20). **R·T·O**

❗ Pre-book only: al.org.uk/events

Part of New Burlington House, purpose-built in 1875 for London's learned societies. Historic apartments with highlights from the library and museum collections on display. Imposing top-lit library with double galleries and marbled columns. Banks & Barry, 1875

The Geological Society of London
⏰ Sat 10am–5pm + Hourly tour (max 20, pre-book only). Last entry 4.30pm. **B**
❗ Pre-book only: (Tours) library@geolsoc.org.uk
Home to the oldest geological society in the world, founded in 1807. The Society has been based at Burlington House since 1874, and now has over 12,000 members worldwide. Banks & Barry, 1873

Canada House
🚶 Trafalgar Square, SW1Y 5BJ
⏰ Sat Tour every 45 mins (10am–4pm, max 20). **D·T**
❗ Pre-book only: eventbrite.co.uk/e/open-house-london-tour-of-canada-house-tickets-47349589898
🚇 Leicester Square, Charing Cross
Canada's diplomatic home in the United Kingdom, the revitalised Canada House serves as a showcase for the very best of Canadian art and design in the 21C. Sir Robert Smirke, 1823

Centre Building
🚶 London School of Economics & Political Science, 2 Houghton Street, WC2A 2AD
⏰ Sat/Sun 10am–5pm (Regular guided tours). Last entry 4.15pm. **T·R·D·A**
🚇 Temple, Holborn
Completed in May 2019, LSE's Centre Building is a state of the art flexible and highly sustainable academic and teaching building. Rogers Stirk Harbour + Partners, 2019

City of Westminster Archives Centre
🚶 10 St Ann's Street, SW1P 2DE
⏰ Sat Hourly tour (11am–4pm, max 20). **B·R·T·O**
🚇 St. James's Park, Victoria
🚌 211,507
Modern red brick building purpose-built to house the City of Westminster's historic records. Opportunity to visit the conservation studio and strongrooms and see treasures of the archives. Tim Drewitt, 1995

Dartmouth House
🚶 37 Charles Street, W1J 5ED
⏰ Sun 10am–5pm (max 450) + Hourly tour (max 20). Last entry 4.15pm. **T·R**
❗ Pre-book only: esu.org/open-house-london/
🚇 Green Park, Bond Street
🚌 22
Grade II*-listed town house boasting a marble courtyard, fine panelling and a Robert Adam fireplace. It is home to the English-Speaking Union, a charity equipping young people with the speaking and listening skills they need to thrive.

Embassy of Hungary
🚶 35 Eaton Place, SW1X 8BY
⏰ Sat/Sun 10am–4pm (max 100, ground and 1st floors) + Tour with the Hungarian Ambassador at 11am (max 40) · piano concert at 3pm (max 80) + Cooking at 12pm (max 20) · Hungarikum show at 3pm (max 80) Last entry 3.30pm. **F·T**

❗ Pre-book only: (Tours) london.events@mfa.gov.hu
🚇 Victoria, Hyde Park Corner
The properties in Belgravia were developed as part of the Grosvenor Estate around 1820. The Embassy is located in a four-storey white stucco house characteristic of the neighbourhood where main builder Thomas Cubitt carried out major projects. Thomas Cubitt, 1820

Embassy of the Republic of Poland
🚶 47 Portland Place, W1B 1JH
⏰ Sat 11am–5pm (max 15, access to first and second floors only. Please bring a photo ID) + A Culinary Tour through the Regions of Poland , ½ hourly + Izabela Czartoryska (1746-1835): The Polish Prophetess at 4pm. Last entry 4.00pm. **R·T**
❗ Pre-book only: london.events@msz.gov.pl
🚇 Great Portland Street, Regent's Park
🚌 453,88
Georgian townhouse built by Robert and James Adam in the years 1776–1793, a fine example of the Adam style of Neoclassical interior design. Seat of the Polish Embassy in London since 1921, it also houses a collection of Polish artworks. James and Robert Adam, 1776

Fitzrovia Chapel
🚶 2 Pearson Square, Fitzroy Place, W1T 3BF
⏰ Sun 10am–5pm (max 60, no access to organ loft) + Debris: a visual exhibition by Paola Musico. Last entry 4.15pm. **D·T·O·Q**
🚇 Goodge Street, Oxford Circus
Loughborough Pearson's red brick building is neat and unimposing from the outside, but inside it is a riot of Gothic Revival design. Golden mosaics reveal the character of the Grade II*-listed chapel, once part of the Middlesex Hospital. JL Pearson, 1891

Foreign & Commonwealth Office
🚶 King Charles Street, SW1A 2AH
⏰ Sat/Sun 10am–5pm. Last entry 4.15pm. **D·R·T**
🚇 Charing Cross, Westminster
🚌 3,11,12,24,87,88,159,453
Grade I-listed Victorian government office buildings. Route includes the magnificent and richly decorated Durbar Court, India Office Council Chamber, Locarno Suite and Foreign Office Grand Staircase. Sir George Gilbert Scott & Matthew Digby Wyatt, 1861

Gap House
🚶 28D Monmouth Road, W2 4UT
⏰ Sat Architect-led tours, ½ hourly (10am–11.30am, max 10).
❗ Pre-book only: gaphousetours.eventbrite.co.uk
🚇 Bayswater, Queensway
🚌 70,23,7,27
Family home with a minimal carbon footprint on a 8ft wide site. Environmentally friendly house, utilising among many eco-friendly devices ground source heat pump heating & rainwater harvesting. RIBA Manser Medal Winner 2009. Pitman Tozer Architects, 2007

Grand Junction at St Mary Magdalene Church
🏃 Rowington Close, W2 5TF
🕐 Sat 10am–4pm (max 50) + tour at 12pm, 1.30pm, 3pm
(max 25) · Architect-led tour at 12.30pm, 2pm (max
20) + Family workshop, 10am. Last entry 3.15pm.
T·F·D·A·O
❗ Pre-book only: (Tours) info@grandjunction.org.uk
🚇 Warwick Avenue, Royal Oak
🚌 6,187,414,18,36
Grade I-listed Victorian Gothic church by G E Street,
architect of the Royal Courts of Justice. The recent
conservation project reveals the original colours of
Daniel Bell's painted ceiling, plus Dow Jones Architects'
new modern wing. GE Street, 1867

HM Treasury
🏃 1 Horse Guards Road, SW1A 2HQ
🕐 Sat 10am–5pm + Film screening of refurbishment
(max 100) · Exhibition space (self-guided). Last
entry 4.15pm. **D·R·T**
🚇 St. James's Park, Westminster
🚌 3,11,12,24,87,88,159
A quadrangular, English Baroque revival building.
Grade II*-listed government office covering the entire
complex, Great George Street constructed 1899–17 in two
phases. Refurbishment completed 2002, now occupied
by HM Treasury. JM Brydon, John McKean Brydon, John
Brydon & Sir Henry Tanner, John Brydon, Sir Henry
Tanner, 1899

Happy Kids Dental Clinic Marylebone
🏃 74–78 Seymour Place London, W1H 2EH
🕐 Sat 10am–5pm. Last entry Sat 4.45pm. **T·R·F·D·O**
🚇 Marylebone, Edgware Road (Circle)
🚌 27,205
Immersive jungle-themed waiting room with i-pads,
consoles and digital games for children. Fun sculptures
and graphics on the walls across two floors, making a
dental visit fun! Modern dental technologies specifically
developed for children.

Horden Cherry Lee Architects Studio
🏃 36-38 Berkeley Square, Berger House, W1J 5AE
🕐 Sat/Sun 10am–5pm (max 30, ground floor access
only). Last entry 4.15pm. **A·O**
🚇 Bond Street, Green Park
🚌 38,22,19,14,9,6
HCL Architects open their ground floor studio in Berkeley
Square. The studio features their recent projects and the
work & research of the late founding partner, Richard
Horden. Architects will be on site and available to
answer questions. Horden Cherry Lee Architects, 2008

Italian Cultural Institute
🏃 39 Belgrave Square, SW1X 8NX
🕐 Sat 10am–5pm. Last entry 4.15pm. **T·O**
🚇 Hyde Park Corner, Victoria
🚌 2,16,52,38,9
Grade I-listed stucco-fronted Belgravia town house.
Library extension built 1960s. George Basevi

Jaguar Suite in Taj 51 Buckingham Gate Suites and Residences
🏃 SW1E 6AF
🕐 Sat Tour, ½ hourly (1pm–4pm, max 6) / Sun Tour, ½
hourly (9am–12pm, max 6). **T·R**
❗ Pre-book only: marketing.london@tajhotels.com
🚇 St. James's Park, Victoria
🚌 11,24,148,211,507
1,832 sq ft of luxury, inspired by classic and
contemporary Jaguar models, from the historic 1960s
E-type to the state of the art C-X75, featuring finest
leather, custom-made wallpaper and damask, ebony
veneer doors, clean-fuel fireplace. Ian Callum, 2011

King's College London, Strand Campus
🏃 Strand, WC2R 2LS
🕐 Sat/Sun 1pm–5pm. Last entry 4.30pm. **D·T**
🚇 Charing Cross, Temple
🚌 1,59,341,243,15
King's Grade I-listed campus includes King's Building
(Sir Robert Smirke 1829/BDP 2004), the College Chapel
(Sir George Gilbert Scott 1864) and newly reopened
Bush House (Harvey W Corbett 1919/John Robertson
Architects 2016). Harvey W Corbett, Sir George Gilbert
Scott, Sir Robert Smirke, 1829

Lancaster House
🏃 Stable Yard, St. James's, SW1A 1BB
🕐 Sat/Sun 9.30am–5pm (max 25) + ½ hourly tour). Last
entry 4.15pm. **D·T**
❗ Pre-book only: (Tours) eventbrite.co.uk/e/open-
house-lancaster-house-tickets-45804103306
🚇 Victoria, Green Park
🚌 6,9,14,19,22,38
Extravagant private palace originally built for the Duke
of York, with magnificent central hall and staircase.
Benjamin Wyatt, 1825

Mark Masons' Hall
🏃 86 St James's Street, SW1A 1PL
🕐 Sun 10am–2pm (max 25) + Regular tours. Last entry
1.00pm. **T·R**
🚇 Green Park
🚌 38,22,19,6,9,14
This stunning Victorian building is situated next door
to St James's Palace. Fronted in stone, the style is
'Grosvenor Hotel' Italianate. Coarse foliage ornament
fronts the building, the grand interiors adapted for
Masonic use in the 1970s. James Knowles Jr, 1866

Methodist Central Hall Westminster
🏃 Storey's Gate, SW1H 9NH
🕐 Sun 1.30pm–5pm + organ recital at 3pm · Dome visit
at 1.30pm (16 yrs+). Last entry 4.30pm. **D·B·R·T·O**
🚇 St. James's Park, Westminster
🚌 11,24,88,159,87,453,148
A masterpiece of Edwardian neo-baroque architecture
opposite Westminster Abbey. Second largest self-
supporting ferro-concrete dome in world. Its Great Hall
was the venue for the Inaugural General Assembly of the
United Nations in 1946. Lanchester & Rickards, 1909

National Audit Office

🏃 157–197 Buckingham Palace Road, SW1W 9SP
🕐 Sat/Sun 11am–4pm (max 12). Last entry 3.45pm. **R·T**
🚇 Victoria
🚌 11,44,170,C1,C10

A prestigious Grade II-listed building. Opened in 1939 by Imperial Airways and subsequently used by BOAC and then British Airways. The building has been the home of the National Audit Office since 1986 and was refurbished in 2009. Albert Lakeman, 1939

New Scotland Yard

🏃 Victoria Embankment, SW1A 2JL
🕐 Sat/Sun 10.30am–4.30pm (max 14, tour access only). Last entry 4.00pm. **T·D·A**
❗ Pre-book only: openhouselondon.open-city.org.uk/ballots/12/entries/new
🚇 Embankment, Westminster
🚌 3,11,24,87,88

The Met Police's home on the Embankment, created from the 1930s Curtis Green building with a new curved glass pavilion entrance and extensions to the rooftop and rear. Winner of the 2017 Prime Minister's Better Public Building Award. Allford Hall Monaghan Morris, 2016

New West End Synagogue

🏃 St Petersburgh Place, W2 4JT
🕐 Sun 10am–1pm. Last entry 12.30pm. **T·O**
🚇 Bayswater, Queensway
🚌 7,23,27,36,70,94,148

Grade I-listed Victorian synagogue, Audsley's masterpiece. Includes metalwork, stained glass and a mosaic; stained glass by NHJ Westlake. Further enrichment 1894–95 included lighting designed by George Aitchison. George Ashdown Audsley, 1877

Plunge Bath

🏃 5 Strand Lane (access via Surrey Street steps), WC2R 2NA
🕐 Sat 10am–5pm / Sun 12pm–5pm. Last entry 4.15pm
🚇 Charing Cross, Temple
🚌 9,15,91,168

The bath, reputed to be of Roman survival, is in fact the remains of a 17C cistern-house for a fountain at the old Somerset House that was converted into a bathing facility in 1776. Owned by the National Trust. 1612

Portcullis House

🏃 Victoria Embankment, SW1A 2LW
🕐 Sat 10am–5pm (Access to Atrium and 1st floor only) + Variety of talks and activities throughout the day, see Open House website for more information. Last entry 4.15pm. **F·D·B·A·R·T·Q**
🚇 Westminster,
🚌 3,11,12,24,87,88,159

Portcullis House contrasts its imposing façade with a generous light-filled courtyard covered by a glass roof at second level and surrounded by a two storey cloister. Extensive collection of Parliamentary portraiture from Gilray to Scarfe. Hopkins Architects, 2001.
parliament.uk/open-house-london

RIBA

🏃 66 Portland Place, W1B 1AD
🕐 Sat 11am–4pm. Last entry 3.30pm. **R·F·D·B·T·O**
🚇 Great Portland Street, Regent's Park
🚌 88,453

Fine example of Grade II*-listed 1930's architecture with many original features and fittings and home to the world-class British Architectural Library collections. Grey Wornum, 1932

ROOM by Antony Gormley

🏃 The Beaumont, Brown Hart Gardens, 8 Balderton Street, W1K 6TF
🕐 Sat/Sun Hourly tour (2pm–5pm, max 6). **R·T**
❗ Pre-book only: eventbrite.co.uk/o/the-beaumont-hotel-10778952168
🚇 Bond Street, Marble Arch
🚌 113,390,139,94

A monumental, inhabitable sculpture placed on a wing of the listed façade of The Beaumont Hotel. The interior, a bedroom, is as important as its exterior: a giant crouching cuboid figure based on the artist's body. Antony Gormley, 2014

Reform Club

🏃 104 Pall Mall, SW1Y 5EW
🕐 Sat Tour every 20 mins (10am–5pm, max 18)/Sun Tour every 20 mins (10am-3pm, max 18). **T·X**
❗ Pre-book only: paul.austin@reformclub.com
🚇 Piccadilly Circus, Charing Cross
🚌 9,94

Built as a Whig gentleman's club and inspired by Italian Renaissance palaces. Lobby leads to an enclosed colonnaded courtyard with complementary glazed roof and tessellated floor. Tunnelled staircase leads to upper floor. Charles Barry, 1841

Romanian Cultural Institute

🏃 1 Belgrave Square, SW1X 8PH
🕐 Sat/Sun 10am–5pm. Last entry 4.45pm. **D·T·O**
🚇 Hyde Park Corner, Victoria
🚌 23,2,9,14,137,148,436,13,390

Situated in one of the grandest and largest 19C squares in London, 1 Belgrave Square was acquired by Romania in 1936 and is now home to the Romanian Cultural Institute. Thomas Cubitt, 1828

Royal Academy of Music – Theatre and new Recital Hall

🏃 Marylebone Road, NW1 5HT
🕐 Sat/Sun Architect-led at 11am, 1pm (max 25, Duration 50 minutes). **X·D·A·T·O**
❗ Pre-book only: ajohns@ianritchiearchitects.co.uk
🚇 Great Portland Street, Regent's Park
🚌 18,453,205,30,27

The Royal Academy of Music's Theatre and new Recital Hall project has created two distinct, outstanding performance spaces for Britain's oldest conservatoire. Winner of 20 awards including RIBA London Building of the Year 2018. Ian Ritchie Architects, 2018

Royal Automobile Club
🏃 89 Pall Mall, SW1Y 5HS
🕐 Sat/Sun Hourly tour (9.30am–11am, max 20). **T**
❗ Pre-book only: racpallmallclubhouse.eventbrite.co.uk
🚇 Charing Cross, Piccadilly Circus
🚌 9,15,159,94,453
Inspired by the French Beaux-Arts, the Royal Automobile Club's pioneering clubhouse was described as the 'Palace of Pall Mall' with thrilling interior spaces in a mix of styles. Mewes & Davis, 1911

Royal College of Nursing
🏃 20 Cavendish Square, W1G 0RN
🕐 Sat Tours ½ hourly (10am–3.30pm, max 15).
D·R·T·O·Q
🚇 Oxford Circus, Bond Street
🚌 12,55,73,22
A cleverly integrated mixture of architectural styles and periods, incorporating a late 1720s house with rare Baroque painted staircase and the purpose-built College of Nursing (1926). Bisset Adams Architects, 2013

Royal Courts of Justice
🏃 Strand, WC2A 2LL
🕐 Sat 10am–4pm + Role of the High Court Tipstaff · Robing demonstrations · Courtroom workshops · Open Court: Q&A with court staff · What happens in a courtroom talk · Legal Costume Exhibition · Visit the cells · Kids corner. Last entry 3.30pm.
F·R·T·O·Q
🚇 Temple, Chancery Lane
🚌 11,15,26,76,341
Street's masterpiece and one of Victorian London's great public buildings. 13C Gothic given a Victorian interpretation. GE Street, 1874

Royal Institution of Chartered Surveyors
🏃 12 Great George Street, Parliament Square SW1 3AD, SW1P 3AD
🕐 Sat Tour every 15 mins (10am–4.30pm, max 15). **D·R·T**
🚇 Westminster, St. James's Park
🚌 11,12,24,148,87,88
Historic Grade II-listed gabled Victorian building purpose-built for the RICS in Franco-Flemish style, with a later addition of a Georgian townhouse to the building. Only surviving Victorian building in the street. Alfred Waterhouse, 1899

Royal Over-Seas League
🏃 Park Place, St James's Street, SW1A 1LR
🕐 Sat/Sun Hourly tour (10.30am–3.30pm, max 20). **T**
❗ Pre-book only: guestrelations@rosl.org.uk
🚇 Piccadilly Circus, Green Park
🚌 6,9,14,19,22,38
Over-Seas House is an amalgamation of two Grade I-listed buildings – Rutland House (James Gibbs, 1736) and Vernon House (1835 rebuilt 1905), with an Art Deco style wing added in 1937. William Kent, James Gibbs, 1736

Royal United Services Institute for Defence & Security Studies
🏃 61 Whitehall, SW1A 6ET
🕐 Sat 10am–5pm (max 10, Limited access to 4th floor) + Guided tour every 20 mins. Last entry 4.15pm. **X·T**
🚇 Westminster, Charing Cross
🚌 159,12,3,11
Grade ll* listed building built as a discreet addition to Banqueting House in 1895; at the time the extension housed their offices, lecture hall and galleried library - a sister library to the National Art Library at the V&A. Edward Ingress Bell, Sir Aston Webb, 1895

Rudolf Steiner House
🏃 35 Park Road, NW1 6XT
🕐 Sun 1pm–5pm (max 100) + ½ hourly tour (max 25). Last entry Sun 4.30pm. **D·B·R·T·O**
🚇 Baker Street, Marylebone
🚌 189,139,13,274,113
Unique example of Expressionist architecture in London with sculptural staircase based on organic plant forms. Grade II-listed. New café area and renovations in 2008. Montague Wheeler, 1926

Savile Row
🕐 Sat 10am–1pm (max 6). Last entry 12.30pm.
🚇 Piccadilly Circus, Oxford Circus
🚌 6,12,14,19,38,88,94

Huntsman
🏃 11 Savile Row, W1S 3PS
Terraced house constructed around 1733, Grade II-listed traditional Georgian construction with retail/tailoring space on ground and basement, and offices on the upperfloors. This year is the centenary of Huntsman moving to Savile Row. Henry Flitcroft, 1733. *huntsmansavilerow.com*

Chittleborough and Morgan
🏃 12 Savile Row, W1S 3PS
Constructed in 1740, Grade II-listed. The property has a tablet commemorating the residence of George Grote the historian. Basement of no.12 Chittleborough and Morgan who are celebrating 50 years since they introduced women's tailoring. Henry Flitcroft, 1740. *chittleboroughandmorgan.co.uk*

Norton and Sons
🏃 16 Savile Row, W1S 3PL
The property dates back to the 1730s and is Grade II-listed, of traditional construction with retail/tailoring space on the ground floor and basement. Henry Flitcroft, 1730. *nortonandsons.co.uk*

Cad and The Dandy & Richard Anderson
🚶 13 Savile Row, W1S 3PH
Grade II-listed, an original Georgian terraced house, consisting of basement and 3-storeys. The property comprises pediment dormered mansards, recessed sashes at second floor level, and cast iron Balconettes (mid 19C) to the first floor. The ground floor of the property contains a Mid 20th century shop front. Henry Flitcroft, 1730. *richardandersonltd.com* & *www.cadandthedandy.co.uk*

Soho Green – Art Loo
🚶 St Anne's Churchyard, Wardour Street, W1D 6BA
🕐 Sat 1pm–5pm (max 5). Last entry 4.15pm. A
🚇 Piccadilly Circus, Leicester Square
🚌 38,19,14
A treasure trove of a toilet – an egg shaped capsule in oak with etched glass hinting at the bodies buried below; and this year revealing a new art interior inspired by Soho. Steven Johnson, 2007

Somerset House
🚶 Strand, WC2R 1LA
🕐 Sat/Sun 11am–6pm + guided tours. Last entry 5.15pm
D·B·R·T·O
🚇 Temple
🚌 6,9,11,15,87,91,176
Grade I-listed restored building of five wings, four of which surround large courtyard. New Wing, overlooking Waterloo Bridge, dates from 1850 by Sir James Pennethorne. Sir William Chambers, 1775

Spencer House
🚶 27 St James's Place London, SW1A 1NR
🕐 Sun 10am–5pm. Last entry 4.15pm. D·T·B·Q
🚇 Green Park
🚌 38,22,19,6,9,14
London's finest surviving 18C town house. Built for the 1st Earl Spencer, the original build took 10 years to complete. Refurbished under Lord Rothschild the State Rooms are among the earliest and finest Neoclassical interiors in Europe. John Vardy & James Stuart, 1756

St Barnabas Church
🚶 St Barnabas Street, SW1W 8PF
🕐 Sat 10am–5pm/Sun 1pm–5pm (ask for admission to the crypt) + Live music 2pm. Last entry 4.45pm.
D·B·R·T·O
🚇 Sloane Square, Victoria
🚌 11,170,C10
Early English style, full of Pre-Raphaelite decoration. Important works by Bodley, Comper and Cundy and windows by Kempe and Tower. First Oxford Movement church. Recently restored 10 bell peal; bell ringing quarter peal once a month. Thomas Cundy, 1850

St John's Smith Square
🚶 Smith Square, SW1P 3HA
🕐 Sat/Sun 10am–5pm. Last entry 4.45pm. D·R·T
🚇 Westminster, Victoria
🚌 C10,507,3,87,88

A rare example of Thomas Archer's work and a masterpiece of English Baroque, this was originally dubbed Queen Anne's Footstool. Grade I-listed building, restored by Marshall Sisson after extensive bombing damage, now a busy concert hall. Thomas Archer, 1714

St Martin-in-the-Fields
🚶 Trafalgar Square, WC2N 4JH
🕐 Sat 10am–5pm (max 70) + Bell Ringing at 11am, 12.30pm, 2pm, 3pm (max 20) · Q&A at 11.30am (max 25). Last entry Sat 4.15pm. D·B·R·T·O
🚇 Leicester Square, Charing Cross
🚌 11,24,29,87,91
One of Britain's finest churches, built in the Italian Baroque tradition and beautifully restored in 2008. Sustainable features include new heating and management systems and lightwell. RIBA Award Winner 2009. Civic Trust Award Winner 2010. James Gibbs, 1726

St Marylebone Parish Church
🚶 17 Marylebone Road, Marylebone, NW1 5LT
🕐 Sat 10am–5pm. Last entry 4.15pm. O
🚇 Regent's Park
🚌 453,30,205,27,18
Grade I-listed monumental Neoclassical building by the architect Thomas Hardwick. It was opened in 1817 and is the fourth parish church built for the parish which has a history stretching back 900 years. Thomas Hardwick, 1813

The Association of Anaesthetists and Anaesthesia Heritage Centre
🚶 21 Portland Place, Marylebone, W1B 1PY
🕐 Sat 10am–5pm (max 60) + Anaesthetist-led tour, every 90 mins (11am–3.30pm, max 15) + demonstration workshops. Last entry Sat 4.15pm.
T·F·D·O
🚇 Great Portland Street, Regent's Park
🚌 88, 453
Large white Grade II-listed building, with Neoclassical portico. Heritage Centre is located in the basement, with many highly decorated meeting rooms throughout the building. Robert and James Adam, 1776
anaesthetists.org/Home/Heritage-centre

The British Academy
🚶 10–11 Carlton House Terrace, SW1Y 5AH
🕐 Sun 11am–4pm + Guided tours, ½ hourly (11.30am–2pm, max 15). Last entry 3.15pm. D·T
🚇 Charing Cross, Embankment
One of London's finest examples of Georgian architecture, Carlton House Terrace was designed by John Nash and constructed from 1827 to 1833. It is home to the British Academy which is the voice of the humanities and social sciences. John Nash, 1827
thebritishacademy.ac.uk

The Caledonian Club

🚶 9 Halkin Street, SW1X 7DR

🕐 Sun ½ hourly tour (10am–4pm, max 15). **D·T**

❗ Pre-book only: clubevents@caledonianclub.com

🚇 Hyde Park Corner, Victoria

Built in the Neoclassical style for Hugh Morrison (1868–1931), this was the last mansion house of its kind to be built in London. The club, founded in 1891, moved to the premises in 1946. Detmar Blow, 1908

The College of Optometrists

🚶 42 Craven Street, WC2N 5NG

🕐 Sun 1pm–5pm (max 50) + Ask the experts (max 10). Last entry Sun 4.45pm. **B·T**

🚇 Embankment, Charing Cross

🚌 3,6,11,12,24

HQ of professional and examining body for UK optometrists occupying two terraced houses, No. 41 (Flitcroft c1730 with later additions) and No. 42 (rebuilt by Tarmac plc, c1989) including Council chamber, print room, library and museum. Henry Flitcroft, 1730

The London Library

🚶 14 St James's Square, SW1Y 4LG

🕐 Sat Hourly tour (10am–4pm, max 20). **T**

❗ Pre-book only: eventbrite.co.uk/e/the-london-library-open-house-21-september-2019

🚇 Piccadilly Circus, Green Park

🚌 6,9,14,19,38

The world's largest independent lending library with over 175 years of history, 1m books & 17 miles of shelves. Atmospheric Victorian bookstacks, Reading Rooms & contemporary RIBA award-winning space provide a unique literary haven. James Osborne Smith, 1898

The Photographers' Gallery

🚶 16–18 Ramillies Street, W1F 7LW

🕐 Sat/Sun 10am–5pm + Latin American Photography 1959 to 2016. Last entry 4.45pm. **D·B·T·0**

🚇 Oxford Circus

🚌 390,94,159,12,73

An elegantly redeveloped Edwardian red-brick warehouse, linked to a steel-framed extension through an external sleeve of black render, terrazzo and Angelim Pedra wood. O'Donnell + Tuomey, 2012

The Queen's Chapel (St James's Palace)

🚶 St James's Palace, Marlborough Road, SW1A 1BG

🕐 Sat/Sun 10am–5pm (max 50). Last entry 4.15pm. **X·D**

❗ Pre-book only: tickets.rct.uk/queens-chapel

🚇 St. James's Park, Green Park

🚌 9,14,19,22,38

The first Palladian style post-Reformation church in England and private chapel of Charles I's bride Henrietta Maria; later extensively refurbished by Sir Christopher Wren in 1682–83. Inigo Jones, 1623

The Royal Society

🚶 6-9 Carlton House Terrace, SW1Y 5AG

🕐 Sat/Sun 10am–5pm (No access to terrace) + Carlton House Terrace Tour, ½ hourly (max 16, tours last 30 mins). Last entry Sat/Sun 4.15pm. **D·T**

🚇 Charing Cross, Piccadilly Circus

Grade I-listed building designed by famed architect John Nash. Built in 1831, these former townhouses have undergone refurbishments throughout their history. The building is now home to the UK's national science academy. Decimus Burton, John Nash, 1831.

royalsociety.org/open-house

The UK Supreme Court (formerly the Middlesex Guildhall)

🚶 Parliament Square, SW1P 3BD

🕐 Sat/Sun 10am–5pm + exhibition. Last entry Sat/Sun 4.15pm. **D·B·R·T·0**

🚇 St. James's Park, Westminster

🚌 11,24,88,159

Sensitive refurbishment of this neo-gothic Grade II*-listed building to become home of UK's highest court. Admire original features including stained glass windows, wood panelling and ornate ceilings. Feilden + Mawson, 2009

Victoria Palace Theatre

🚶 126 Victoria Street, SW1E 5EA

🕐 Sat/Sun Tour, hourly (10am–11am, max 15). See Open House website for accessability. **T·D**

❗ Pre-book only: victoriapalacetheatre.co.uk/openhouse

🚇 Victoria

🚌 507,148,24,11

The Victoria Palace Theatre, magnificently restored for the 21C reopened on 6 December 2017 with the European premiere of Lin-Manuel Miranda's acclaimed, Pulitzer Prize-winning Hamilton. Frank Matcham, 1910

Victoria Wharf

🚶 348–352 Ladbroke Grove, W10 6DW

🕐 Sat/Sun 10am–5pm (max 10). Last entry 4.15pm. **A**

❗ Pre-book only: alexandra.hellyer@cgluk.com

🚇 Kensal Green, Kensal Rise

🚌 452,316,228,70,52,28,23,18

Designed by Child Graddon Lewis for Westminster Community Homes and Westminster City Council, Victoria Wharf is an award-winning 100% affordable housing scheme comprising 22 homes (21 x 1 bed, 1 x 2 bed). Child Graddon Lewis, 2018

Westbourne Park Baptist Church

🚶 Corner of Porchester Road and Westbourne Park Villas, W2 5DX

🕐 Sat 10am–5pm/Sun 1pm–5pm + Church, Developer and Architect presentation and tour, every 90 mins (11am–4pm, max 20). Last entry 4.15pm. **T·R·F·D·A·0**

🚇 Royal Oak

🚌 36,18

A church with a hall, meeting rooms and offices, a children's library and 33 affordable units of accommodation made up of 1, 2 and 3 bedroom flats. Allies and Morrison Architects, 2019

Westminster City Hall
🚶 64 Victoria Street, SW1E 6QP
🕐 Sat 10am–5pm (19th floor Lord Mayor's reception rooms only). Last entry 4.30pm. **T·D**
🚇 St. James's Park, Victoria
🚌 11,24,148,507
Recently refurbished 1960s tower block offering floor to ceiling views across Westminster and beyond. Visit the Lord Mayor's parlour on the 19th floor where historical gifts and regalia tell the story of Westminster. Burnet Tait & Partners, 1966

Westminster Quaker Meeting House
🚶 52 St Martin's Lane, WC2N 4EA
🕐 Sat 10am–5pm. Last entry 4.15pm. **T·R**
🚇 Covent Garden, Leicester Square
,Opened in 1883, with front doors added in the 1920s. It was bomb-damaged in 1941 and rebuilt in 1956. Grade II-listed registered place of worship, it contains a peaceful meeting room and 1950s wood panelling and fittings. WW Lee and JA Tregelles, 1883

Westminster Reference Library
🚶 35 St Martin's Street, WC2H 7HP
🕐 Sat 10am–5pm + Historical tour, at 10am, 2pm, 11am (max 15) + Beauty of Architecture at 10am. Last entry 4.15pm. **T·O**
🚇 Piccadilly Circus, Leicester Square

• Victoria Wharf

Built in 1918 Westminster Reference Library has served the public for over 90 years. Situated on the site of Sir Isaac Newton's house, the architecture reflects Newton's original building alongside charming Edwardian features. AN Prentice, 1926

Wigmore Hall
🚶 36 Wigmore Street, W1U 2BP
🕐 Sat 10am–3pm (max 100) + Performances · Family Workshops. Last entry 2.45pm. **R·F·T**
🚇 Bond Street, Oxford Circus
🚌 390,7,94,139
One of the world's great concert halls, Wigmore Hall specialises in chamber and instrumental music and song. Refurbished in 2004, it is renowned for its intimacy, crystalline acoustic and beautiful interior, with a capacity of 552 seats. Thomas E Collcutt, 1901
wigmore-hall.org.uk

Walks & Tours

Engineering Walking Tour
🚶 Meet: in front of, One Great George Street, SW1P 3AA
🕐 Sat 10am (max 40).
❗ Pre-book only: london@ice.org.uk
🚇 Westminster, St. James's Park
A walk through the engineering past, present and future of London, travelling from Westminster along the river to London Bridge with expert guides explaining how the city has been shaped by engineers like Brunel & Bazalgette. James Miller, 1913

Secret Belgravia
🚶 Meet: outside Portland Place (opposite Marks & Spencer), Cardinal Place, Victoria Street, SW1E 5JE
🕐 Sat, ½ hourly (10am–3.30pm, max 25, Duration 90 minutes). **D·Q**
🚇 Victoria, St. James's Park
🚌 507,148,24,11
Walk a fashionable residential area with a Westminster Guide and discover stunning architecture, including terraces, squares and mews, together with fascinating stories of famous people.

Secrets of the Devil's Acre
🚶 Meet: outside Portland House (opposite Marks & Spencer), Cardinal Place, Victoria Street, SW1E 5JE
🕐 Sat, ½ hourly (10.15am–3.45pm, max 25, Duration 90 mins). **D·Q**
🚇 St. James's Park, Victoria
🚌 507,11,24,148
Tour of Victoria's unfamiliar streets with a Westminster Guide to discover social history, noted architects and Victorian philanthropists.

Index

Credits & Acknowledgements

Open City is a charity promoting a people-centred approach to the design of our city.

Director
Rory Olcayto

Trustees
Alison Brooks RIBA
Richard Ehrman
Stephen Howlett CBE
Crispin Kelly (Chair)
Alan Leibowitz
Alan Stanton OBE RIBA
Jayden Ali

Individuals Benefactors
Andrew McManus
David Neilson
Julian Peddle
Julie Taylor
Nigel Grey-Turner
Norman Franklin
Paul Carter
Richard Hughes
Robin & Sue Hodges
Tim Harris
Tom Smith
William Hewlett

Founder
Victoria Thornton OBE HonFRIBA

Open City Team
Adrianna Carroll-Battaglino
Tours Manager
Ailsa Cullens
Learning Coordinator
Annie Simpson
Open House Marketing
& Project Manager
Jeni Hoskin
Deputy Director
Ruby Maynard-Smith
Conference Producer

Open City Team; continued
Sian Milliner
Open House Project &
Volunteer Manager
Sophie Draper
Head of Learning

Volunteers
Alan Jacobs, Alasdair Bethley,
Alison Surtees, Bill Green, Bob
Dawes, Catherine Day, David
Taylor, Elizabeth Nokes, Leonora
Robinson, Miriam Sullivan, Peter
Bury, Richard Purver, Rick Smith,
Rob Hurn, Robin Key, Steve Kerr,
Stuart Rock, Sue Thorburn, Ulla Kite

Youth Advisory Panel
Aramide Elegbede
Beulah Kuku
Beyonce Brookman-Amissah
Carley Bucknell
Charlotte Bell
Erdem Kuslu
Khairat Abimbola
Lily Nguyen
Michelle Zheng
Qi Weoi Wong
Robinson Sivalingam
Sanjukta Hazarika
Shah Shivani
Shivang Bansal
So Sum Lee

Special thanks to
Alastair Carruthers, Kathryn
Lovering, Beck Road Residents
Association, Sven Muendner, Steve
Lavers, Luke O'Donovan, Henning
Stummel, Mike Tonkin & Ann Liu,
Alex Michaelis, Michael Russum,
Jestico + Whiles, Julia Barfield,
Jon Wright, Benedict O'Looney,
Linda Davies

Special thanks to: continued
Grant Smith, Margaret Baddeley,
Stephen Senior, Ralph Ward, David
Garrard, John Lyon's Charity,
Canary Wharf Group, Kings Cross,
Here East, City of London, 30
St Mary Axe, Harriet Thompson,
Tascha Von Uexkull, Luke Tozer,
Anthony Boulanger and Yeoryia
Manolopoulou, James Macdonald
Wright, Patrick Wynniatt-Husey,
Roger Zogolovitch, Alex Ely,
Richard Lavington, Clare Donnelly,
Sebastien Ricard, Ian Simpson and
Rachel Haugh.

Thanks also to all the property
owners, reps and managers; all the
architects, landscape architects
and engineers; the developers
and builders and of course, our
volunteers, for their incredible
goodwill, free time and enthusiasm
for Open House London.

Print
Circulation: 92,000
Typefaces: Miller, Brown, ITC
Officina Serif
Printed by CPI

Contact
openhouselondon.org.uk
open-city.org.uk
@openhouselondon2019
@openhouselondon
@opencityorg

18 Ensign Street London E1 8JD
hello@open-city.org.uk
020 3006 7008

Open City is a registered charity:
1072104

Itineraries

Self-guided daily itineraries curated to make the most out of Open House London – booking not required

Cycle time
Total cycle between all buildings on that itinerary

Social Housing: Saturday 10am–3.30pm

(Cycle time: 1 hr 25 mins)
- **10am: Alexandra and Ainsworth Estate**
Rowley Way, NW8 0SN
- **10:40am:** Walk to Swiss Cottage → Jubilee Line to Baker Street → Bakerloo line to Latimer Road Station → 2 min walk
- **11.20am:Silchester Estate**
Freston Road, W10 6TT
- **12:20pm:** Latimer Road Station → Circle/ Hammersmith Line to Barbican → 5 min walk
- **12.55pm: Lunch Break**
- **1.30pm: Golden Lane Estate**
Fann Street, EC1Y 0RD
- **2.15pm:** Walk to Old Street Bus Stop N (EC1Y 1AU) → Bus 141 towards Palmers Green to Kings Crescent Estate → 4 min walk
- **3pm: Kings Crescent Estate**
Murrain Road N4 2BN

Families: Saturday 10am–2.30pm

(Cycle time: 28 mins)
- **10am: Freemasons Hall, drop-in activities**
60 Great Queen St, WC2B 5AZ
- **12pm:** Walk to Holborn → Central line to St Pauls → 5 min walk
- **12.30pm: Museum of London, family tour**
150 London Wall, EC2Y 5HN
- **1:30pm:** Walk to St Pauls → Central Line to Tottenham Court Road → 6 min walk
- **2pm: The Building Centre, drop-in actitivites**
26 Store St, Fitzrovia, WC1E 7BT